Grandma Moses

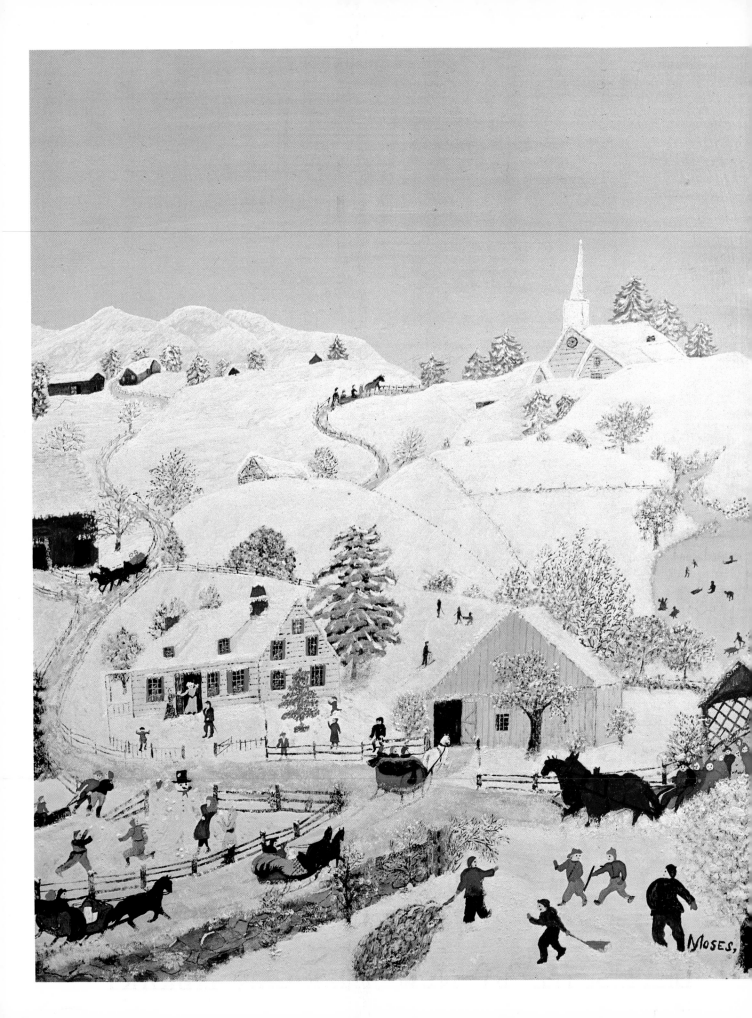

OTTO KALLIR

Grandma Moses

NEW CONCISE N A L EDITION

HARRY N. ABRAMS, INC.
PUBLISHERS, NEW YORK

DISTRIBUTED BY NEW AMERICAN LIBRARY

Frontispiece: *White Christmas.* 1954. 23¾ x 19¾".
Collection Mr. and Mrs. Irving Berlin

Nai Y. Chang, *Vice-President, Design and Production*
John L. Hochmann, *Executive Editor*
Margaret L. Kaplan, *Managing Editor*
Barbara Lyons, *Director, Photo Department, Rights and Reproductions*
Ann Goedde, *Index*
Christy S. Nettles, *Designer*

Library of Congress Cataloging in Publication Data
Kallir, Otto
  Grandma Moses.

  An abridgment of the 1973 ed. published by Abrams.
  1. Moses, Anna Mary (Robertson) 1860-1961. I. Moses, Anna Mary Robertson, 1860-1961.
ND237.M78K322   759.13   74-31269
ISBN 0-8109-2053-0

Library of Congress Catalogue Card Number: 74-31269
Text copyright © 1973, 1975 by Otto Kallir
Illustrations copyright © 1973, 1975 by Grandma Moses Properties, Inc.,
24 West 57th Street, New York, N.Y. 10019

The excerpts from Grandma Moses's *My Life's History,* 1952, edited
by Otto Kallir, are reprinted by permission of Harper & Row, New York.
The excerpts from Edward R. Murrow's interview with Grandma Moses
on "See It Now," 1955, are quoted by permission of CBS News

Acknowledgments

My thanks, above all, go to

HILDEGARD BACHERT

whose intimate acquaintance with Grandma Moses and her art and whose longtime collaboration with me have greatly helped me in writing this book,

to

NANCY GARNIEZ

for her constructive assistance, especially in the compilation of the data,

and to

MY WIFE

for the invaluable help and understanding she has given me throughout.

Special mention should be made of those who very early recognized the unique quality of Grandma Moses's art and helped to make her known: Louis J. Caldor, the artist's "discoverer," Sidney Janis, Allen Eaton, Thomas J. Watson, and Ala Story.

I recall with gratitude the members of Grandma Moses's family for making available over the years much documentary material, particularly records and letters which were used in the preparation of this book: Winona R. Fisher, Loyd R. Moses, Forrest K. Moses, Hugh W. Moses, Dorothy Moses, Fred E. Robertson, and Mrs. B. Russell Robertson.

Grateful acknowledgment is made to the museums which furnished photographs and data on paintings: The Phillips Collection, Washington, D.C.; The Metropolitan Museum of Art, New York; Museum of Art, Rhode Island School of Design, Providence; Memorial Art Gallery of the University of Rochester, N.Y.; New York State Historical Association, Cooperstown; The Shelburne Museum, Shelburne, Vt.; The Bennington Museum, Bennington, Vt.; The Fine Arts Gallery of San Diego, Calif.

Special appreciation is expressed to Dr. Armand Hammer, Victor J. Hammer, and his staff for their helpful cooperation, as well as to all the collectors who have supplied information on the Grandma Moses works in their possession.

Finally I wish to thank all those who have made possible the publication of this book, especially Harry N. Abrams and Fritz Landshoff, as well as Nai Y. Chang, who contributed the artistic design. Valuable assistance was given by Geoffrey Clements, who photographed many paintings in color and black and white.

CONTENTS

Author's Note

IN THIS BOOK AN ATTEMPT IS MADE to present and examine the art and personality of Anna Mary Robertson Moses. The author's close contact with the painter over a period of more than twenty years and his intimate knowledge of her work have made this undertaking possible. Since the first New York show all documentary material pertaining to the artist and her work has been preserved, thus forming the basis for a systematic study. Pertinent information previously published in books and articles has also been included. Nearly sixteen hundred pictures, created between the years 1918 and 1961, are catalogued, and many of them reproduced. The more awkward attempts, the sketchy small pictures, the incomplete works are shown along with the refined, finished paintings, for all are of interest in forming a valid impression of Grandma Moses's oeuvre.

It will be seen how the compelling urge of an old woman never to remain idle after having worked hard all her life, but to make something pretty and pleasing for her own enjoyment and the pleasure of those around her developed into an all-inclusive, consciously planned creative activity.

The art and personality of Grandma Moses are inseparable. Her paintings remain for everyone to see and judge for himself. Her personality, however, can best be evoked by her own writings—letters and autobiographical notes—and through first-hand reports of those who met her personally. Particular emphasis has therefore been laid upon the evidence of people who were able not only to describe her appearance and behavior, but also to find and uncover the roots of her vitality and strength.

1

BEGINNINGS

Unless otherwise noted, all works are in oil and tempera on Masonite or cardboard.

"I, Anna Mary Robertson…"

2. *The Childhood Home of Anna Mary Robertson Moses.* 1942. 14 x 28″. Formerly collection Louis J. Caldor

I anna Mary Robertson, was born
back in the green meadows and wild
woods, on a Farm in washington, co.
In the year of 1860, Sept 7,
of Scotch Irish Paternal ancestry.
    Here I spent the first ten years
of my life with mother Father
and Sisters and Brothers,
those were my Happy days, free
from care or worry, helping

3. Anna Mary's mother,
   Mary Shannahan Robertson

4. Anna Mary's father,
   Russell King Robertson

mother, rocking Sisters creadle
taking sewing lessons from
mother sporting with my Brother
making rafts to float over the
mill pond,
Roam the wild woods gathering
Flowers, and building air castle
                1870,
now came the hard years,
Schooling was in those days in
the country three months in
summer three in winter,
little girls did not go to school
much in winter, owing to the
cold, and not warm enough
clothing, there for my School days
were limited,
altho I was Kept busy helping at
Home, and the neighbors,
   when twelve years of age I left
Home to earn my own living as
then was called a hired girl,
   This was a grand education
for me, in cooking, House
Keeping, in moralizeing and
mingleing with the out side world

   I went to live with a Family by
the name of mrs & mr Thomas
white sides, they were lovely
people, while well along in
years,

I was cared for by them as a
child of their one,
    Presbyterians by creed,
one of my duties was to drive the
Horse "old black joe" to church for
them on Sunday mornings, and
place boquets on the Pulpit in
the church, and always remember the
                    in
text,
living with the whitesides
for three years, caring for
mrs whiteside who was an invalid
and died,
    Then I Kept house for mr white
side for a year till his nephue
and wife could come and take
care of the Farm, and Him,
    I was very proud in those days,
could get up such fine dinners.
for his Friends who came far off
                        from
to see Him,

    when the minister came and I
could bring out the fine linen and
the china tea set, and the heavy
Silver, then with hot bisquits
home mad butter and Honey, with Home
cured dryed beef, I was proud,
    But I some times now, think they
came for eats more than to see Him,
    then mr whiteside died,
and I drifted away from that
neighborhood,

5. Anna Mary at the age
   of four

6. Anna Mary at the age
   of fifteen

7. Anna Mary as a bride, 1887

8. Thomas Salmon Moses, the bridegroom, 1887

1880.
Still woorking as a hired girl, and
care ing for the sick
  Those were busy days,

In the Fall of 1887,
nov 9 I married Thomas Solmon moses,
a Farmer by occupation
we left on our wedding trip for
north Carolina- to take charge of
of a Horse ranch in north carolina,
But we never reached there,
we were Kidnaped at Staunton, V, a.
or I should say over perswaded,
to go no father south
  So we hired a Farm near Staunton
verginia for a year to see if we
would like the south,
and the people there were over
anxious for northeners or westners to
come in and build up the State,
They were in a way helpless
sence the colared help had been
  taking from them,
  we remained on this Farm one
year, then moved farther down
the valley on to a six hundred
acre dairy Farm,
  Here I commenced to make Butter
in pound prints and ship it to
the white Sulphur Springs, w, va,
I also made potato chips, which was
a novelty in tho days,
this we continued for severel years.
Here our ten children were Born,
  and there I left five little graves
in that beautifull Shenadoah valley,

Coming to New York State Dec 15, 1905, with our five children to educate and put on there one footing,

we bought a Farm and went in to the dairy business selling milk, and doing genarel Farm woork,

Here my oldest daughter married and left Home, Here my two oldest sons bought a Farm and struck out for them selves,

Here Jan 15, 1927. my Husband died, my yongest son and wife taking over the Farm,

Leaving me unoccupied, I had to do somthing, so took up painting pictures in worsted, then in oil,

9. Anna Mary Moses with two of her youngest children, Hugh and Anna, c. 1904

This autobiographical sketch was written by Anna Mary Robertson Moses in 1945. It is an outline of the years up to her husband's death in 1927, that is to say, the time preceding her career as a painter.

The astonishing story of Anna Mary Robertson Moses's development has aroused the interest of the American and the European public for more than three decades. As "Grandma Moses" she has become known all over the world. Wherever her pictures were shown, they met with exceptional response—in the United States, in Western Europe, and in Russia. People everywhere have been impressed by her paintings, which so vividly depict life in rural America, the changing seasons, the daily chores and pleasures of farm life, of which the artist was a part for close to a century.

Early Attempts

10. *Fireboard.* 1918. Paper on cardboard, 32¼ x

ALTHOUGH ANNA MARY MOSES STARTED PAINTING SERIOUSLY only in her old age, one cannot set an exact date for the beginning of her artistic activities, because, almost without being aware of it, she had from early childhood on done painting and decorating in her home. "When I was quite small," she once wrote,

> my father would get me and my brothers white paper by the sheet, it was used for newspapers. He liked to see us draw pictures, it was a penny a sheet and it lasted longer than candy. My oldest brother loved to draw steam engines, the next brother went in for animals, but as for myself I had to have pictures and the gayer the better. I would draw the picture, then color it with grape juice or berries, anything that was red and pretty in my way of thinking.

But the inclination for painting, shared also by her father and other members of the family, was always subordinated to the duties and obligations of everyday life. Anna Mary did not have the leisure to develop her talent, either in her early youth, as a young housewife in

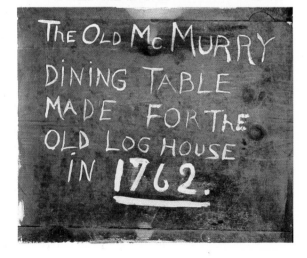

11–15. "Tip-up" table and details. c. 1920.
Collection Mrs. Hugh W. Moses

Virginia, or after the family returned to the State of New York in 1905. But her artistic urge often expressed itself in a desire to decorate objects of daily use around the house. Two examples have been preserved: a fireboard and a table (plates 10–15). She wrote about the fireboard:

> One time I was papering the parlor, and I ran short of paper for the fireboard. So I took a piece of paper and pasted it over the board, and I painted it a solid color first, then I painted two large trees on each side of it, like butternut trees. And back in it I did a little scene of a lake and painted it a yellow color, really bright, as though you were looking off into the sun light. In the front, to fill in that space, I brought in big bushes. I daubed it all on with the brush I painted the floor with. It run on three or four years, and we re-papered the parlor and papered over the picture. When we re-papered the room again a few years ago, we took the paper off the fireboard, but the colors had faded somewhat. That was my first large picture.

About the table she wrote:

> I have an old tip-up table, on which I paint. My aunt gave it to me thirty-five years ago, it was built for a log cabin. . . . The table was made of pine planks, under the top between the standards there was a box in which they kept their pewter dishes. . . . Then one day my aunt sent it to me for a flower stand; I have painted scenes on the standards and covered the top with postal cards, and now use it for my easel.

The painting on the fireboard is dated May 10, 1918, and those on the table were done about 1920. It is interesting to note that these first attempts already show a painterly technique rarely found in works of self-taught artists.

Louis Caldor Discovers
Anna Mary Moses

16. *Mt. Nebo on the Hill.* Embroidery, 10 x 14″. Formerly collection Louis J. Caldor

ONLY IN HER LATE SEVENTIES, when housework became too strenuous for her, did Mrs. Moses start to make pictures that were meant to be framed and hung on the wall. Dorothy Moses, wife of her youngest son, Hugh, who shared the home with her, tells about her mother-in-law's artistic efforts:

> While she was at her daughter's [Anna Moses's] home in Bennington [in the 1930s] she started making yarn pictures, which were very beautiful—as she designed her own pictures and they were done in lovely bright colors. . . . She gave away many and also sold some. . . .
>
> When her sister Celestia called on us one day and saw these

17.
The Old Hoosick Bridge, 1818.
Embroidery, 10 x 14".
Formerly collection Louis J. Cald[...]

pictures, she told her she should try to paint some—she "knew" she could as long as she could make such beautiful ones in yarn. For her first picture Grandma used a piece of canvas which had been used for mending a threshing machine cover, and some old house paint. We told her it was very good and to try and paint more—which she did. . . .

Some of the first she painted, Hugh and I took along with some yarn pictures down to the Woman's Exchange in Thomas's Drugstore in Hoosick Falls where they were put on display in the window. This is where the ball started rolling for Grandma. One day [Easter 1938] Louis Caldor, an art collector from New York who was passing through Hoosick Falls, stopped at the drugstore and was very much amazed at the wonderful collection. He went in and asked all about the pictures and who the artist was and where she lived. Later he came here and met Grandma. He asked her to paint some pictures for him, which she did, and which he brought to New York. . . .

Louis Caldor made many efforts to interest people in these pictures. He was turned down everywhere. Now and then he was told that the works he showed were quite "nice" but unimportant, and not in line with contemporary art; above all, nobody wanted to waste time and money in promoting an unknown artist who was close to eighty. Caldor had almost given up trying when in 1939 he chanced to hear of plans for a show, "Contemporary Unknown American Painters," to be held in the Members' Rooms of the Museum of Modern Art in New York City. Its organizer was Sidney Janis, a member of the museum's Advisory Board. Caldor went to see Janis, who selected three paintings by Anna Mary Moses.

The exhibition took place from October 18 to November 18, 1939. The three paintings, listed as loans from Louis J. Caldor, were *Home, In the Maple Sugar Days,* and *First Auto* (correct title: *The First Automobile;* see plate 31). Aside from the works by Grandma Moses, the show contained pictures by seventeen other artists: Patsy Santo, Samuel Koch, Ella Southworth, Gregorio Valdes, Morris Hirshfield, Cleo Crawford, Byron Randall, R. J. Bump, Rev. W. S. Mulholland, Hazel Knapp, Fred Fredericks, W. Samet, Alex Fletcher, Bernard Frouchtben, Flora Lewis, Gene Frances, and Dorothy B. Leake.

When the exhibition closed, Louis Caldor's loans were returned to him. About half a year went by after this initial success without Caldor being able to achieve anything more for the artist. However, he remained in touch with her, encouraged her to continue painting, and sent her painting material of more professional quality than she had used in the beginning. He then heard of a new gallery that had recently opened, whose owner was said to be interested in folk art. So Mr. Caldor came to see me for the first time.

First One-Man Show

IN THE FALL OF THE YEAR 1939 I had opened a branch of my Paris Galerie St. Etienne on Fifty-seventh Street in New York City. In Paris, as well as previously in Vienna, I had mainly concentrated on twentieth-century Expressionist art, but I also had a special liking for folk art and "primitive" painting. I was therefore interested when Caldor offered to show me American folk art that he had collected on business trips through New York State.

Among other objects, he brought pictures which he said had been done by an old woman who lived on a farm in Eagle Bridge, New York, about thirty miles from Albany. These were small pictures, some of them painted, others embroidered in yarn. Their artistic quality varied greatly; some had doubtless been copied from prints and illustrations, but quite a few were very good.

One painting in particular commanded my attention. It was a sugaring-off scene (plate 18). In a snow-covered clearing, people were busy collecting sap from the trees and carrying it in large buckets to a kettle over a fire, children were running around or waiting for the maple candy being prepared by the figure at the left, a sleigh piled with wood for the fire was being unloaded, a team of oxen was approaching—it all added up to a well-balanced scene of animated activity. But what struck me more than this was the way in which the artist had handled the landscape. While the figures were done in a rather clumsy fashion, the landscape was painted with astonishing mastery. Though she had never heard of any rules of perspective, Mrs. Moses had achieved an impression of depth, passing from the tall bare trees in the foreground, the huts and large, clearly outlined groups, to hazy tones in the distance, where smoke rising from the chimney mingled with the bluish gray of an early morning in winter, creating an atmosphere of compelling truth and closeness to nature.

I asked to see more, and Caldor said that he kept a number of pictures in his car, which was parked in Riverdale, a half-hour's drive away. They could only be inspected after 8 P.M., since he worked all day. Eager to get a more definite impression, I agreed to this rather strange way of presenting an artist. We drove out and, the parking lot being unlit, Caldor showed me the pictures by the beam of a flashlight; they were piled up on the back seat of his car.

18. *Bringing in the Maple Sugar.* 1939 or earlier. 14 x 23″. Collection Otto Kallir

19. *Home for Thanksgiving.* 1940 or earlier. 10½ x 12½″. Formerly collection Louis J. Caldor

Some of the pictures had great artistic quality, others were uninteresting attempts or obvious copies. There were also more yarn pictures, which did not seem to fit in with the rest. Only later did I realize that Mrs. Moses, in her desire to create pictorial scenes, had at first embroidered pictures. The term "picture" meant the same to her whether the scene was embroidered or painted. Still, the positive impression of what I had seen predominated, and I told Mr. Caldor that I would be willing to give the artist a one-man show at my gallery, on condition that the choice of works be left to me.

After the pictures had been assembled at the gallery I was able to examine them at leisure. All were in old frames, either from the Moses attic or from those of neighbors. The size of a painting was determined by the available frame. Most were on cardboard or Masonite, a few on canvas. Grandma Moses later described her way of preparing a picture:

> well I like masonite tempered presd wood. the harder the better,
>   I prefer it to canvas, as it will last longer,
>   I go over this with linseed oil, then with three coats of flat white paint, now I saw it to fit the Frames.
>   A picture with out a fraim is like a woman without a dress. In my way of thinking.

The artist had written a title on the back of almost every picture, usually in pencil. Some, like *Where the Muddy Missouri Rolls,* also bore lengthier inscriptions:

WHERE THE MUDDY MISSOURI ROLL[S] ON TO THE SEA
WHERE MAN IS A MAN, IF HE IS WILLING TO TOIL,
AND THE HUMBLE MAY GATHER THE FRUIT OF THE SOIL.

This was obviously quoted from a poem that had influenced her choice of subject.

Many of the titles Grandma Moses gave her pictures, then and later, indicate what she considered to be the essential content of a painting. In this first show there were such titles as *Apple Pickers* (plate 22), *All Dressed Up for Sunday,* and *The Old Churchyard on Sunday Morning.* Each bespoke the artist's involvement with a given theme. One felt that what she tried to express was always a personal experience, what she depicted was always something she had been part of. Whether the picture was of a washday or a Sunday, it was *her* washday, *her* Sunday.

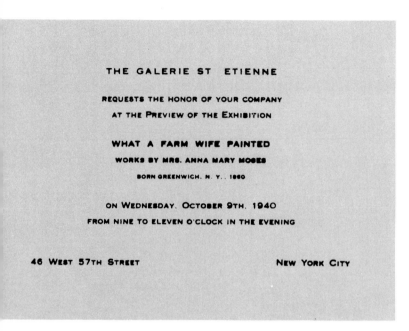

PAINTINGS BY ANNA MARY (ROBERTSON) MOSES

Born Greenwich, N.Y., 1860

1. Down in the Glen
2. Where the Muddy Missouri Rolls
3. The Old Red Sleigh
4. Farm Along the River
5. Village in Winter
6. The Covered Wagon
*7. Backyard at Home
8. Starry Eyes
*9. All Dressed Up for Sunday
10. Guardian Angel
11. The Hills of New England
12. On the Bridge
13. The Burning at Troy, New York
14. Home from the Honeymoon
*15. Bringing in the Hay
16. The Old House at the Bend of the Road
17. A Fire in the Woods
18. The Old Sugar House Among the Trees
19. Bringing in the Sugar
20. Shenandoah Valley (South Branch)
*21. Home
22. In the Maple Sugar Days
23. The Old Automobile
24. Shenandoah Valley, 1861 (News of the Battle)
25. Cambridge in the Valley
26. Turkey in the Straw
27. A - On the Road to Greenwich
    B - The Waterfalls
28. A Winter Visit
29. The Old Churchyard on Sunday Morning
30. Apple Pickers
31. At the Old Well
32. The Village by the Brookside
33. September Hills (Loaned by Miss Ona Robertson)
*34. Mt. Nebo-on-the-Hill (Loaned by Louis J. Caldor)

*Scenes from Mrs. Moses' own farm

GALERIE ST. ETIENNE
46 West 57th Street
New York City

Invitation to the first one-man show   21. List of the pictures exhibited

Even when she took material for a picture from a print, magazine, or newspaper, she strove not merely to produce a copy, but to transform the subject into something of her own. For example, she gave her personal touch to a Currier and Ives print, *Home for Thanksgiving;* in color and atmosphere her painting (plate 19, listed as *A Winter Visit* in the first exhibition) far surpasses the print. She had created something fresh and new.

The exhibition opened on October 9, 1940, under the unassuming title "What a Farm Wife Painted." It contained thirty-four small-size pictures, with the exception of two or three that exceeded twenty inches in width. There was no catalogue, but the visitors were given a mimeographed list of the paintings on exhibit.

The general reaction was surprisingly favorable. The simplicity and candor of the pictures, the artist's ability to express in a clear, uncomplicated way what she had to say, established immediate contact between work and beholder. This impression was strongly echoed by

22. *Apple Pickers.* 1940 or earlier. 13 x 12½″. Formerly collection Louis J. Caldor

many newspaper notices; a leaflet containing some of the first reviews was printed at the time and distributed.

We had invited the artist to the opening of the show but she declined, saying she did not need to come since she knew all the pictures anyway.

The name "Grandma Moses" appeared for the first time in an article in the *New York Herald Tribune* of October 8, 1940, which read: "Mrs. Anna Mary Robertson Moses, known to the countryside around Greenwich, New York, as Grandma Moses, began painting three years ago, when she was approaching 80." From then on Anna Mary Robertson Moses became known as Grandma Moses.

Grandma Moses Comes To New York

Shortly before the end of the show at the Galerie St. Etienne, Gimbels Department Store requested the pictures for an exhibition to be held in the store's auditorium for a Thanksgiving Festival on November 14. The exhibition hall was larger than my gallery, so a number of paintings not previously shown, as well as some "worsted" pictures, were added.

Grandma Moses was invited to the festivity, and this time she accepted. She arrived by train, accompanied by Mrs. Carolyn Thomas, the owner of the drugstore in Hoosick Falls where Louis Caldor had found her pictures.

Since 1905, when she had passed through on her way back from Virginia to her native village, she had been in New York only once or twice. The immense changes that had altered every facet of the city were bewildering. After having spent almost eighty years of her life in the country, seldom meeting anyone beyond the realm of her daily life and experience, Grandma Moses was suddenly confronted with several hundred strangers who had come to see her.

Louis Caldor had advised her to take along some homemade bread and preserves. She followed his suggestion and expected to talk about her products, remembering that only a few years earlier, when she had exhibited both her preserves and some paintings at the Cambridge Fair, she had won a prize for her jams while her pictures remained unnoticed.

But now people had come to Gimbels to see her pictures and to meet the artist. She later described her entrance into the hall:

> Someone handed me one of those little old ladies' bouquets and then someone pinned something on me, it felt just like a black bug, but I couldn't look down. It was a microphone, I was on the air. They took me by surprise, I was in from the back woods, and I didn't know what they were up to. So while I thought I was talking to Mrs. Thomas, I spoke to four hundred people at the Thanksgiving Forum in Gimbels' auditorium.
>
> Afterwards, oh it was shake hands, shake, shake, shake—and I wouldn't even know the people now. My, my, it was rush here, rush there, rush every other place—but I suppose I shouldn't say

that, because those people did go to so much bother to make my visit pleasant.

The following day Grandma Moses, accompanied by Mrs. Thomas, came to see me at my gallery. It was our first meeting. As far as I remember, we talked about her trip and her impressions of the city, hardly at all about her painting. Shortly afterward she returned to Eagle Bridge. At that time I did not in the least expect that within a few years a close cooperation in all matters concerning her artistic work would develop between us, as well as a warm and enduring personal friendship.

The public's reaction to the larger display of Grandma Moses's pictures at Gimbels was an interesting indication of future trends. While many judged them with kindly condescension, there were also those who, even though favoring contemporary modern art forms, recognized her work as a valid artistic expression.

In January 1941, the exhibition was sent to the Whyte Gallery in Washington, D.C., where it was received with even more favorable comment than in New York. The artist had come to the attention of the public.

23.
Grandma Moses and Carolyn Thomas
at Gimbels Auditorium,
November 14, 1940

New York State Prize

24.
Old Oaken Bucket.
1941. 25 x 31″.
Collection John N. Irwin II

DURING THE INTERVAL BETWEEN HER FIRST SHOW IN NEW YORK in
October 1940 and an exhibition at the Syracuse Museum of Fine Arts
(now the Everson Museum of Art) in May 1941, Grandma Moses had
gained considerable assurance. She now ventured into larger-size pictures, and their composition was on a broader, freer scale. One of
these new paintings was *Old Oaken Bucket* (plate 24), which illustrates
a popular song she had learned in her youth. Explaining how she came
to paint it, she wrote:

> That winter I had the grippe, and they kept me in bed, and I
> planned mischief then. When I was lying there, I thought I was
> going to paint the story of the "Old Oaken Bucket," because I
> knew how it originated. I painted it when I got up, that was the

25. *The Old Oaken Bucket.* 1943. 23½ x 30″. Collection Hildegard Bachert

first one I tried, but later I painted it again and could remember more of the details.

Then I was requested to send several pictures out to the gallery in Syracuse, where they had an exhibition. I sent the "Old Oaken Bucket," the "Checkered House," and a picture with a young colt in it. Hugh and Dorothy persuaded me to attend the show, so we went to Syracuse. My picture, "The Old Oaken Bucket," took the New York State Prize, and Mr. Thomas J. Watson bought it.

Artistic Progress

A ONE-MAN SHOW THE FOLLOWING YEAR should be mentioned. It was held from December 8 to December 22, 1942, at the American-British Art Center in New York, whose director, Ala Story, had begun to take an interest in the artist. Thirty-two paintings were on display, among them one listed in the catalogue as *Black Horses* (plates 26, 27; Grandma Moses herself had titled this picture *Lower Cambridge Valley*). The quality of the painting so impressed me that I consider it the turning point in my evaluation of the artist.

If up to that time I had looked upon Grandma Moses's work as interesting and appealing folk art, I suddenly realized that here was an outstanding painter. Her progress within two short years was astonishing. Whereas the early pictures are for the most part small, the figures often cramped in little surrounding space and the colors of the landscapes without much range, in *Black Horses* a new conception seems to have emerged, as though the artist's eyes had been opened to broad vistas of nature.

There was the view of the Cambridge Valley and the panorama of the distant mountain range and, above all, there was the subtle blending of muted colors. Forests, meadows, hills, and fields planted with a variety of crops were all painted in their own appropriate tones, yet formed a harmoniously integrated whole. To keep the picture from being a mere landscape, Grandma Moses had "brought in" (as she would say) two cantering black horses in the lower right foreground which attract the beholder's attention. A brown horse, with two children astride, stands docilely on the left, counterbalancing the other group. The artist later noted that the black horses had belonged to her great-grandfather and that one of them was killed in the Battle of Walloomsac during the Revolutionary War.

In the following years Grandma Moses created many new paintings that confirmed the fact of her development. In most of her early work she had represented single objects, such as a covered bridge, an old mill, a waterfall, an ancient car. The subject itself was all-important and the artist used the landscape as a setting; she did not as yet possess the ability she was soon to acquire to create a landscape which would not merely serve as surrounding scenery.

26.
Black Horses.
1942. 20 x 24".
Collection Otto Kallir

This development can be traced by comparing early and later versions of the same theme. One of the pictures included in the first exhibition was *The Burning of Troy* (plate 29), done in about 1939. It shows a covered bridge on fire. The idea for this painting derived from an illustration and story (plate 28) Mrs. Moses had cut out of a Troy, New York, newspaper, which "77 years later" recalled the catastrophe of Saturday, May 10, 1862. By a few pencil lines on the clipping she had indicated how she intended to change the oval illustration into a rectangular painting. More important, her imagination transformed the black-and-white newspaper print into a dramatic scene of flaming reds and dark billowing clouds of smoke, harsher and cruder colors than she would use in later years but forcefully evocative of the terrible event. This first version makes use of most of the elements shown in the newspaper illustration: the horse and cart looming very large in the foreground, the figures of running men carrying buckets darkly outlined against the flaming interior of the bridge, the brick structure supporting the bridge, and even a small boat tied to a post at the river's edge. The representation of the subject is all that matters, the bridge itself filling the entire width of the picture, flames and smoke reaching up to the top, leaving just enough space at the sides to indicate the approaches to the bridge and the river it spans.

27. *Black Horses* (de

In 1943 the artist used the same theme for a large painting titled *The Burning of Troy in 1862* (plate 30). But it shows an entirely different mood, less dramatic, more picturesque. It is now a wide landscape, serene in spite of the burning bridge that dominates the center of the painting. The hurrying figures and the horse and buggy have become less prominent. There is a cluster of charming houses and trees on the far river bank, apparently removed from danger. To the left of the bridge the river flows quietly through a hilly countryside painted in soft hues, the sky is high and clear above the burning bridge, and on the right a willow tree is delicately outlined against the river. Distant hills melt into the pale blue of the horizon.

THE BRIDGE THAT STARTED THE GREAT FIRE OF 1862

A COW started the great fire of Chicago. An earthquake started the great fire of San Francisco. But Troy's Great Fire was started by an old covered bridge.

From New York Bay to the head of navigation at Waterford, it was the first bridge ever built across the Hudson. Nearly a third of a mile long, it was wide enough to accommodate a railroad track, a carriage road, and a footway.

On Saturday, May 10, 1862, it nearly destroyed the city of Troy. A gale was blowing from the northwest, when a spark from a locomotive lodged in the shingles on the roof. In a twinkling, the entire bridge was in flames and the wind had carried burning embers to all parts of the city.

The fire started at noon. By six o'clock in the evening, seventy-five acres in the heart of Troy had been "swept over as by the hand of a destroying fiend." "Tears and despondency," says a historian, "could not recall the burned property which had been slowly accumulated by the incessant industry of many years." But by the latter part of July, 181 buildings had been rebuilt, and by November, all but a few of the burned lots were covered with new and superior structures.

Once again, the famous "enterprise of the Trojans" had not failed. And this bank is proud to have played a part in rebuilding the stricken city. Today, 77 years later, the Manufacturers National joins with other Troy banks in looking forward to a great industrial and commercial future.

28.
Newspaper clipping of 1939 about the Great Fire of 1862

29.
The Burning of Troy.
c. 1939. 9 x 11¼".
Formerly collection Louis J. Caldor

30.
The Burning of Troy in 1862.
1943. 19 x 30"

31. *The First Automobile.* 1939 or earlier. 9¾ x 11½″.
Formerly collection Louis J. Caldor

32. *Automobile, 1913.* 1943. 17¾ x 21¼″.
Formerly collection Artur Schnabel

There are several more versions of this subject, the last one—a small picture—painted in 1959. Grandma Moses had kept the clipping from the Troy newspaper all that time.

Three other paintings, each to my knowledge an original composition, also demonstrate the artist's progress: *The First Automobile* (1939 or earlier), *Automobile 1913* (1943), and *The Old Automobile* (1944) (plates 31–33). In the earliest, the clumsy car takes up the greater part of the foreground, framed by a sketchy landscape dominated by two trees in bloom. In the second version, *Automobile 1913*, the landscape predominates. In the center foreground there is again an open car with four people in it, as clumsy as the previous one. It evidently had been put in after the landscape was completed. Its motion and noise are indicated by two shying horses. Three children watch the unfamiliar sight, a farmer plows his field, a tree-shaded house with barn and small cottages are scattered in the valley. A dark sky over distant hills gives the picture a somewhat somber aspect.

One year later Grandma Moses took up the subject for a third time. Now the old car, though again placed in the center of the foreground, has become incidental in a delicately painted landscape; the hues of

33. *The Old Automobile.* 1944. 18¾ x 21½″. Private collection

the forests fade into ever softer greens toward the background, and
the coloring of the hills conveys an impression of great distance. Everything is quiet and at peace; it could be a scene of a hundred years
ago, were it not for the newfangled contraption before whose rattling
and speed, filling the air with visible dust clouds, the horse in front of
a buggy rears in terror.

34.
The Hitching Post.
1948. 15 x 19¼".
Private collection

35.
The Doctor.
1950. 20 x 24".
Collection Otto Kallir

36.
The Mailman Has Gone.
1949. 16¾ x 21½″.
The Shelburne Museum,
Shelburne, Vt.

Grandma Moses often chose to title a picture for a detail quite subordinate to the general composition. In *The Hitching Post* (plate 34), for instance, two windblown trees dominate the scene, rather than the horse-and-buggy being tied to the hitching post that gives the picture its name.

The title of a charming summer landscape with trees and meadows and children playing out of doors is *The Doctor* (plate 35). A man and a woman are standing in front of a large house; evidently the doctor has just arrived on horseback and is talking to the lady of the house who has come out to meet him.

A very dramatic landscape with falling snow and a dark, stormy sky bears the title *The Mailman Has Gone* (plate 36). There is a roadside mailbox, and among a number of people a man is proudly holding up a perhaps long awaited letter.

The narrative content has become part of an all-over visual impression. The fluid technique, far removed from that of a "primitive," can be traced even in Grandma Moses's earliest pictures; she rapidly gained assurance and mastery as her work progressed.

After the 1942 exhibition at the American British Art Center and others at various galleries in the following years, the work of Grandma Moses became widely known. As a result, she received many letters from people who wrote that they liked a certain painting they had seen and wanted her to "paint just such a picture" for them. Among the themes most in demand were Over the River to Grandma's House, The Old Oaken Bucket, Catching the Turkey, The Checkered House, and Sugaring Off. Although Grandma Moses did not enjoy these "orders," she obliged, because, as she said, she did not want to disappoint her friends. This explains the frequent recurrence of these titles.

It is interesting to note, however, that the artist hardly ever copied her paintings exactly. She found ways to vary the composition of a given theme, now as a winter scene, now as a spring, summer, or fall landscape. This gave her the means to change the atmosphere and tone of a painting.

If one calls to mind how many artists have simply copied their successful paintings upon order, one can only admire how this untaught woman avoided repeating her own work. What she did retain in each variant were the characteristics of any specific theme.

37.
Thanksgiving Turkey.
1943. 16 x 20″.
The Metropolitan Museum of Art, New York
Bequest of Mary Stillman Harkness, 1950

38.
Checkered House.
1943. Canvas, 36 x 45″.
IBM Corporation, Armonk, N.Y.

39.
Checkered House.
1955. 18 x 24″

The *Checkered House* (plates 38, 39), for example, always shows a large building with a red-and-white checkerboard design, barns and sheds, a wide road in the foreground alive with horses pulling carriages, riders on horseback, and men in uniform. In her youth she had seen this building, which was a landmark near Cambridge, New York. Later she wrote about it: "The Checkered House is old. . . . It was the Headquarters of General Baum in the revolution war, and afterwards he used it as a Hospital, then it was a stopping place for the stage, where they changed horses every two miles, oh we traveled *fast* in those days."

Looking at two variations of the *Checkered House,* I once asked her how she managed to represent the same motif in a fresh form. She said that she visualized the picture she was about to paint as though framed in her window and that she had only to imagine she was looking out on the scene either from the right or from the left and that accordingly all parts of a composition would shift into place.

The figures that populate her landscapes are for the most part "types" who perform certain standard chores: the men carrying wooden buckets in " sugaring off " pictures, for instance (plate 40), or the ones catching the turkey (plates 37, 42). Sometimes there are soldiers in old uniforms, indicating a historical setting (plates 38, 39).

40.
Sugaring Off in Maple Orchard.
1940. Canvas, 18⅛ x 24⅛″.
Private collection

41. *Sugaring Off*
Maple Orchard (det

Such figures were often taken from books or old prints, or from the newspaper clippings which she kept in a box. This helps to explain their recurrence in Grandma Moses's paintings, whereas the landscape is always the original artistic expression of her own vision. Remarkably enough, the animals in her pictures are seldom stereotyped in the way that her human figures are. Rarely did she copy them; they are painted with natural ease and abandon, with the emphasis not on details of their appearance but on their movements, which are astonishingly well observed. One need only study the horses in her paintings (see plate 119): in the winter pictures some of them trot heavily through the snow, straining to draw a laden sleigh; others are unburdened and light in their movements or even try to break out. This seemingly effortless touch, achieved also in the landscapes, was not at her disposal in the human figure.

The blending of two distinct components—sensitively felt and beautifully represented nature scenes, painted in an almost Impressionist manner, with primitive though often colorful human figures—into artistic harmony constitutes what has become known and recognized the world over as the Grandma Moses style.

42. *Catching the Turkey.* 1940. 12 x 16″. Formerly collection Louis J. Caldor

The Early Years to 1946

43. *Home in Winter.* c. 1938. 6 x 16″. Galerie St. Etienne, New York

44. *A Fire in the Woods.* 1940 or earlier. 10¼ x 15″. Formerly collection Louis J. Caldor

45.
The Daughter's Homecoming.
1943. 19¾ x 23½"

46.
Grandma Going to the Big City.
1943. 21 x 24".
Sidney Janis Gallery, New York

47. *Home of Hezekiah King in 1800, No. 4.* 1943. 23 x 29″

48. *Mt. Nebo in Winter.* 1943. 20½ x 26½″. Private collection

49. *The Sun Has Gone Down.* 1944. 6 x 9″. Private collection

50.
In Harvest Time.
1944. 12 x 17″

51. *Out for the Christmas Trees.* 1944. 24 x 29½″.
Collection Anson Brooks

52.
The Lookout, 1777, Vermont. 1945. 17 x 21″.
Formerly collection Bernard M. Douglas

53. *Hurricane in Hoosick Falls.* 1945. 15¾ x 20"

54. *Early Springtime on the Farm.* 1945. 16 x 25¾". Private collection

55.
Wash Day.
1945. 17¾ x 23½″.
Museum of Art,
Rhode Island School of Desi
Providence

FAR LEFT:
56.
Wild Roses.
1945. 10¾ x 9¼″.
Private collection

LEFT:
57.
Wild Daisies.
1945. 11¾ x 7¾″.
Private collection

2

GROWING
RECOGNITION

"Grandma Moses: American Primitive"

HAVING REALIZED HER IMPORTANCE AS AN ARTIST and witnessed the public's growing interest, I decided, in 1945, to write a book on Grandma Moses. I had often visited her at her home in Eagle Bridge and we naturally discussed the project. From our many conversations and even more from her letters, I found, to my delight, that her ability to express herself was not limited to painting. She had a most vivid and personal style, as well as a spelling all her own. It was fascinating to listen when she told stories of her family and of events she had witnessed or been told about in her youth, some of historical interest, others just local anecdotes.

Feeling that here was a rich source of first-hand information about rural life in nineteenth-century America, I encouraged Grandma to write down what came to her mind whenever she felt like doing so. In the course of a year she sent me three autobiographical sketches, one of which is reproduced in facsimile at the beginning of the present volume. She sent along a letter, saying in her modest way: "Here is my life's history, can you make anything out of it? . . . You see, I don't know how to go about such things."

She also agreed to write comments on the forty paintings to be reproduced in the book. They were not only descriptions of the pictures, but also stories about the depicted events. Everything was written in her own clear and meticulous hand and was so charming and original that I decided to have the comments reproduced in facsimile opposite each illustration.

The book was published in 1946 (Dryden Press) under the title *Grandma Moses: American Primitive*. Louis Bromfield, who had been interested in the artist for a number of years, wrote the introduction. The book proved an immediate success, and was republished in 1947 (Doubleday) with additional colorplates. Widely reviewed in the American press and in some European papers, it drew increased attention to Grandma Moses. Museums and art centers the country over asked to present her work.

Reproductions and Christmas Cards

58. *Sugaring Off.* 1943. 23 x 27″. Private collection. First color reproduction, 1948

GRANDMA MOSES HAD NEVER HAD THE IDEA of selling her paintings for high prices; still less would the thought have entered her mind that she might receive money from reproductions of her pictures. She had always been a conscientious and thrifty housekeeper and she could not understand why she should get more for a painting than she had asked; it seemed to her almost an offense. I had already become familiar with this attitude in the course of the first exhibition. Two or three of her works had been sold for a substantially higher sum than what Louis Caldor had paid her. Not having met Mrs. Moses personally at the time, I suggested to Caldor that she be sent an additional amount. No sooner had the check been mailed than it was returned by Mrs. Moses with the remark that everything had been paid for, she was not owed anything, and she did not want the money.

Later on I once sent her twenty dollars above the price she had indicated for a picture. She kept it this time but wrote: "In regard to paying for paintings you do not have to pay more then I ask." (October 3, 1945) On a previous occasion she had written: "Don't pay me in advance as it puts me under obligation, and that I don't want now. Ive got to that age where I want to keep my House in order." (September 15, 1943)

Soon after the first exhibitions, requests came to reproduce Moses paintings. In order to protect them from unauthorized use, all her pictures were registered at the Copyright Office in Washington. Large, excellent-quality color reproductions of her important pictures were printed (plate 58) which could be afforded by wide circles and contribute to making the artist's work known.

Christmas and greeting cards also helped to spread her popularity. The firm of Brundage Greeting Cards published the first set of sixteen Grandma Moses Christmas cards in 1946. Then, in 1947, Hallmark acquired the right to reproduce the artist's paintings on Christmas and greeting cards and published them for many years.

When Grandma Moses received a large sum of money in royalties from the first Christmas card venture in 1946, she was at a loss to understand how she came to get it, and she did not cash the check. Visiting her some time later, I inquired why she had not done so, whereupon she produced it and seemed puzzled. I tried to explain that some of the paintings she had sold were earning all this money for her by being reproduced on Christmas cards and that she was participating in what they brought. She shook her head but promised to follow my suggestion and take the check to the bank in Hoosick Falls. The next day, the cash was lying in bundles on the table, and she said she had kept her word.

Seeing that Grandma Moses was not able to cope with such business matters, it was decided to have a lawyer take care of her financial affairs. Starting in 1947, all receipts from the sale of paintings and all royalties derived from copyrights went to Sylvester Scott of Hoosick Falls; he was a longtime friend, personally interested in the artist's work, and he administered her income almost up to the time of her death.

Documentary Film

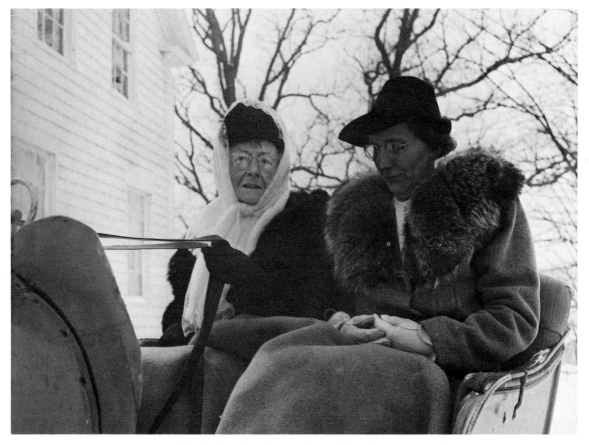

59. Grandma Moses with her daughter-in-law, Dorothy, during making of documentary film. Photo by Erica Anderson

ALA STORY, WHO SHARED MY CONVICTION of the artist's importance, had been working closely with me since 1945—our association lasted many years. In 1946 we began making plans for a film on Grandma Moses. Erica Anderson, who was to gain fame with her movie on Albert Schweitzer, went up to Eagle Bridge from time to time and took color pictures of the artist, her home, her family, the setting of her daily life, and the surrounding countryside. They were as yet disconnected color shots with no guiding script. The motion picture producer Jerome Hill then arranged the material to form a documentary, which was completed in 1950. Archibald MacLeish wrote and narrated the text; the music was composed by Hugh Martin and arranged by Alec Wilder. The film received the "Certificate of Nomination for Award" from the Academy of Motion Picture Arts and Sciences.

Visit to Washington

In May 1949, Grandma Moses was invited to go to Washington, D.C., to receive the Women's National Press Club Award. The President of the United States was to present "certificates of achievement" to six women who were being honored "for their outstanding contributions to their respective fields for the year 1948."

Grandma Moses left her home in Eagle Bridge on May 12 in the company of her daughter-in-law Dorothy. They arrived in New York by train. A wheelchair had been prepared at the station to take Grandma to a taxi. "That was humiliating to me, but I couldn't have walked it," she later wrote. She and Dorothy spent two nights at our home in New York.

The press wished to meet her, so I arranged a small exhibition of the artist's paintings at my gallery.

The next day the *New York Herald Tribune* wrote:

> There was a host of reporters, photographers and radio people in the room when Grandma walked in. . . . After surviving the ordeal by flash bulbs she moved over to a sofa, where she faced a solid ring of reporters with a devil-may-care attitude. . . . The questions came thick and fast and mixed up. She not only displayed the utter independence of the elderly but it was evident that she was having the reporters on a bit. . . . When asked if she was excited at the prospect of seeing President Truman and Mrs. Franklin D. Roosevelt, who also is receiving the award, she said, "No. Not at all." . . . Somebody asked if she wanted to paint the New York City scene.
>
> "It doesn't appeal to me," she said.
>
> "You mean it doesn't appeal to you as painting material?" someone asked.
>
> "As any material," said Grandma crisply.

With characteristic understatement she called her painting a pleasant occupation. "As I finish each picture, I think I've done my last, but I go right on," she said.

On the evening of May 14 the official dinner took place in the Presidential Room of the Statler Hotel in Washington. Seven hundred guests attended, among them the diplomatic corps, the

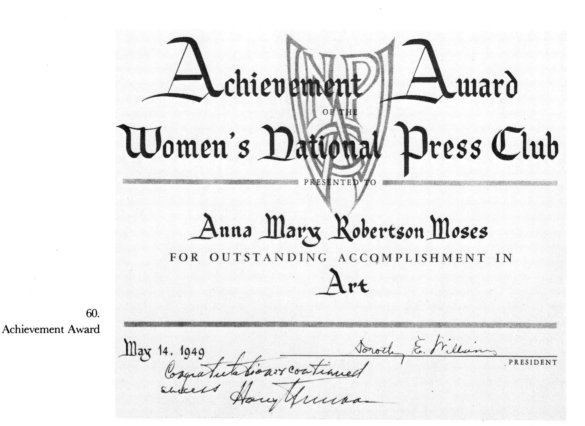

Supreme Court Justices, and the members of the President's Cabinet with their wives. When Grandma Moses entered the hall, she received a big ovation, which she smilingly acknowledged without interrupting her progress toward the dais, where she was seated next to Mrs. Truman. The President handed her the award "for outstanding accomplishment in Art," which he had inscribed for her.

The other recipients were: Mrs. Franklin D. Roosevelt for her work as Chairman of the United Nations Human Rights Commission; Mary Jane Ward, author of *The Snake Pit*, a novel which focused attention on the need for improving mental institutions; Madeleine Carroll for outstanding achievement in the theater; Dorothy McCullough Lee, the first woman to be elected mayor of a city exceeding 500,000 (Portland, Oregon); and Marjorie Child Husted, of General Mills, Inc., for achievement in business.

During the dinner Grandma Moses carried on a lively conversation with the President and his wife. He told me afterward how charmed and impressed he was by her and added that he would very much like to see her again and that therefore, if at all possible, he would attend a tea to which the award recipients had been invited by Mrs. Truman the following day.

61.
Grandma Moses receiving
the Women's National
Press Club Award from
President Harry S Truman,
May 14, 1949

THE WHITE HOUSE
WASHINGTON

May 26, 1949

Dear Grandma Moses:

I certainly appreciated your good letter of May
twenty-third. I am glad you enjoyed your visit
to Washington.

Mrs. Truman and I were delighted to see you
at the dinner and to have you at the Blair House
for tea. My piano playing doesn't amount to
much but I am glad you enjoyed it.

I hope you have many, many happy years ahead
of you.

Sincerely yours,

Harry Truman

Mrs. Anna Mary Robertson Moses
Eagle Bridge
New York

62. Letter from President Truman
to Grandma Moses, May 26, 1949

When we arrived at Blair House, where the Trumans were living while the White House was being remodeled, the President was already there and he again chatted with Mrs. Moses. "After the tea," Grandma recalled, "we had a terrific thunderstorm, so we sat down on a couch to wait till the shower was over. President Truman sat beside me and said, 'Don't be afraid, as this is a large building with many lightning rods on it.' Maybe he thought Grandma might be afraid. I talked with him, and I could not think but that he was one of my own boys. I even asked him to play something on the piano." At first he was reluctant and suggested he would turn on the radio instead, but Mrs. Moses insisted, so he smilingly went to the piano and played a minuet by Paderewsky. "That was a delight," she wrote. "Then the shower was over, and he ordered his own car to take us to the Hotel Statler, that was an honor."

Next day Grandma Moses visited the Phillips Gallery, where a large loan exhibition of her paintings had been arranged. In 1941 Mr. and Mrs. Duncan Phillips had been the first to acquire a Grandma Moses picture for an American museum; they subsequently added several more to their collection (see plate 142).

When Grandma Moses and Dorothy returned home on May 20, "her many friends, neighbors and relatives in Eagle Bridge were joined by

63.
July Fourth.
1951. 23⅞ x 30″.
The White House, Washington, D.C.

folks from all over Rensselaer County who came to welcome Mrs. Moses. . . . Several hundred automobiles jammed the village's only street, as an estimated 800 persons—almost twice the population of Eagle Bridge—assembled at the World War II Honor Roll in the center of the little community. . . . She was back home again after receiving the largest welcome the small village could give. . . ." (*Troy Record,* May 21, 1949) School children sang and presented her with flowers. The Hoosick Falls High School band played and escorted her all the way home.

Perhaps of the honors she had received, she enjoyed most the welcome she got in Eagle Bridge. "In a way I was glad to get back and go to bed that night," she wrote later.

When President and Mrs. Truman moved into the remodeled White House, I wrote to Mrs. Truman on March 21, 1952: "As I have seen in the papers, the White House will be reopened on April lst. It would be a great pleasure to me to dedicate on this occasion an original painting by Grandma Moses to the White House and to the American people, if the President and you would approve of my intention, and if there is a place for it." My suggestion was accepted, and *July Fourth* (plate 63), which the artist had painted in August 1951, has been hanging at the White House ever since.

Moving to a New House

64. Grandma Moses's old house, Eagle Bridge, N.Y.

65. Grandma Moses on the front-porch steps of the old house, c. 1946

GRANDMA MOSES WAS NOT TO STAY MUCH LONGER in the old farmhouse, although she referred to it as "home" for the rest of her life. Her youngest son, Hugh, who had taken care of the Moses farm, had died suddenly in February 1949. Grandma stayed on with her daughter-in-law Dorothy, but her two surviving sons, Forrest and Loyd, were building a more comfortable ranch-style house for her across the road. She moved into it in April 1951. Her daughter, Winona Fisher, came from California to care for her and eventually took over more and more of the tasks that Grandma had been doing herself, such as letter writing, making entries in the Record Book, and sometimes writing labels for pictures. Aside from seeing to it that her mother was comfortable, Mrs. Fisher had a keen understanding of her significance as an artist and as a personality. After Mrs. Fisher's death in 1958, Forrest Moses and his wife Mary moved in with Grandma and took care of her.

66. *Grandpa's House.* 1951. 9¼ x 12″. Private collection. This picture shows the house to which the artist moved in April 1951. It was built by Forrest Moses, who was often called "Grandpa"

67.
Grandma Moses in front of
the new house, 1952

First European Exhibitions

68–70. Posters of the first Moses exhibition to travel in Europe

SHORTLY AFTER WORLD WAR II, European papers and magazines had begun to take notice of Grandma Moses. Many articles, frequently accompanied by illustrations, were published on the story of Anna Mary Robertson Moses and on the attention her work was receiving in the United States. A desire to see the original paintings was repeatedly expressed, and in 1950 a collection of fifty pictures was assembled and sent to Europe under the sponsorship of United States Information Centers or embassies. The exhibition was shown in Vienna, Munich, Salzburg, Berne, The Hague, and Paris. While the initial reaction to the "Grandma Moses phenomenon" had been one of skepticism, a first-hand acquaintance with the artist's work brought about a complete change of attitude. The enthusiastic response to the shows surpassed all expectations. Great numbers of visitors and many favorable reviews and comments bore witness to the surprise and pleasure the originality of her art had evoked. "Grandma Moses is one of the key symbols of our time. . . . She is clearly an artist, whose paintings reveal a quality identical with genius. . . ." wrote a critic for the noted London magazine *Art News and Review.*

These European exhibitions and some lectures on American folk art I had given met with such interest that in 1954 the Smithsonian Institution organized the show "American Painting: Peintres Naïfs from 1700 to the Present." It was circulated in Europe by the United States Information Agency. The collection, which included works by Grandma Moses, presented a cross-section of American folk painting. The confrontation of European art circles with what had been until then a totally unfamiliar form of American painting proved most instructive.

In contrast to Europe, no art schools had existed in America until well into the nineteenth century. People who painted had to find their own technical and artistic means of expression. The importance of this art had not been recognized until fairly recently. Within the framework of the show, Grandma Moses proved to be not so much an isolated figure as a link in a long chain. Each of these untaught artists had found his individual way of expressing ideas of his time and experiences of his daily life. Like all "peintres naïfs," they painted for pleasure in their spare time. Edward Hicks (1780–1849), the painter of the *Peaceable Kingdom,* was a Quaker preacher; John Kane (1860–1934), a manual laborer, mainly depicted the industrial landscape of Pittsburgh; Horace Pippin (1888–1946) took his inspiration from a Negro cultural background. Grandma Moses was a farmwife and her work re-creates the American rural scene.

71. Opening, Grandma Moses exhibition, Paris, December 1950: M. Bizardel, Director of Fine Arts, Musées et Bibliothèque de la Ville de Paris, with the French Primitive painter Camille Bombois and Mme Bombois

72. At the opening of the Grandma Moses exhibition in Paris, December 1950: Darthea Speyer, then Assistant Cultural Officer of the U.S. Embassy, Paris, with Jean Cassou, art historian, then chief curator of the Musée National d'Art Moderne, Paris

"My Life's History"

73.
My Homeland.
1945. 16 x 20″

GRANDMA MOSES'S AUTOBIOGRAPHY, *My Life's History,* is the most important source of first-hand information about the artist.

The ability to express herself in a highly personal and original way has already been mentioned. I was convinced that what had appeared in print in 1946–47 was but a small part of what she had to say. Therefore, I urged her to write more about her life. She wrote a short piece titled "I Remember," which was published in the *New York Times Magazine* in 1948. It began:

> What a strange thing is memory, and
> Hope, one looks backward, the other forward,
> The one is of to day, the other is the tomorrow
> memory is History recorded in our brain,
> memory is a painter it paints pictures
> of the past and of the day,

Her autobiography was to open with these words. In the course of the next few years she jotted down little stories and sketches, sending in all 169 handwritten pages; of these only 37 deal with the years in which she had become a world-famous artist, an indication of how little importance she attached to her success as a painter, as compared to the vivid recollections of the full life she had led before as farmwife and head of a large family.

When Grandma Moses came to New York in 1949 I tried using a tape recorder to spare her the trouble of writing down her memories. But she disliked microphones; she preferred, she said, to write everything herself. After the principal content of the book had been written and its general plan had emerged, she dictated connecting passages at her home in Eagle Bridge. Some corrections in spelling were made at her insistence, although the editor was reluctant to alter what he regarded as part of her characteristic way of expressing herself.

Descriptions of everyday life on the farm alternate with recollections of historical events, such as the death of President Lincoln and the still strained relations between North and South long after the Civil War. Many of these memories form a lively commentary to the paintings that illustrate them.

At the end of the book Grandma Moses summarizes:

> In the foregoing chapters I have tried to tell you many true facts as they were in my days. It is hard in this age for one to realize how we grew up at all. I felt older when I was 16 than I ever did since. . . .
>
> Things have changed greatly and still are changing, can they change much more? . . .
>
> And yet I wonder sometimes whether we are progressing. In my childhood days life was different, in many ways, we were slower, still we had a good and happy life, I think, people enjoyed life more in their way, at least they seemed to be happier, they don't take time to be happy nowadays. . . .
>
> I have written my life in small sketches, a little today, a little yesterday, as I thought of it, as I remembered all the things from childhood on through the years, good ones, and unpleasant ones, that is how they come, and that is how we have to take them. I look back on my life like a good day's work, it was done and I feel satisfied with it. I was happy and contented, I knew nothing better and made the best out of what life offered. And life is what we make it, always has been, always will be.

The book was published in 1952 (Harper); it subsequently appeared in England and, in translation, in Germany and Holland.

74.
Grandma Moses,
Otto Kallir, and Lillian Gish
in Eagle Bridge, 1952

David Shaw wrote a dramatization which was televised in March 1952, with Lillian Gish playing the role of Grandma Moses.

Several years later, on one of my visits, Grandma Moses gave me a composition written in her own hand in the year 1874. She had later added a penciled line: "This was last day of school." I seem to remember her telling me that she had given this speech in class at the end of her last school year. It is titled "Let Home Be Made Happy." Anna Mary was fourteen at the time, yet her handwriting already resembles that of the mature woman.

Even though the teacher must have helped formulate the text, the ideas it expresses give insight into the young girl's mental capacity. The guidelines for "good and happy living" she set down at that time are no different from those she practiced throughout her life. She must have treasured this paper, for she kept it from youth on into her old age.

The artistic inclination that showed itself so early is revealed by her remarks on the importance of bringing happiness and harmony to a home by decorating it and making it ever more beautiful: ". . . then let man be happy in adorning his home. in making his home the dwelling of happiness and comfort. let him as far as circumstances will permit be industrious in surrounding it with pleasing objects in decorating it within and without with things that tend to make it agreeable and attractive. . . ."

7
"Let home be made happy
written by Anna Mary in 18"

Let home be made happy.

Industry is a homely virtue yet worthy of all praise. even nature herself reads us a lecture upon it. Let us go for a moment from the homes of men to the quiet forest.

here we shall find no discord or tumult of worldly traffic. it is silent. but look around and see what has been done by the busy hand of nature. will you look at nature and see her with industrious fingers weaving flowers and plants and grasses and trees and shrubs to ornament every part of the earth. and will you go home no wiser for this hint? Will you go home to that dear spot upon which the heart should shine as the sun in spring-time shines upon the flowers. and permit it to be the scene of idleness negligence and waste.

Will you permit it to be a naked shelter from the weather. like the den of a wild beast. will not adorn it by your industry as nature adorns the fields and the forest.

if you say that this is somewhat fanciful and should be regarded rather as an illustration then let it be so. still are not the works of nature designed to have an influence of this kind upon us. then let man be happy in adorning his home. in making his home the dwelling of happiness and comfort. let him as far as circumstances will permit be industrious in surrounding it with pleasing objects in decorating it within and without with things that tend to make it agreeable and attractive. let industry and taste make home the abode of neatness and order a place which brings satisfaction to every inmate and which in absence draws back the heart by the fond memories of comfort and contents let this be done and this dear spot will become more surely the home of cheerfulness. kindness and peace. The parents who would have their children happy must be persevering in bringing them up in the midst of a pleasant. cheerful. a happy home.

there are many happy homes scattered all over our land some are princely abodes in the city others beautiful suburban residences. but among them all there are none more homelike and peaceful than those quiet farmhouses we find among the green hills and fields of the country and none seem more deserving to be called dear home in them we find freedom from the weary rounds of fashion. The wife and mother finds time to devote herself to her children. and her examples and influence impress on their minds those principles which will govern their whole after life.

Waste not your time in gathering unnecessary wealth for them but fill their minds and souls with seeds of virtue.

Let children join with their parents in trying to make home a happy place they can at least practice obedience to parents and kindness to all around. For if you do not when you come to leave Oh! how much you will think of home. but leave it you must soon the lapse of years will bring around the time when you are to go from home you are to leave that dear old place to go out in the world to meet its temptations and to contend with its storms The day will come in which you are to leave the fireside of so many endearments the friends endeared to you by so many acts of kindness. you are to say "Goodbye" to your Mother you are to leave a Father's protection to go forth and act without an adviser. and rely upon your own unaided judgment you are to bid farewell to Brother and sister no more to see them but on occasional visits at your home.

Oh! how cold and desolate will the world appear. how your heart will shrink from launching forth to meet its tempest and its storms. Then you will think of thy own happy home and sigh.

Mid pleasure and palaces though we may roam Be it ever so humble there's no place like home.
Farewell peaceful cottage farewell happy home
Forever I'm doomed a poor exile to roam
This poor aching heart must be laid in the tomb
Ere its cease to regret the endearments of home.

Ceramic Tiles

ANNA MARY'S DESIRE TO MAKE HER SURROUNDINGS PLEASING TO THE eye remained with her throughout her life. There exist a number of objects decorated by her own hand, such as the case of an old clock and those tree mushrooms known popularly as "the Artist's Fungus," which become hard as wood when dried. On these she painted small landscapes. When Mrs. Helen C. Beers, a friend who lived in a neighboring town, suggested in 1951 that she try making sketches on ceramic tiles, she took up the idea with great pleasure. The comparatively easy technique and the playful, noncommital way she could jot down "what the mind may produce," as she once wrote, appealed to her. Mrs. Beers, who worked in ceramics as a hobby, provided six-inch-square tiles and ceramic paints, and instructed the ninety-one-year-old artist in their use.

Over a period of about a year, Mrs. Moses did eighty-five tiles. Some are simple designs, almost drawings, with spare use of color; others are little paintings whose flowing colors make interesting effects on the ceramic background. Mrs. Beers glazed and fired the completed tiles (plates 77–82).

77–8
Ceramic til
1951–52. Each 6 x 6
Numbered and title
on the reverse by the arti

No. 2: *A House*

No. 16: *Narrow Road*

76.
Painting made
on a tree mushroom

No. 35: *Playing*

No. 26: *Church Goers*

No. 42: *Hilltop*

No. 51: *The Marsh*

1946 to 1953

83.
Covered Bridge with Carriage.
1946. 27½ x 21½″.
The Shelburne Museum, Shelburne, Vt.

84.
A Tramp on Christmas Day.
1946. 16 x 19⅞″.
The Shelburne Museum, Shelburne, Vt.

85. *Taking Leg Bale for Security.* 1946. 27 x 20¾″. Collection George M. Newell

86. *The Spring in Evening*. 1947. 27 x 21″. Private collection

87. *Mary and Little Lamb.* 1947. 24 x 34½". Collection Mrs. F. Kallir

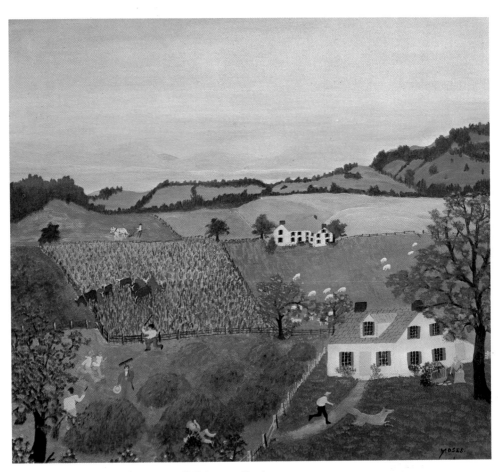

88. *Little Boy Blue.* 1947. 20½ x 23". Private collection

89. *A Fire in the Woods.* 1947. 24 x 36¼". Private collection

90.
The Dividing of the Ways.
1947. 16 x 20".
Private collection

91.
The Church in the Wild Wood.
1948. 16¼ x 20″.
Collection Mrs. William Hayward

92.
The Thunderstorm.
1948. 20¾ x 24¾″.
Private collection

93. *Candle Dip Day in 1800.* 1950. 9 x 9¼".
Private collection

94. *The Meeting House.* 1949. 18¾ x 26¼"

95.
Flying Kites.
1951. 18¼ x 24″.
Collection Mrs. Arthur Choate, Jr.

96.
It Snows, Oh It Snows.
1951. 24 x 30″.
Collection Mrs. F. Kallir

97.
Blacksmith Shop.
1951. 16 x 28″.
Collection Mrs. Forrest K. N

98. *Hoosick River, Summer.* 1952. 18 x 24″. Private collection

3

FAME

New York Herald Tribune Forum, 1953

AMONG THE EVENTS IN WHICH GRANDMA MOSES took part during the last decade of her life was the 22nd Annual Forum arranged by the *New York Herald Tribune* in October 1953. The theme chosen for that year was "New Patterns for Mid-Century Living." The symposium took place in the Grand Ballroom of the Waldorf-Astoria Hotel and was attended by two thousand delegates. The opening address was to have been delivered by Dag Hammarskjold; it was read in his absence by Dr. Ralph Bunche. Among other prominent speakers were John Foster Dulles, Secretary of State, and Francis Henry Taylor, Director of the Metropolitan Museum of Art in New York.

Grandma Moses came to New York with her daughter, Mrs. Fisher. Her appearance was scheduled for the third session, on October 20. The subject for that day was "Time on Our Hands," and the discussion centered on "how the extra hours, the leisure time created by technical advances could best be put to use." After I had given a brief address on "Amateur Painters in America," I introduced the artist and we had an informal conversation—we had discussed it in general terms, but it was not rehearsed.

When she came onto the stage, a little bent but walking with firm steps toward her chair, she was given a standing ovation. Smiling, she faced the crowd, took her seat, and, producing a handkerchief, waved to the audience. This gesture of gracious and spontaneous response brought renewed cheers and applause. It was characteristic of her complete lack of self-consciousness and immediately created an atmosphere of warmth between her and the audience. In the following dialogue she answered all my questions without a moment's hesitation, sometimes interspersing her answers with joking remarks, to the great delight of her listeners. The way in which she spoke about the subject closest to her heart—her painting—and the great modesty with which she regarded her artistic achievement were received by the audience with increasing admiration. The impression Grandma Moses made was expressed by an editorial published in the *New York Herald Tribune* of October 22, 1953:

> For all who suffer from what might be called living strain—and many do complain about the malady—a few minutes' exposure to

New York *Herald* Tribune

ANNUAL FORUM

•

SPEAKER'S TICKET

TUESDAY, OCTOBER 20, 1953   1:45 P.M.

WALDORF-ASTORIA HOTEL

Please take the Park Avenue Elevators to the third floor West Foyer.

Grandma Moses

99. Grandma Moses's ticket

100. Grandma Moses with her daughter, Winona R. Fisher, and Otto Kallir,
filmed for NBC-TV News, after the *Herald Tribune* Forum

the presence of Grandma Moses is powerful therapy. On Tuesday this ninety-three-year-old lady made one of her rare trips to the city from her up-state home in Eagle Bridge, N.Y., to appear at the annual *Herald Tribune* Forum. Some said that she stole the show. Others were impressed with her astonishing vitality, her mental alertness, her humor, simplicity, graciousness, enjoyment of the occasion, and so on. The plain fact is, everybody felt reinvigorated while in her presence. . . .

She holds within herself, in utter unawareness, the wisest secrets of life, secrets composed of many elements, yet as natural and immediate in their expression as a child's smile. While many distinguished persons were appearing before the Forum, a little old lady of ninety-three stepped into their midst and endeared herself to all by her simple aliveness. . . .

Grandma Moses and
Edward R. Murrow, 1955

IT HAD LONG BEEN MY WISH to observe Grandma Moses while painting, but she seemed reluctant to let me watch, so I did not insist. It turned out that she did not consider it proper for a gentleman to enter her bedroom, which she used as a studio. Situated on the second floor of the old house, it was reached by a steep staircase which she climbed countless times a day. After she moved into the new house, she painted in a small room behind the kitchen, and there I could sometimes watch her at work for a few minutes.

Then, in 1953, Edward R. Murrow, the radio and television commentator, wrote to Grandma Moses about interviewing her for television. This seemed to me a good opportunity to film the step-by-step creation of a painting. I knew from experience that she could face any unfamiliar situation or person with complete self-assurance, yet I felt a little uneasy at the thought of a meeting between two such entirely different personalities. However, the importance of the project prompted me to persuade Grandma Moses to go through with this rather strenuous task. Mr. Murrow and his associate, Fred Friendly, agreed to the idea wholeheartedly. The project remained in the planning stage for two years; it was finally realized for Mr. Murrow's television program "See It Now."

The crew of CBS technicians stayed in Eagle Bridge not only for the interview itself, which took place on June 29, 1955, but until the artist had completed an entire painting in front of the cameras. We were in the midst of a heat wave, not exactly the best time to spend many hours under hot floodlights. Everyone was a little tense and uncomfortable, everyone except Grandma Moses, who remained cool and unruffled throughout. The crew had brought along two large movie cameras; one was mounted high above the table on which the artist worked, the other faced her at a distance of about fifteen feet. It was thus possible to take pictures of Grandma Moses as she painted and at the same time to follow the progress of her work in every detail. The artist, who was close to ninety-five, worked for several days under the hot lamps.

101.
Grandma Moses painting in the room
behind the kitchen.
Photo by Ifor Thomas

She had chosen one of her favorite subjects, a sugaring-off scene. After grounding a Masonite board with flat white paint that she applied with a broad housepainter's brush, she took a pencil and drew a fine line across the upper part of the board to mark how far the sky would go. She then took a narrower brush and began to paint the sky, starting at the left. While working, she explained that it was going to be an overcast winter's day; otherwise she would have painted the sky a light blue or a blackish gray, according to whether she wanted to represent a sunny day or perhaps an oncoming snowstorm. After completing the sky, she again took the pencil and indicated with a few delicate lines the contours of mountains and hills. She then proceeded to paint these, either squeezing the various colors directly onto a fine brush or mixing them in small bowls and thinning them with turpentine; for this purpose she often used the lids of preserve jars. She now painted the distant mountains in shades of blue and the closer hills in brown and greenish tones. Without finishing the upper part of her painting, she again took up her pencil and began drawing objects in the foreground, trees and houses, all in scarcely visible outlines, as if only to reserve a certain place for each. After doing

102. *Sugaring.* 1955. 11⅛ x 16″

this, she began to work on the whole picture, now in this, now in another part, here a tree that reached over the entire surface up to the top, there some small shrubs and trees to form a border in the foreground. Once in a while she would interrupt her work for a moment, close her eyes, and then quickly fill in an empty space with the outline of a house, because "something had been missing here." But there was never any prolonged pause that might indicate that the artist was uncertain how to proceed. She always appeared to be following a plan and to know exactly what was to come next and what the final result was to be.

She painted the figures directly into the picture without first sketching them. It was interesting to see how she repeated certain types from previous versions of that specific subject. She seemed to know their exact functions so well that she could easily put them in their proper places. While working on a house or a tree, she sometimes interrupted

103. Grandma Moses and Edward R. Murrow, June 29, 1955. Interview for "See It Now."
Grandma Moses painted *Sugaring* during and after the interview

herself to dab a few spots of brown, blue, or red here and there; these would become dresses, shoes, or the hat of a man who could soon be recognized. After she had taken up a fine brush and indicated face and hands by little pink spots, she sometimes used a match or even a pin to put in the eyes and the mouth, "because the brushes are not fine enough." One could observe her imagination at work and see how each figure she painted meant something to her. After completing the painting (plate 102), she took "glitter" from a box and sprinkled it on the snow that covered the ground and the branches. A friend had in previous years tried to dissuade her from this "treatment" of her pictures, but she could not understand his objection. She said that if he had ever seen the snow on a sunny day, he would realize that it glitters.

The interview with Edward R. Murrow began after the painting was grounded and sketched. Grandma Moses did not share the general excitement; she had watched the complicated preparations with amusement and a trace of irony.

The "tip-up" table, which she had decorated with landscapes long before, had been brought into the living room for her to work on. After a few opening questions by Ed Murrow, Grandma pushed aside her painting and began interviewing her interviewer. She put a piece of paper before him and told him to draw something. When he protested, saying he could not draw, she replied with her usual remark that anybody could and that there was nothing to it. After that, the interview developed into a lively conversation touching upon many subjects, no longer a matter of questions and answers but an animated give-and-take that did not lag for a moment. Those present were somewhat taken aback by Murrow's last question: "What are you going to do for the next twenty years, Grandma Moses?" Without faltering for a second, seriously and calmly, she raised her hand and said: "I am going up yonder. Naturally—naturally, I should. After you get to be about so old you can't expect to go on much farther."

> MURROW: But you don't spend much time thinking about it or worrying about it. Do you?
> GRANDMA MOSES: Oh, no. No. No. You don't worry because you think, well, what a blessing it will be to be all united again. I'm the last one left of my sisters and brothers. . . .
> MURROW: So this is something that in a sense you have no fear about or no apprehension?
> GRANDMA: Oh, no. Go to sleep and wake up in the next world. I think that's the way. Did you ever know when you went to sleep?
> MURROW: No, I don't think so.
> GRANDMA: When the last thought came—you didn't know.
> MURROW: No. That's true.
> GRANDMA: You might wake up the next morning and think, well, that's what I was thinking about, but you didn't know when that last thought came. Well, that's the way you'll go to sleep.

Murrow, so poised and aloof, was visibly taken off guard by the turn of the conversation and closed the interview with the words: "Well, you will leave more behind you than most of us will, when you go to sleep."

Ed Murrow and all who had witnessed the interview felt that it had been an unforgettable experience. When CBS arranged a program on April 30, 1965, in commemoration of Edward Murrow's death, the last part of his interview with Grandma Moses was included among the most memorable moments of his broadcasting career.

Painting the Eisenhower Farm

For "Grandma", Moses, a real artist —

From a rough amateur —
with best wishes

Dwight D. Eisenhower
France, March 1952.

...om the Eisenhowers, *Marnes la Coquette*

OUR POND AT
VILLA SAINT PIERRE
ORIGINAL BY D.D.E.

Card from General Dwight D. Eisenhower

GRANDMA MOSES HAD ALWAYS ADMIRED GENERAL EISENHOWER, and he in turn had long shown interest in her art. Himself an amateur painter, he had devoted much time to this hobby before becoming president.

In 1952, while still in France, he sent Mrs. Moses a reproduction of one of his paintings with a hand-written inscription. She treasured this tribute to her art, and had it framed and hung in her living room.

Toward the end of 1955, President Eisenhower's Cabinet decided to mark the third anniversary of his inauguration by giving him a Grandma Moses painting. It was agreed that she would paint a picture of the Eisenhower Farm at Gettysburg, Pennsylvania.

She had never been there, and was uncertain how to comply with this unusual request, but she felt greatly honored by the "order" and was ready to try her best. She was sent about twenty black-and-white and color photographs showing house and grounds from all sides. Using this material as a guide, she created two paintings each giving a different view of the farm. The more representative one (plate 105) was selected and given to the President in a surprise meeting of the Cabinet on January 18, 1956. Vice President Richard M. Nixon acted as master of ceremonies. The next day's issue of the *New York Times* reported:

> The President obviously was happy both with the painting and
> with the artistic liberties the famous artist had taken with his

105. *The Eisenhower Farm.* 1956. 16 x 24″. The Dwight D. Eisenhower Library, Abilene, Kan.

Gettysburg property. Farmer Eisenhower is proud of his growing herd of Black Angus cattle. He owns only one Holstein and one Brown Swiss. But Grandma Moses painted four Holsteins to three Angus cattle grazing in the pastures. General Eisenhower was delighted to see the recently built golf green, which had grown in size in the transfer from a photograph to an oil canvas. "I wish it was that big," said the President to Mrs. Eisenhower. He spotted his three grandchildren—David, Susan, and Barbara Eisenhower—riding in the pony cart. The Great Dane that usually precedes them looked more like a wire fox-terrier.

106. A letter to President Eisenhower

Grandma Moses
Eagle Bridge
New York

Jan. 12 1956.

Mr. President,

I was very honored to be asked to paint a picture of your home in Getrysburg.

Although most of my paintings are memories and imagination, I tried to do this for you and hope it will please you.

My very best wishes for your continued good health on your third anniversary, as our President.

Very sincerely,
Grandma Moses.

Historical Themes

GRANDMA MOSES REPEATEDLY USED HISTORICAL EVENTS she had been told about or which occurred in her lifetime as subjects for her paintings.

When President Lincoln was assassinated in 1865, Anna Mary was not quite five years old, but the event remained vivid in her mind throughout her life. In 1957 she painted a small picture (plate 108) showing a village street, with the doors of the church and the houses draped in black bunting. In recollecting this very early experience, she wrote:

> One day, mother, aunt Lib and I, we left Greenwich to come down to grandma's, just above Eagle Bridge where she lived. Mother was driving the buggy, an old fan horse, a gentle horse. . . . I don't remember the trip so much until we got down into Coila. . . .
>
> Mother noticed that everything was trimmed in black. I remember her saying, "Oh, what has happened?" It was war times. . . . She went into the store and asked what had happened. The pillars on the store were all wrapped in black bunting. And this man told her that President Lincoln was shot the night before. And I remember her coming back to the buggy and she said to aunt Lib, "Oh, what will become of us now?" And if she hadn't used those words, I don't suppose I would have ever remembered it.

Grandma Moses was especially interested in the history of her neighborhood and knew a great deal about it. The Revolutionary War, in which some of her ancestors had taken part, particularly fascinated her. In 1953 she painted three pictures of the Battle of Bennington (plate 107), which had taken place close by—the site is marked by a monument. In preparation for her work she looked up many historical details in reference books. In the first two versions she painted the monument in the background; when it was pointed out to her that this was an amusing error, since naturally no monument existed at that time, she made a third painting without it.

Grandma Moses never ceased to follow current events with lively interest and understanding. In 1959 Alaska became the forty-ninth state of the Union. During the preceding year there had been much discussion about how the new flag should look with one star added to forty-eight. The idea stimulated Grandma's recollections, for she had many times witnessed the growth of the United States and the changing of the flag.

107. *The Battle of Bennington.* 1953. 18 x 30½″

108.
Lincoln.
1957. 12 x 16⅛″.
Collection Shirley Futterman

109.
Old Glory.
1958. 12 x 16″

She made a design for the new American flag, basing it on "the first flag with stars and stripes [which] was that of Ticonderoga. It had a circle of thirteen. Why not fill the others in?" she wrote. It was a sketch of just the flag without background, on a 12-by-16-inch board. She called it *Old Glory* (plate 109). On a second small oil painting dated the same day, December 6, 1958, Grandma Moses showed this new flag being hoisted to the accompaniment of salvos from two cannons at the foot of the flagpole.

Hundredth Birthday, September 7, 1960

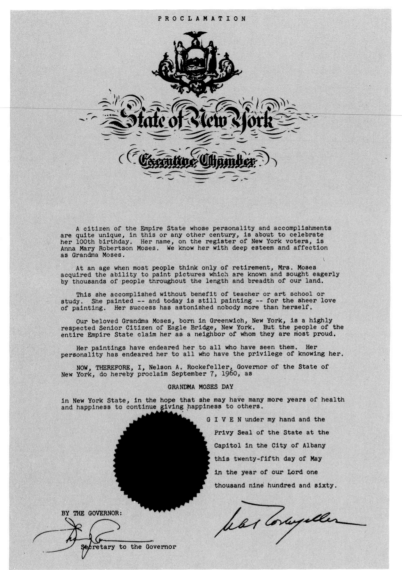

PROCLAMATION

State of New York

Executive Chamber

A citizen of the Empire State whose personality and accomplishments are quite unique, in this or any other century, is about to celebrate her 100th birthday. Her name, on the register of New York voters, is Anna Mary Robertson Moses. We know her with deep esteem and affection as Grandma Moses.

At an age when most people think only of retirement, Mrs. Moses acquired the ability to paint pictures which are known and sought eagerly by thousands of people throughout the length and breadth of our land.

This she accomplished without benefit of teacher or art school or study. She painted -- and today is still painting -- for the sheer love of painting. Her success has astonished nobody more than herself.

Our beloved Grandma Moses, born in Greenwich, New York, is a highly respected Senior Citizen of Eagle Bridge, New York. But the people of the entire Empire State claim her as a neighbor of whom they are most proud.

Her paintings have endeared her to all who have seen them. Her personality has endeared her to all who have the privilege of knowing her.

NOW, THEREFORE, I, Nelson A. Rockefeller, Governor of the State of New York, do hereby proclaim September 7, 1960, as

GRANDMA MOSES DAY

in New York State, in the hope that she may have many more years of health and happiness to continue giving happiness to others.

G I V E N under my hand and the Privy Seal of the State at the Capitol in the City of Albany this twenty-fifth day of May in the year of our Lord one thousand nine hundred and sixty.

BY THE GOVERNOR:

Secretary to the Governor

110.
Proclamation by Governor
Nelson A. Rockefeller, 1960

PREPARATIONS FOR THE HUNDREDTH BIRTHDAY of Grandma Moses began early. In May 1960, Governor Nelson A. Rockefeller issued a proclamation declaring September 7 "Grandma Moses Day" in New York State.

As the day approached, many newspapers requested personal interviews. Fearing that it would be too strenuous for the centenarian to have dozens of reporters descend on her home in Eagle Bridge, her family allowed only a very few to see her. One of the most sensitive reports was written by Joy Miller of the Associated Press, whose article was published nationwide on September 4:

Your impression of Grandma Moses is that she is very fragile and very old. She's sitting in the living room, looking small at one end of a big sofa, wearing a blue print dress and pink sweater, with a black ribbon around her throat. Her arthritic fingers are curled together in her lap. You advance hesitantly. How do you address America's best known primitive painter? . . . Is it too forward to call her "Grandma"? . . . Do you have to shout?

But she has sighted company. Her face lights up in a gamin grin, her hazel eyes sparkle behind their spectacles. Her welcoming hand grasps yours with startling vigor.

As she chats about this and that, the character of a remarkable woman emerges: kindly, humorous, unaffected, indomitable, with sight and hearing in admirable repair. You become aware that her seemingly frail 100-pound frame supports a spirit that's at once robust and ageless.

From the beginning of September, mailbags full of cards and letters swamped the Eagle Bridge Post Office. Hundreds of telegrams arrived, piles of gifts were stowed away in the sunporch of the farmhouse, where Grandma Moses took loving care of her geraniums, African violets, and coleus. President and Mrs. Eisenhower, Vice President and Mrs. Nixon, and former President and Mrs. Truman sent birthday tributes. President Truman had never failed to remember Grandma's birthday since their meeting in 1949.

For the benefit of friends and neighbors who could not come on the 7th, which was a working day, Grandma Moses's family gave a birthday party at her home on Sunday the 4th. After this, Forrest and Mary Moses had to hold open house for more than a week to accommodate the steady stream of visitors. In the midst of all this excitement Grandma Moses was cheerful and serene and seemed to enjoy everything. When she had realized that her efforts to discourage an elaborate celebration would fail, she said: "I'm going to sit right here, just so, and the others can do the work. I wish they wouldn't fuss, but it's a nice excuse for the young people to get together."

Several weeks went by before the excitement subsided and she could go back to the quiet life she had been leading of late.

In honor of Grandma Moses's hundredth birthday, the IBM Gallery of Arts and Sciences arranged a loan exhibition, "My Life's History," which ran from September 12 to October 6, 1960. The gallery had been inaugurated five years earlier with a comprehensive Moses show.

111. Grandma Moses and Thomas J. Watson, 1955

Although Thomas J. Watson, the artist's longtime friend and active supporter, had died in 1956, his family remained interested in her work, as did the art department of IBM.

The pictures for the birthday exhibition were selected to depict events from the life of the artist as she remembered them. Most of the captions that accompanied the paintings were taken from her autobiography, but a few quotations from the previous book, *Grandma Moses: American Primitive*, were also included.

Prominent personalities who had taken a personal interest in the artist and in her work formed the honorary committee. Among them were former President and Mrs. Truman, Eleanor Roosevelt, Irving Berlin, Jean Cassou, Walt Disney, Lillian Gish, and Thornton Wilder.

"The Night Before Christmas"

112. *Waiting for Santa Claus.* 1960. 12 x 16".
Grandma Moses Properties, Inc., New York

113. *Santa Claus II.* 1960. 16 x 24".
Grandma Moses Properties, Inc., New York

EARLY IN 1960 GRANDMA MOSES'S STRENGTH HAD BEGUN TO FAIL. She could no longer walk around very much and was more and more confined to the house; painting lifted her spirits and gave her a fresh incentive every day. At that time a proposal was made by Bennett Cerf and Robert Bernstein of Random House that she illustrate Clement C. Moore's famous poem, *The Night Before Christmas.* The idea of creating pictures for a Christmas story did not appeal to her. She had declared time and again that she only wanted to paint scenes and situations she knew from her own experience. She once wrote to me (March 4, 1944): "Some one has asked me to paint Biblical pictures, and I say *no* I'll not paint something that we know nothing about, might just as well paint something that will happen 2 thousand years hence."

Still, she took up the project, for she liked the poem and knew it by heart. At first she dutifully tried to follow the text and painted scenes and objects familiar to a child's conception of Christmas—stockings hanging by the fireplace, candy canes, and toys (plates 112, 113). As her work progressed, her imagination unfolded. *So Long till Next Year* (plate 114), one of the many paintings done for the book (though finally not published in it), was obviously meant to conclude the series. This work far transcends any factual illustration.

It is a pure artistic expression of almost dreamlike quality and is also remarkable in that this effect is achieved entirely by means of color. The intense blue of a deep, clear winter night is illumined by an almost white moon that bathes the unrealistic feathery branches of the trees in a silvery light; stars are scattered across the dark sky. There are only these two colors, blue and white, except for a few beautifully distributed patches of red—Santa's coat and the red chimneys. The reindeer, quite substantial and lifelike in the other illustrations, are, as they should be, otherworldly apparitions receding into the beyond. One can imagine a child, still half asleep yet expecting the miraculous, stepping to the window in the middle of the night and experiencing this vision of a transformed world.

Grandma Moses's work on the book, begun in March 1960, was interrupted by the commotion caused by her hundredth birthday. She completed the pictures in November of 1960, but did not live to see the book's publication in 1962. It has since become very popular and is read and shown every year on the December 24th telecast of the CBS-TV children's program "Captain Kangaroo."

114. *So Long till Next Year.* 1960. 16 x 24". Grandma Moses Properties, Inc., New York

The Last Months

115. Grandma Moses on her 101st birthday, September 7, 1961

ON JULY 18, 1961, FORREST AND MARY MOSES took Grandma to the Health Center at Hoosick Falls. Forrest wrote me: "Grandma feels good, only for her legs, they are so weak; her hearing is good again and her voice is strong." She had fallen several times, and it was decided that she would be better off under professional care. Grandma Moses was quite unhappy at the nursing home, and hoped her stay there would be only temporary.

As long as she had been at home she had continued to paint, completing more than twenty-five pictures after her hundredth birthday. At the nursing home, however, she was not allowed to do what had become her most important activity. Her physician, Dr. Clayton Shaw, who had been the family's doctor for fifty years, felt that she "would not rest if she had her paints."

THE WHITE HOUSE
WASHINGTON

September 5, 1961

Dear Grandma Moses:

I want again to send you my warmest best wishes
as you reach another milestone in your long and
celebrated career.

Your painting and your personal influence continue
to play a large and valuable role in our national
life.

Both Mrs. Kennedy and I want to wish you best
health and happiness in the years ahead.

Sincerely,

Grandma Moses
Eagle Bridge, New York

116. Letter from President John F. Kennedy

During one of his visits she hid the doctor's stethoscope. When he asked, "Where's my stethoscope?" Grandma Moses replied: "That's what I won't tell you. I hid it. It's a forfeit. You take me back to Eagle Bridge and you'll get back your stethoscope."

Just before her 101st birthday I visited her and found her in good spirits. She was mentally alert and full of plans. "As soon as I get back home, I will start painting again," she said. Asked how she would celebrate her birthday this year, she said: "Much as I enjoy visiting with my friends and neighbors, I have come to see that *one* hundred-year celebration is enough for anybody, and I would like to spend my 101st birthday the same as my first day, very quiet."

Again Governor Rockefeller proclaimed September 7 as Grandma Moses Day in New York State. On that day the Health Center at Hoosick Falls was described as resembling "one huge bowl of flowers," for at Grandma's request the bouquets were shared by the other patients at the home. Among the tributes she received was a letter from President John F. Kennedy.

In October 1961, Random House published *The Grandma Moses Story Book*, a collection of stories for children by various authors, illustrated with her paintings. This was the last of her books the artist saw published.

The Death of Grandma Moses

EARLY IN THE AFTERNOON OF DECEMBER 13, 1961, Dr. Shaw called from Hoosick Falls to tell me that Grandma Moses had passed away a short while before. "She just wore out," he said. Her death had been expected for some weeks; she had grown steadily weaker, her mind had begun to wander, and she slept for long hours. Her daughter-in-law Dorothy had been at Grandma Moses's bedside every day during these last weeks and months.

News of the artist's death was broadcast over all radio networks and published nationwide on the front pages of newspapers. Her passing brought words of sympathy from all over the country.

President Kennedy issued the following statement:

> The death of Grandma Moses removes a beloved figure from American life. The directness and vividness of her paintings restored a primitive freshness to our perception of the American scene. All Americans mourn her loss. Both her work and her life helped our nation renew its pioneer heritage and recalled its roots in the countryside and on the frontier.

Governor Nelson A. Rockefeller said the death of Grandma Moses "is a loss to all of us in New York State and to those everywhere who loved simplicity and beauty. She painted for the sheer love of painting, and throughout her 101 years, she was endeared to all who had the privilege of knowing her."

Of the numerous editorials on her life, her artistic achievement and its meaning for our time, one tribute is reprinted here from *The New Yorker* of December 23, 1961:

> The death of a very old person seems no more natural, no less an untoward incursion, than the death of a young one. Perhaps death seems natural only to Nature herself—and even she may have some doubts. Yet we cannot think of the life, now concluded, of Anna Mary Robertson Moses without cheerfulness. To live one allotted span as a farm wife and the mother of ten children, and then, at the age of seventy-six, to begin another, as an artist, as Grandma Moses, and to extend this second life into twenty-five years of unembarrassed productiveness—such a triumph over the normal course of things offers small cause for mourning. If we do mourn, it

117.

The Reverend Joel B. Miller conducting graveside rites for Grandma Moses, December 16, 1961. UPI Photo

is for ourselves; she had become by her hundredth year one of those old people who, as old buildings civilize a city or spindly church spires bind up a landscape, make the world seem safer. Shaw and Brancusi were examples; Churchill and Schweitzer still are. They pay the world the great compliment of being reluctant to leave it, and their reluctance becomes a benediction.

Grandma Moses was buried on December 16 in a hilltop grave in Maple Grove Cemetery, Hoosick Falls, overlooking the Hoosick Valley. About a hundred friends and neighbors joined with the family in a fifteen-minute Episcopal service conducted at her Eagle Bridge house by the Reverend Joel B. Miller, Rector of St. Mark's Episcopal Church in Hoosick Falls, of which she had been a member. The house was so crowded that mourners stood in the hall and in the kitchen. The priest interpolated into the service phrases of his own which had reference to Grandma's special gifts as an artist, but there were no eulogies.

A thirty-five-car cortege proceeded from the house to the cemetery some five miles distant, with Washington County sheriff's deputies as escort to the county line and Rensselaer County deputies taking over at that point. The day was clear and bright and bitter cold, with temperatures in the low teens, but almost all those at the house continued to the cemetery. Along the route, groups of people waited in front of their homes to pay their last respects.

At the graveside, Father Miller read briefly from the burial service of the Book of Common Prayer. Anna Mary Robertson Moses was buried next to her husband, Thomas Salmon Moses, her son Hugh, and her daughter Winona. The services were marked by the simplicity that was the keynote of Grandma Moses's life. Father Miller said: "It was exactly what she would have wanted—a simple, farmhouse, family funeral."

118.

The grave: Thomas S. Moses/his wife/ Anna Mary Robertson/Winona R. Fish At left, grave of Hugh W. Moses. Maple Grove Cemetery, Hoosick Falls, Photo by John Woodruff

1953 to 1961

119. *Joy Ride.* 1953. 18 x 24″

120.
Bennington.
1953. 18 x 24″.
Collection George Eisenpresser

121. *The Thrashers.* 1954. 18 x 24½″

122. *Sugaring Off.* 1955. 18 x 24″

123. *A Blizzard.* 1956. 15⅞ x 24″. Private collection

124.
Wind Storm.
1956. 16 x 24″.
Private collection

125.
Snowed In.
1957. 12 x 16″

126. *Balloon.* 1957. 15⅞ x 24″. Collection Otto Kallir

127. *Old Times.* 1957. 16 x 24″

128.
A Blizzard.
1958. 16 x 24⅛″

129. *Eagle Bridge Hotel.* 1959. 16 x 24″

130. *Sugar Time.* 1960. 16 x 24″

131. *Get Out the Sleigh.* 1960. 16 x 24″

132. *White Birches.* 1961. 16 x 24″

Exhibitions, 1962 — 1972

133.
Corn.
1958. 16 x 23⅞".
Pushkin Museum, Moscow, U.S.S.R.

A PHENOMENON OFTEN OBSERVED is that the public's interest slackens after an artist's death; his fame becomes dimmed, his name no longer appears in the news. Then, sometimes, he is rediscovered. Finally the pendulum that has swung far out in both directions levels off to an objective and lasting evaluation.

Such a development seemed very likely in the case of Grandma Moses. So much had been written about her exceptional rise to fame in old age, and now the appealing aura surrounding her person faded with her passing. But the public's interest, far from diminishing, has steadily grown as her art, stripped of anecdotal embellishments, emerges and speaks for itself.

One-man shows and museum exhibitions that took place in the decade following the artist's death were received with great interest. In November 1962, a memorial show was held at the Galerie St. Etienne, New York. The catalogue reproduced details of pictures to draw attention to various characteristics of the artist's painting technique.

A traveling show, sponsored and circulated by the Smithsonian Institution (1962–64) found the greatest response. The collection was presented at museums in nine American cities and thereafter in eight European countries, finally going to Russia at the invitation of the

113

Soviet Ministry for Culture. It was exhibited at the Pushkin Museum in Moscow in December of 1964. "The show was very well received by the public, once they had overcome their initial surprise," wrote the Counselor for Cultural Affairs of the United States Embassy in Moscow. "Judging by the comments we heard . . . the evident delight that Grandma Moses took in the execution of all her work was the most impressive aspect for the Soviets. They were surprised, and quite pleased, to find a total absence of 'social message'. . . . I would judge that 100,000 viewers would not be too generous an estimate. . . . There were lines of people waiting to see the show. . . . The Embassy regards the Moses exhibit as a successful and very valid effort . . . to increase Soviet understanding of the United States and its people."

From 1964 on, the Hammer Galleries, New York, in cooperation with the Galerie St. Etienne, has been presenting Moses exhibitions at Christmas time.

In 1963, 1965, and 1967 the Bennington Museum in Vermont arranged Grandma Moses shows that met with such lively response that the idea of establishing a more permanent exhibition arose. The Grandma Moses Gallery was opened in a wing of the museum on May 10, 1968. Beginning with her first known picture, the *Fireboard*, "worsted" pictures, and small early paintings, the collection contained prominent works from the artist's two productive decades. In addition, photographs, exhibition posters, and documents conveyed a vivid impression of her life and the development of her fame as an artist. The Grandma Moses Gallery was closed after the 1972 season.

The most comprehensive Moses exhibition ever assembled, titled "Art and Life of Grandma Moses," was presented at the Gallery of Modern Art in New York in 1969. A total of 141 paintings lent by museums and collectors all over the country showed a cross-section of the artist's entire oeuvre.

Shortly after Grandma Moses's death the little one-room schoolhouse in Eagle Bridge, where Anna Mary had gone to school, was up for sale. Her son Forrest and daughter-in-law Mary acquired it and had it moved to a site next to the old Moses farm. Leaving the original structure untouched, they filled it with countless memorabilia, including the old shop sign of Thomas's Drugstore in Hoosick Falls, where Louis Caldor had first seen her pictures, as well as objects and souvenirs she had assembled from childhood on. The schoolhouse was opened to the public in 1966. It has recently been acquired with its entire contents by the Bennington Museum and set up adjacent to it.

134. The Grandma Moses Gallery, 1968–72, at the Bennington Museum, Bennington.

The Grandma Moses Stamp

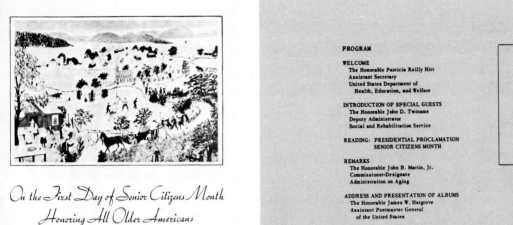

IN 1969, THE UNITED STATES GOVERNMENT paid tribute to the memory of Grandma Moses by issuing a six-cent stamp, an honor accorded to but a few American artists.

Senator Kenneth B. Keating first brought up the idea on the Senate floor in 1960, on the occasion of the artist's forthcoming hundredth birthday. The *Congressional Record* of June 20, 1960 (vol. 106, no. 113), includes the following statement:

> Mr. President, one of the leading citizens of my State is, in the fullest sense of the word, a citizen who belongs to all the world. She is Anna Mary Robertson Moses of Eagle Bridge, N.Y., better known everywhere as Grandma Moses.
>
> This great lady and artist has brought an inspiring message to people all over the world. Not only has Grandma Moses become a legend in her time; she has also demonstrated to elderly people

everywhere that the opportunity for achievement and satisfaction really knows no age. By her example and through her paintings she has projected a wonderful and indelible image of America to the four corners of the globe.

In my view, the message of Grandma Moses and all she stands for could be communicated ideally through the issuance of a commemorative stamp bearing one of her paintings. It would be a fitting tribute on the occasion of her 100th birthday on September 7 of this year. I have made this suggestion to the Postmaster General and I am hopeful an affirmative response will be forthcoming.

It took nine years for Senator Keating's idea to be realized. When the decision to issue the stamp was finally reached, J. Carter Brown, Director of the National Gallery of Art in Washington, D.C., was asked to suggest a painting. He recommended *July Fourth* (see plate 63), owned by the White House, as a suitable subject. The design for the stamp is a detail from that painting. Printed on a two-plate Giori press in six colors, in an edition of 166,630,400, the stamp was released in a ceremony in Washington on May 1, 1969, marking the beginning of Senior Citizens' Month.

136. The Grandma Moses stamp

4

THE RANGE OF GRANDMA MOSES'S ART

From Amateur to Professional

In the beginning Grandma Moses worked more or less casually, taking pleasure in painting as she had in doing needlework of different kinds throughout her life. A study of her paintings shows that she made repeated use of motifs borrowed from various sources, combining and recombining them in much the way an experienced housewife uses elements of different patterns in making clothing for her family and decorative objects for her home. At times she also copied from reproductions.

It is not possible to trace all the pictures, mostly of small size, which Grandma Moses made in the period before her true development as a painter. Their style is very inconsistent, and their artistic quality depends more on her feeling for the subject and, perhaps, for the intended recipient of the picture than on her concern with the painting as such.

Then there are the pictures which Louis J. Caldor assembled between 1938 and 1941. The first Moses works to appear at an exhibition were three paintings displayed at the Museum of Modern Art in 1939 and those in her one-man show at the Galerie St. Etienne in 1940. Some of Caldor's purchases may have been painted years earlier, and we know about the exhibited pictures only that they were done previous to the shows.

It is a remarkable phenomenon that Grandma Moses's mind always remained alert, open, and eager to take up new suggestions if they appealed to her. Thus, within the period of a very few years, what had at first been a hobby and pleasant pastime became a full-time professional activity. She even learned to manage some sort of "bookkeeping" with regard to her work, conscientiously filling orders and requests, noting data and prices, and personally supervising the shipping of her paintings.

In November 1941, when people had begun to be interested in Grandma Moses, her youngest brother, Fred E. Robertson, a talented self-taught artist in his own right, gave her a book in which to record her paintings. The book is bound in black boards; it measures 7¾ by 10 inches and bears the word "Record" in gold lettering on the cover. The pages are numbered from 1 to 152, and the first one is inscribed in Fred Robertson's hand (plate 137). To make it easier for his sister to keep

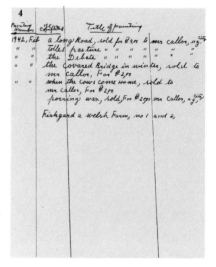

137–39.
Pages from the artist's Record Book

Anna Mary Robertson Moses
Eagle Bridge, N. Y
Born Sept 7, 1860

1944:
Date of Painting *June 25*

Number of Painting *608.*

Title *the sun has gone down.*

GRANDMA MOSES
Anna Mary Robertson Moses

Date of Painting *Oct 12, 1955,*

Number of Painting *1695,*

Title *September.*

The copyright of this painting is the property of
GRANDMA MOSES PROPERTIES, Inc.
46 West 57th Street, N. Y. C.

140–41. Labels used by Grandma Moses
on her pictures (original size)

records, he put headings on the first few pages (plates 138, 139).

Record Book entries for the years 1941–45 reflect a period of exuberant activity. Grandma Moses found herself suddenly popular, her work in great demand. Requests came in the mail and from travelers who made a detour through Eagle Bridge to buy a painting directly from the artist. Many pictures dating from this period were not recorded in her book.

At this time, Grandma Moses began noting more frequently the amounts for which she sold her pictures. A comparison of prices with dimensions indicates that she priced them according to size. On page 18 (1943), for example, a picture measuring 6¼ by 8 inches is listed as having been sold for $2; one measuring 11½ by 13¾ inches brought $5; and one 23 by 26¾ inches brought $15.

It is not possible to establish at what point Grandma Moses began to put numbers on her paintings. The logic of her early system of numbering defies analysis. The first pictures on which numbers appear were painted in 1941 but bear such numbers as 2010, 202, 2211! A painting dated February 9, 1942, is numbered 9, while in January of that year she used 29 and 199. Such discrepancies also appear in the Record Book. On page 24 the number 469 is followed by 500; on pages 31–32 there is a jump from 808 to 1000; on page 35 Grandma Moses "progressed" from 1099 to 1010, but on page 39 from 1099 to 1100.

However, from page 39 (that is, following 1945) up to the last painting, entries were made in a quite systematic manner. After 1955 they were written by Mrs. Winona Fisher and, after Mrs. Fisher's death in 1958, by Forrest Moses.

At about the same time that Fred Robertson gave Grandma Moses the Record Book, he also presented her with labels to paste on the reverse side of her pictures. On these labels she was to enter date, number, and title. When the supply of labels ran out in 1950, new ones were printed (plates 140, 141). In later years the new type of label was filled in by Mrs. Fisher and by Forrest Moses.

A catalogue and index of all works by Grandma Moses known to me is included in the book *Grandma Moses,* published in 1973 by Harry N. Abrams, Inc., New York. Altogether, nearly 1600 pictures have been recorded which the artist created in the course of about thirty years.

Evolving Her Own Style

142. *Hoosick Falls, N.Y., in Winter.* 1944. 20 x 24″. The Phillips Collection, Washington, D.C.

GRANDMA MOSES HAS BEEN CALLED a "primitive" painter, a term generally applied to artists who have had no professional training. She shared with other so-called "primitives" a naive and almost childlike approach to her subject, not worrying whether she would be able to solve a problem with the artistic means at her disposal. However, as her technical ability progressed and developed, so did her gifts as a painter, and she achieved works which far outrank what one is wont to label "primitive." It cannot be said of many artists—whether professional or self-taught— that they have created a distinctive style of their own, as has Grandma Moses.

The artist's work is basically concerned with one theme: life on the farm and in the country. But on closer study, it reveals an astonishing variety of treatment and subject matter.

Landscapes

143. *Hoosick Valley (from the Window)*. 1946. 19½ x 22″. Private collection

MOST OF HER PAINTINGS ARE LANDSCAPES, often depicting the countryside where New York borders Vermont. This is "Grandma Moses Country," the region she knew and loved for a lifetime, where year after year she watched the passing of the seasons. This landscape often forms the setting for the specific events and activities she pictured. Towns, villages, and particular buildings in the area that had played a role in her life— Bennington, Hoosick Falls, Williamstown, the schoolhouse in Eagle Bridge, the Whiteside Church—became her subjects.

She attained the highest artistry in some of the pure landscapes, such as two works that represent the countryside as she saw it from her house: *Hoosick Valley (from the Window)* and *Hoosick River, Winter* (plates 143, 146). The one depicts a spring day, with fruit trees in bloom. There is no "action," the barely indicated figures of grazing cattle only serving

144. *Williamstown.* 1946. Canvas, 36 x 48″. Collection Mrs. Rockefeller Prentice

145.
The Whiteside Church.
1945. 9¾ x 17″.
Private collection

146. *Hoosick River, Winter.* 1952. 18 x 24″. Private collection

to emphasize the tranquillity of the scene framed by the window and its white-dotted net curtains. In *Hoosick River, Winter* the cold starkness of a winter's day is simply and beautifully rendered; the frozen river is seen between snow-covered fields and bare trees; the distant hills are gray. The hunters in the foreground underscore the mood. The stillness of winter is upon the land.

The landscape of Virginia, where the artist lived in her early married years, was equally dear to her. She frequently painted "that beautiful Shenandoah Valley" and the various places where she and her husband had lived and raised their children.

Apple Butter Making (plate 147) evokes a recollection from this time. It is set in the orchard and meadows of the "Dudley Place" near Staunton, Virginia, where the family lived for eight years. "Just a common farm,"

147. *Apple Butter Making*. 1947. 19¼ x 23¼″. Galerie St. Etienne, New York

she later described it. The large house in the foreground at the right can be identified as the family's actual abode; a photograph that Grandma Moses kept shows a house almost identical with the one in the picture. This work is interesting both in its well-planned and tidily executed composition—the many people, each busy with a particular chore, are in correct proportion to their surroundings—and in its color scheme of predominating greens and reds. The chief color accent is provided by the meticulously painted red-brick house with green shutters and a white portico. A kettle for boiling down the cider and apples hangs over an open fire in the orchard. In spite of the importance of the house, the circular spot of fire is, so to speak, the heart of the painting, because of its concentration of color and its decisive part in the process of the work. Beyond a faintly visible white fence in the background is the river bank. Here, as in so many of the artist's pictures, trees play an important role; she loved them especially and observed their various shapes and tones. In this summer painting they are bushy with abundant deep-green foliage. There is an interesting detail in the left foreground: the figure of a woman dressed in a gown of pale mauve, a color that does not otherwise appear in the painting. It is said that Grandma Moses sometimes used this color when she put herself into a picture.

Between 1943 and 1950, Grandma Moses created about twenty very large paintings measuring up to 36 by 48 inches. She was first encouraged to venture into this format by Ala Story, who sent her two large canvases in the summer of 1943 and suggested that she paint two winter scenes. The bedroom in which Grandma worked in the "old home" was far too small to accommodate a large table or easel; she

148. The Moses family in front of the Dudley Place in Virginia, c. 1892

therefore had to lay the canvases on her bed while painting—a strenuous procedure for a woman in her eighties. She first did a painting of a winter landscape, *Over the River*, and then, instead of another snow picture, *Checkered House* (see plate 38). During the following years, Mrs. Story sent her more large canvases. In between, the artist also did several paintings of similar size on Masonite board, her favorite material ("it will last longer").

Considering that only a few years earlier Grandma Moses's first timid attempts had been small paintings in which she depicted specific objects and narrowly defined scenes, one cannot but be amazed at the daring and confidence with which this very old woman undertook the task of painting such large pictures. They are freely and harmoniously composed, giving full scope to her imagination, and they rank among her very best.

A number of them deal with themes the artist had taken up formerly in smaller pictures, but the large versions never give an impression of being empty, artificially enlarged, or "filled in" to make use of the greater space. Sometimes the large canvas is a summing up of many previous artistic experiments and achievements, as for instance *Grandma Moses Going to Big City* and *Grandma Moses's Childhood Home* (plates 149, 150). These two works are especially interesting for the sense of rhythm they convey.

In *Grandma Moses Going to Big City*, the very accurately rendered compound of the Moses farm is circled by a country road leading from in front of the buildings into the background. A driveway goes up to the house and on it there is the old car that will take Grandma to the railroad station. This beautifully composed painting, in which everything is in perfect proportion, is, by the way, another example of an incidental scene that gives a picture its title.

In *Grandma Moses's Childhood Home* the rhythm is especially marked. Two wide circles formed by roads surround buildings, meadows, and orchard; they are linked by a large barn in the center.

Out for Christmas Trees (plate 151), painted on Masonite, is one of the artist's most popular and frequently reproduced pictures. It is the ideal example of a "Grandma Moses" if one has come to think of her mainly as an artist of the winter scene. Strong and simple, it is painted in tones of white and deep green. Among the clusters of fir trees a few tall trees that have shed their foliage stand out, their bare, snow-covered branches

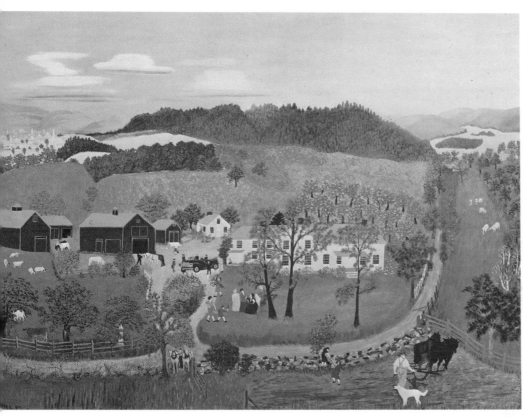

149. *Grandma Moses Going to Big City.* 1946. Canvas, 36 x 48″. Private collection

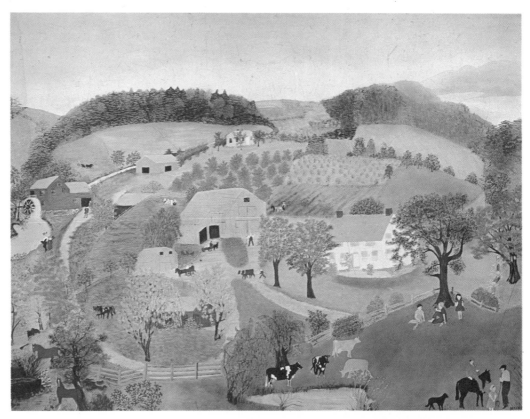

150. *Grandma Moses's Childhood Home.* 1946. Canvas, 36 x 48″. Collection Alfred J. Ostheimer III

151. *Out for Christmas Trees.* 1946. 26 x 36″. Private collection

silhouetted against a gray sky. Horse-drawn sleighs are arriving or leaving; the movement of the animals is masterfully observed. The figures are comparatively small and do not detract from the overall atmosphere of a winter landscape. There is a typical tiny "aside": a small boy stands beside a little fir tree, no taller than himself, probably intending to chop it down and carry it home for his own.

The Barn Dance and *Country Fair* (plates 152, 153), which show a wealth of charming detail integrated into the surrounding landscape, are the last large paintings Grandma Moses created. She was nearly ninety at the time, and conceded that the physical strain was getting to be too much for her. From then on she returned to smaller pictures.

While the majority of Grandma Moses's landscapes are static and show nature in a mood of undisturbed peace, she also did a number in which it is in a state of turmoil. A disturbance in the atmosphere is generally represented by windblown trees bending under a gale and, as in her blizzard and thunderstorm pictures, by a sky dark with menacing clouds. People and animals hurry for shelter, frightened and helpless before the forces of nature.

152. *The Barn Dance.* 1950. Canvas, 35 x 45″. Hammer Galleries, New York

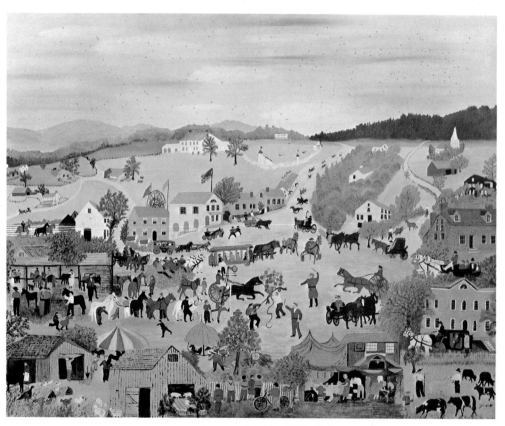

153. *Country Fair.* 1950. Canvas, 35 x 45″. Collection David H. Griffin

154. *A Storm Is on the Waters Now.* 1947. 16 x 20¼". Collection Margaret Mallory

A Storm Is on the Waters Now (plate 154) is a powerful, almost eerie evocation of impending danger. Under a black sky and past dark, storm-tossed trees, two white horses gallop in terror toward a white house, conveying a mood of inescapable violence in an almost Surrealist fashion.

Taking in Laundry (plate 155) is not quite so dramatic. It shows people busy salvaging their day's work before the oncoming storm, but still able to cope with nature.

Another painting that depicts commotion, though not in a threatening way, and that stands out for its subject matter, composition, and imagination is *Halloween* (plate 156), painted in 1955. It records the many activities characteristic of that particular October night. Barrels

155. *Taking in Laundry*. 1951. 17 x 21¾″. Private collection

of cider and buckets of harvested apples are being prepared for the customary apple dunking, which has already begun inside the house. Jack O'Lantern pumpkins glow in the dark—for it is evening, with a pale moon beginning to shine. There seem to be goblins everywhere, or just boys playing all kinds of tricks. The children are running around, either to admire the pumpkins or because they are scared. Little white faces pop up, it is not clear whether of ghosts or real people. The wildest pranks are going on on the roof, where a cart is being rolled back and forth to make uncanny noises in the house below. Two tiny yet very conspicuous "witches" seem almost to float in mid air, little white phantoms quite other-worldly in the midst of robust country folk. The colors of the painting are strong and warm, especially in the foreground:

156. *Halloween.* 1955. 18 x 24"

rich tones of red, brown, and dark green; a view into the house shows a
blazing fire in a red brick fireplace. This vivid detail is counterbalanced
by a group of men unloading barrels from a horse-drawn cart; the
simplicity and strength with which the artist has shown them is remi-
niscent of Bruegel. A white fence in the very foreground closes in the
manifold lively scenes. Gradually, as they fade into the background, the
colors become more subdued: gray houses and dark, distant hills, and
finally, above all the commotion, a quiet, cold wintry sky. The composition of this remarkable painting is unified and softened by the tall
trees, their yellow autumn foliage spreading, as it were, a delicate veil
over the bustling life below.

Interiors

SOMETIMES THE ARTIST WOULD DEVIATE from her familiar path. She was not satisfied with painting only what the public had come to expect. Time and again she tried to tackle problems that posed a challenge, as though to prove to herself that she could still learn and progress. Such experiments often resulted in extraordinary achievements. She continued to the very last her earnest endeavors at "improving" instead of just making it easy for herself. This seems all the more remarkable since people did everything they could to make her repeat what had led her to fame.

One of the problems she tried to cope with was interiors. Some customs and festivities that she remembered demanded an indoor setting. The artist was aware that her scant knowledge of perspective and her inadequacy in depicting human figures were more evident in such paintings than in her landscapes. She wrote in a letter to a friend: "I tryed that interior but did not like it so I erased it, that dont seem to be in my line. . . . Well maybe I try again." In spite of these difficulties she actually did more than twenty interiors in the course of the years.

One of the earliest was *Christmas at Home* (plate 157), painted in 1946. In order not to omit anything that goes into the celebration of a joyful family Christmas, Grandma Moses made the room far larger than it would be in an average farmhouse. It easily accommodates a huge Christmas tree, two tables in the foreground festively decked in white and laden with refreshments, a fireplace flanked by two windows in the center of the back wall with two elderly men seated in front of it. There are some two dozen figures in this lively and cheerful picture, old and young, besides a baby in a cradle, two dogs, a cat, and Santa Claus himself bringing in packages. Even the doorway is not deserted—a boy is about to enter with logs for the fire. This painting, eminently naive, is filled with the joy of storytelling, every detail a beloved experience and memory.

Another interior, *The Quilting Bee* (plate 158), painted in 1950, is remarkable both for its folkloristic content and its composition. Here is Grandma Moses's description of the custom:

> Back in Revolutionary War times quilting bees were a necessity as well as a thing of art. The women took great pride in their needle work. Every well regulated house had one room set aside which was

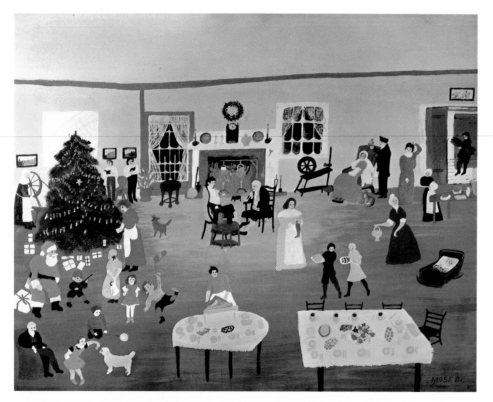

157.
Christmas at Home.
1946. 18 x 23″.
Collection Mrs. F. Kallir

158.
The Quilting Bee.
1950. 20 x 24″.
Private collection

called the quilting room; the quilting frames were set up on the backs of chairs or stands. The women of the neighborhood would gather to sew, sometimes at night, but candle light was very poor for fine stitches, which the women of those days prided themselves in. Some of the designs were beautifully done, such as the Sunflower, Rising Sun and Friendship, where each one wrote her name in the center of the block. There are a few of those old quilts scattered through the country, highly cherished by their owners.

This interior is composed in a somewhat more sophisticated way than *Christmas at Home*, yet the overall appearance is that of a "primitive" painting. Whereas in the earlier work the figures and objects seem scattered around to fill in any space, *Quilting Bee* is clearly divided into three planes—background, middle ground, and foreground. Here, too, the room is very large, almost a hall, with three windows and the indication of a beamed ceiling. The windows look out onto a landscape of delicate hues—the ones in *Christmas at Home* are dark, indicating that it is night. The main activity takes place in the upper center of the picture, where a large frame bears a many-colored quilt on which eight women are working. To the left stands an old-fashioned iron cooking stove with busy women around it. In the foreground a table with a white cloth is set for the meal. The composition of a picture with two almost equally large areas placed parallel to each other might have become clumsy, but the artist has successfully solved the problem by loosening up the composition with many incidental figures and by showing a fairly wide amount of floor space between the furnishings of the room. The general impression is one of almost stylized order with the colorful quilt forming the focal point.

Views out of windows, as seen in this painting, were themes occasionally taken up by the artist. They might show a sunny landscape, or indicate the night outside, or be "blind," giving a shut-in impression. Once in a while she would combine the view into a house with the surrounding landscape or give glimpses into rooms as though the fourth wall had been opened up, like a doll's house. Examples can be found in the paintings for *The Night Before Christmas*.

Perhaps Grandma Moses's two most unusual interiors are the pictures *In the Studio* (plate 159), done in 1944, and *Rockabye* (plate 160), painted thirteen years later, in 1957. In both of them she attempted self-portraits, to my knowledge the only ones she ever did. Though she quite often included herself among the figures populating a scene—carrying

159.
In the Studio.
1944. 18 x 23½".
Sidney Janis Gallery, New York

a milk pail, standing in a doorway, or about to enter a carriage—these are always featureless representations.

Since the subject had not appeared in her work before, it is very likely that she painted the first picture at the suggestion of a friend, coping with the theme as best she could. The artist was certainly too modest and not introspective enough to consider doing a self-portrait for its own sake. She is therefore surrounded by many objects of her daily life—her own small paintings decorate the walls, a huge and colorful flower arrangement stands on the table to her right, a vase with tall black-eyed susans in a corner on the floor. Two large, partly curtained windows in the rear are like pictures in themselves, one giving a view of the garden with a girl beneath a tree, the other of a path leading up to one of the familiar red barns. Grandma occupies the center of the scene, seated in a wide rocking chair, yet she seems to have lavished more care on the objects in the room than on herself. Her dress is plain and unadorned, while even the upholstery of the chair shows a design. The pale gray of the dress contrasts with the strong tones of flowers and dark heavy furniture. It is interesting that she is not wearing the glasses to which she was accustomed at that time—her eyes, two dark dots, look out at the beholder in an almost uneasy way.

Rockabye, the later, far smaller painting, reveals more of the artist's personality. In contrast to the almost cluttered appearance of the earlier picture, here the setting is a rather bare living room. Grandma,

160.
Rockabye.
1957. 11⅞ x 16″.
Private collection

seated to the left in a wicker chair, dominates the composition. A dark-green curtain with white dots provides a lopsided but very effective background. It is touching to note the accuracy and detachment with which Grandma Moses saw herself. There she is, the little frail old lady, as others may have seen her, with no embellishment, no softening light. She is wearing her familiar black-and-white print dress, there is a narrow black ribbon around her neck, and her gray-stockinged feet and very characteristic shoes are side by side, a bit apart, in a not too graceful but most realistic way.

The features of Grandma's face here, too, are not very marked and her glasses, clear and sparkling in real life, are strangely dim and opaque. She is holding a baby on her lap, but in an unconcerned manner which perhaps reflects her matter-of-fact and totally unsentimental attitude. There is a second child in a cradle to the right; nearby, a chair with a dog; toward the back, a table with trinkets and a settee with cushions. More striking than these is the carefully drawn linoleum that covers the floor in a pattern of dark and light squares outlined in green.

There is a window in the back, but it, like Grandma's glasses, is "blind" and permits no view to the outside. If one were tempted to interpret this work psychologically, one might say that it conveys a sense of both calm and resignation. The very old woman and the tiny new human being—a circle of life that has come full way around.

Last Paintings

161.
The hands of
Grandma Moses

THE ARTIST RETAINED THE STEADINESS OF HER HAND into her very old age. Supporting her right hand with the left, she would fill in with absolute accuracy the finest details, such as window slits in distant small buildings or the eyes in human faces. Then gradually, toward the end of 1959, some of her pictures show a changed way of painting whereby the subject matter is almost dissolved into color. This can be observed in *Autumn Leaves* and *Last Snowfall* (plates 162, 163), painted when she was ninety-nine, and in *Falling Leaves* (plate 164), *The Deep Snow*, and *Vermont Sugar*, painted in the last year of her life. There are, of course, human figures, barns, fences, and even a cart or two in these pictures, but they are more roughly daubed in, as though—which may well have been the case—the artist had become impatient with detail and mainly wanted to bring out the general impression of a nature scene, whether the yellow leaves of autumn or the softly falling snow.

162. *Autumn Leaves.* 1959. 16 x 24"

163. *Last Snowfall.* 1959. 16 x 24"

164. *Falling Leaves.* 1961. 16 x 24″. Collection Walter K. Rush

165. *Untitled: Sugaring Scene.* c. 1961. 16 x 24″. Private collection

166. *Rainbow*. 1961. 16 x 24″

Grandma Moses gave the title *Rainbow* to the very last picture she completed (plate 166). Its label bears the number 1997 and the date June 1961. After Grandma Moses's death, Emily Genauer wrote about this painting in the *New York Herald Tribune* of December 14, 1961:

> The pale rainbow she lightly sketched in that picture, arching over a lush summer landscape of her beloved Cambridge Valley . . . will never be strengthened now, as she had planned to strengthen it. No matter. It will remain a strong enough span for those looking at it—or, indeed, at any of her pictures—to be able to reach her simple, peaceful, idyllic nineteenth-century world from their own frantic world of today.
>
> A span leading only to escape need not be strong. Nostalgia and dreams are stout enough materials for its fashioning. But Grandma Moses' span was made of faith. So strong was her own, so certain her conviction that the earth and all growing things . . . are proof that there *is* a meaning to life, that somehow, looking at her pictures we are reassured.

Epilogue

167. *In Harvest Time.* 1945. 18 x 28″. Private collection

THE WORLD OF GRANDMA MOSES is bright and serene; man is in perfect harmony with nature, the tasks he performs are dictated by the daily necessities of farm and country life, as unquestionable as rain or sunshine. Nowhere is there a sign of overwhelming toil; nothing is either good or bad, everything is natural. If Grandma Moses permits herself any personal slant, it is expressed by her strong and charming sense of humor. Mischief of any kind is always good-natured fun—the *Halloween* picture is full of it.

When the artist, departing from the serenity that emanates from most of her paintings, does represent a disturbance, it is not man-made but springs powerfully from nature, as in her representations of stormy and windswept landscapes.

142

168. *A Frosty Day.* 1951. 18 x 24″. Private collection

169. *A Frosty Day* (detail)

170.
Green Sleigh.
1960. 16 x 24″

Never could she have re-created the beauty of a landscape, the changing seasons, the activities that they entail—plowing, haying, harvesting, sugaring—had she not deeply felt and loved nature in all its aspects and varying moods. But it would not have occurred to her to represent them for their pure aesthetic value or to "romanticize" a scene. She painted what she saw and intimately knew, and the beauty which radiates from her work is the natural result of her vision.

No doubt some present-day critics find the world of Grandma Moses too simple, too unproblematic, lacking in the awareness of the strife and grief that overshadow our lives. Although she certainly had experienced them, what she expressed in her art are the everlasting sources of vitality from which man draws his strength, courage, and hope. She has shown an image of her country far different from what has come to be regarded as "typically American," and the image is truer and more enduring.

Jean Cassou, the former director of the Musée National d'Art Moderne in Paris, one of the foremost European authorities on modern art, has expressed most concisely and beautifully what Anna Mary Robertson Moses's work means to the world of art and to our time. He wrote on the occasion of the artist's hundredth birthday:

> The Primitives are the salt of the earth. Through their existence alone does contemporary art, so knowing, so sophisticated and daring, preserve in its depth sources of freshness and life. Thus the Cubists had at their side the Douanier Rousseau, and their marvelous intellectual speculations were counterbalanced by the companionship of this pure heart, inspired by the genius of the people and of nature. The United States through its "avant-garde" is making the most daring aesthetic experiments, but also has its primeval forces, its springs of fresh water. From her small-town vantage point, the adorable Grandma Moses comes to the defense of the countryside, the empire of foliage and birds, and upholds the rights of nature. She would have us know that there is still a bit of paradise left on this earth and that art may reach out as far as it will with its most advanced branches, because it is deeply rooted in the rich soil of Grandma Moses's garden.

"How Do I Paint?"

171. Grandma Moses's painting table

EagleBridge April 7th 1947.

How do I Paint?
well first I get a frame, then I saw my
masonite board to fit the frame.
    Then I go over the board with Oil,
Then give the board three coats of flat
white paint,
    Now it is ready for the scene, what
ever the mind may produce,
    A land scape picture, an Old Bridge A
Dream, or a summer or winter scene,
    Child hoods memory, what ever one fancys,
    But always somthings pleasing and
cheerful and I like bright colors and
activity,
    Why do I use masonite or hard wood
to paint on?
    Becaus it will last many years longer
than canvas,
    Some times the frames are hard to
obtain, they may be pretty frames but
in a delapidated condistion,

then I must use hammer and nails
with plastics, the frames should
allwise blend with the painting for
best affect,

why did I start to paint in my old
age?,

well to tell the truth, I had neuritus
and artheritus so bad that I could do
but little work, but had to keep busy
to pass the time away, I tryed worsted
pictures, then tryed oil,

and now I paint a great deal of the time,

It is a very pleasant Hobby if one
does not have to hurry,

I love to take my time and finish
things up right,

At first I painted for pleasure,
Then I was called upon to do more than
I could, to live up to my promises,

when I first commenced to paint
with oil, I thought every painting
would be my last one,

So I was not so interrested,

Then the reqwests commenced to come,
from this one and that one,
"Paint me one just like that one"
So I have painted on and on till now,

Those that I have keept track of are "1775"
But that is not all of them,

I think I'm dowing better work then at
first,

But it is owing to better brushes and
paint,

I don't advise any one to take it up as
a buisness proprosition, unless they
really have talent, and are crippled
so as to deprive them of phyical labor,

Then with help they might make
a living,

But with taxes and income tax there
is little money in that kind of art
for the ordinary artis

But I will say that I have did remarkalle
for one of my years. and experience,

thanks to mr Louis Coldor, mr Otto Kallin and
Alla Story, through those, life has been a
Success,

As for publicity, that I'm too old to care
care for now,

Some times it makes me think
of a dream that my Father once told at
the breakfast table one morning many
years ago,

He said, "I had a dream about you last
night anna mary"

was it good or bad Pa,?
And he said that depends on the future,
Dreams cast their shadows before us,

He dreamed, I was in a large Hall
and there were many people there,

They were claping their hands and shouting
and I wondered what it was all about, and
looking I saw you anna mary coming
my way, walking on the shoulders of
men, you came right on steping from
one shoulder to another waving to me,

Of late years I have often thought
of that dream, since all the publicty
about me, an of Mother saying, to Father,
"Now Russell anna mary would look nice
walking on mens shoulders"!

She saw the folly of that dream,
Or did she? did that dream cast its
shadows before?

I often wonder, now that I'm getting
letters from all most every country on the
Globe,

and such kind wellwishing letters,
and they come to Grandma from far away,

I love to have visitors, they are awlwise
walcomed, and they bring in news of the
owter world, which is realy delightful,

172. *Over the River.* 1943. Canvas, 34 x 45″. Collection Mrs. Jack Kapp

Biographical Outline

1860 September 7, Anna Mary Robertson is born in Greenwich, N.Y.

1872–87 Works as a hired girl on neighboring farms.

1887 November 9, marries Thomas Salmon Moses.

1887–1905 Lives and farms in Virginia. Ten children are born, of whom five die in infancy.

1905 Returns to New York State; purchases a farm in Eagle Bridge.

1909 Her mother dies in February, her father in June.

1918 Paints her first large picture, on the fireboard in her parlor.

c. 1920 Paints landscapes on the panels of her "tip-up" table and occasional pictures for relatives and friends.

1927 January 15, Thomas Salmon Moses dies.

1930s Lives in Bennington from about 1930. After the death of her daughter Anna Moses in February 1932, she cares for two grandchildren. Embroiders "worsted" pictures. Returns to Eagle Bridge in 1935. Begins to paint in earnest. Exhibits pictures along with preserves at country fairs.

1938 Exhibits pictures in Thomas's Drugstore, Hoosick Falls, N.Y., where Louis J. Caldor discovers them.

1939 October 18 to November 18, three paintings are included in a show of "Contemporary Unknown American Painters" in the Members' Rooms of the Museum of Modern Art, New York.

1940 October 9, the opening of her first one-man show, titled "What a Farm Wife Painted," at the Galerie St. Etienne, New York. In November, visits New York to attend an exhibition of her work at Gimbels Thanksgiving Festival.

1941 New York State Prize is presented to her for *The Old C Bucket* at the Syracuse Museum of Fine Arts (now Everson Museum of Art).

1946 Publication of *Grandma Moses: American Primitive* by Kallir, with an introduction by Louis Bromfield and a biographical notes by Grandma Moses. The first Christ cards reproducing her paintings are published.

1949 In February, her youngest son, Hugh, dies. In May, Women's National Press Club Award, "for outstand accomplishment in Art," is presented to Grandma Mose President Harry S Truman in Washington, D.C. In June receives an Honorary Doctorate from Russell Sage Coll Troy, N.Y.

1950 Erica Anderson creates a documentary color film, narration by Archibald MacLeish.

1951 Grandma Moses receives an Honorary Doctorate from Moore Institute of Art, Philadelphia.

1952 *My Life's History* by Grandma Moses is published.

1953 Grandma Moses is guest speaker at the *New York He Tribune* Forum in New York.

1955 Edward R. Murrow interviews Grandma Moses for a tele in his "See It Now" series.

1958 October 14, her daughter Winona Fisher dies.

1960 Paints pictures illustrating *The Night Before Christmas,* Clement C. Moore.

1960, 1961 Governor Nelson A. Rockefeller proclaims the artist's bi day "Grandma Moses Day" in the State of New York.

1961 In June, paints her last picture, *Rainbow.* December Grandma Moses dies at the Health Center, Hoosick Fa

Selected Bibliography

Grandma Moses by Otto Kallir. The story of her life and work. With the catalogue of her pictures. Harry N. Abrams, Inc., New York, 1973.

BOOKS WRITTEN OR ILLUSTRATED BY GRANDMA MOSES
(in chronological order)

Grandma Moses, American Primitive. Edited by Otto Kallir. Introduction by Louis Bromfield. Comments on forty paintings and a brief autobiography by Grandma Moses. First edition: Dryden Press, New York, 1946. Second edition: Doubleday & Co., Garden City, New York, 1947.

Christmas. Facsimile edition of the handwritten manuscript. 500 copies. Galerie St. Etienne, New York, 1952.

My Life's History. Edited by Otto Kallir. Trade edition and a special autographed, numbered edition of 270 copies bound in half-leather. Harper & Row, New York, 1952. British edition: André Deutsch, London, 1952. German edition: *Meine Lebensgeschichte.* Ullstein Verlag, 1957. Dutch edition: *Het verhaal van mijn leven.* A. W. Bruna & Zoon, 1958.

Christmas with Grandma Moses. Phonograph record of Christmas music with commentary spoken by Grandma Moses. Paintings, photographs, and quotations from the artist's writings in the descriptive booklet bound into the record album. RCA Victor No. LOP–1009, 1958.

The Grandma Moses Storybook. Stories and poems by 28 writers. Edited by Nora Kramer. Illustrated by Grandma Moses. Biographical sketch of the artist by Otto Kallir. Random House, New York, 1961.

The Night Before Christmas. Clement C. Moore. With pictures by Grandma Moses especially painted for this book. Random House, New York, n.d. [1962].

CHILDREN'S BOOKS
(in chronological order)

Graves, Charles P. *Grandma Moses, Favorite Painter.* Garrard Publishing Co., Champaign, Ill., 1969.

Armstrong, William H. *Barefoot in the Grass: The Story of Grandma Moses.* Doubleday & Co., Garden City, New York, 1971.

BOOKS PUBLISHED DURING GRANDMA MOSES'S LIFETIME IN WHICH HER WORK IS DISCUSSED
(in chronological order)

Janis, Sidney. *They Taught Themselves: American Primitive Painters of the 20th Century.* Dial Press, New York, 1942.

Ford, Alice. *Pictorial Folk Art in America, New England to California.* The Studio Publications, Inc., New York & London, 1949.

Lipman, Jean, and Winchester, Alice. *Primitive Painters in America, 1750-1950.* Dodd, Mead & Co., New York, 1950.

Jasmand, Bernhard, and Kallir, Otto. *Sonntagsmaler: Das Bild des einfältigen Herzens.* Verlag Otto Aug. Ehlers, Berlin & Darmstadt, 1956.

Eliot, Alexander. *Three Hundred Years of American Painting.* Time, Inc., New York, 1957.

Bihalji-Merin, Oto. *Modern Primitives: Masters of Naive Painting.* Harry N. Abrams, Inc., New York, 1959.

REPRODUCTIONS
(in chronological order)

Series of 16 Christmas cards, 1946. The Brundage Company, New York.

Numerous Christmas and greeting cards, 1947–55; 1964–69. The Hallmark Company, Kansas City, Mo.

Four color reproductions, 1948–49. Besides the regular edition, 100 prints of each subject were numbered and signed by the artist. Two additional color reproductions were published in 1963 and 1965 respectively. Arthur Jaffe Heliochrome Company, New York.

"The Four Seasons." Set of four color reproductions, 1956. Donald Art Company, Port Chester, New York.

Series of 12 Christmas and greeting cards, 1957. R. Oldenbourg, Graphische Betriebe, Munich, Germany.

"Six of My Favorite Paintings." Portfolio of six color reproductions, 1959. Catalda Fine Arts, Inc., New York.

Portfolio of eight color reproductions, with an Appreciation by John Canaday, 1967. Art in America, New York.

Set of four color reproductions, 1973. Limited edition of 3000 numbered prints of each subject. American Heritage Publishing Company, Inc., New York.

PERIODICALS

An extraordinary amount of material has been published about Grandma Moses in newspapers and periodicals around the world. Some of the more significant articles published during the artist's lifetime are listed here in alphabetical order by author.

Fisher, Barbara E. Scott. "Go Ahead and Paint." *Christian Science Monitor Magazine,* January 5, 1946.

Grafly, Dorothy. "Primitive and Primitives." *American Artist,* October 1949.

Herbert,François. "Grandma Moses, 100 ans peintre." *Paris Match,* December 10, 1960.

Kutner, Nanette. "Grandma Moses: Norman Rockwell Talks About His Neighbor." *McCall's,* October 1949.

Lansford, Alonzo. "Grandma Moses." *The Art Digest* (now *Arts),* May 15, 1947.

Lipman, Jean. "Fourth of July Art." *Cosmopolitan,* July 1956.

Roden, Max. "Die amerikanischen Primitiven." *Die schönen Künste* (Vienna), 1947.

Schoenberg, Harold C. "Grandma Moses—Portrait of the Artist at 99." *The New York Times Magazine,* September 6, 1959.

Seckler, Dorothy. "The Success of Mrs. Moses." *Art News,* May 1951.

Soby, James Thrall. "A Bucolic Past and a Giddy Jungle." *The Saturday Review of Literature,* November 4, 1950.

Sullivan, Frank. "An Afternoon with Grandma Moses." *The New York Times Magazine,* October 9, 1949.

Stahly, François. "Grandma Moses/Morris Hirschfield." *Graphis* (Zurich), Vol. 7, No. 35, 1951.

Thompson, Dorothy. "The World of Grandma Moses." *Ladies' Home Journal,* January 1957.

Waldinger, Ernst. "Die Geschichte eines amerikanischen Erfolges." *Annabelle* (Zurich), March 1947.

Woolf, S.J. "Grandma Moses, Who Began to Paint at 78." *The New York Times Magazine,* December 2, 1945.

List of Major Exhibitions

9 October 18–November 18
Contemporary Unknown American Painters: Opening Exhibition of the Advisory Committee of the Museum of Modern Art
The Members' Rooms, The Museum of Modern Art, New York. Included 3 paintings by Grandma Moses. Catalogue includes Introduction by Sidney Janis

0 October 9–31
What a Farm Wife Painted: Works by Anna Mary Moses
Galerie St. Etienne, New York. 33 paintings, one embroidered picture. Mimeographed list of the pictures

November 14–25
Auditorium, Gimbels, New York. 50 paintings and embroidered pictures

1 January
Whyte Gallery, Washington, D.C. One-man show of 26 paintings

May
New York State Art Show
Syracuse Museum of Fine Arts (now Everson Museum of Art), Syracuse, N.Y. Included 3 or more paintings by Grandma Moses (*The Old Oaken Bucket* received the N.Y. State Prize)

42 February 9–March 7
They Taught Themselves: American Primitive Painters of the 20th Century
Marie Harriman Gallery, N.Y. Included 3 paintings by Grandma Moses. Catalogue with *A Statement by André Breton*

December 7–22
Anna Mary Robertson Moses: Loan Exhibition of Paintings
American British Art Center, New York. 32 paintings. Catalogue

43 November
Grandma Moses
E.B. Crocker Art Gallery, Sacramento, Calif. 30 paintings

44 February
New Paintings by Grandma Moses–The Senior of the American Primitives
Galerie St. Etienne, New York. 32 paintings

April 2–29
Grandma Moses – The Senior of the American Primitives
James Vigeveno Galleries, Los Angeles. 21 paintings. Catalogue

September 6 – October 9
Syracuse Museum of Fine Arts (now Everson Museum of Art), Syracuse, N.Y. One-man show of 23 paintings

December
Grandma Moses
Galerie St. Etienne, New York. 36 paintings

1944–45 *Grandma Moses*
Traveling Exhibition: South Hadley, Mass.; Williamstown, Mass.; Amherst, Mass.; Nashville, Tenn.; Manchester, N.H.; Washington, D.C.; Dillon, Mont. 20 paintings

Portrait of America
Metropolitan Museum of Art, New York. Exhibition of 150 paintings conducted by Artists-for-Victory, Inc., presented in many leading museums in the United States after the New York show. Included one painting by Grandma Moses

1945 May 1–31
Grandma Moses: The Senior of American Primitives in Her Initial San Francisco Showing
Maxwell Galleries, San Francisco, Calif.

October 28–November 17
Recent Paintings by the Senior of American Primitive Painters: Grandma Moses
James Vigeveno Galleries, Los Angeles, Calif. 30 paintings. Catalogue

November 13–18
Women's International Exposition: Woman's Life in Peacetime
Madison Square Garden, New York. One-man show

1945–46 *Grandma Moses*
Traveling Exhibition: Utica, N.Y.; Norfolk, Va.; Claremont, Calif. 20 paintings

1945–49 *Painting in the United States, 1945*
Carnegie Institute, Pittsburgh, Pa. Each show included a different painting by Grandma Moses. Catalogues

1946 February 25–March 23
Exhibition of Paintings by Grandma Moses
The American British Art Center, New York. 44 paintings.
Catalogue

October 20–November 16
Recent Work by America's Beloved Grandma Moses
James Vigeveno Galleries, Los Angeles, Calif. 32 paintings.
Catalogue

946–47 *Grandma Moses*
Traveling Exhibition: Manitowoc, Wis.; St. Paul, Minn.;
Lubbock, Tex.; Zanesville, Ohio; Ithaca, N.Y.; Lock Haven,
Pa.; Chicago, Ill. 20 paintings

1947 May 17–June 14
Grandma Moses: Paintings
Galerie St. Etienne, New York. 34 paintings. Catalogue
includes *How Do I Paint?* by Grandma Moses

947–48 *Grandma Moses*
Traveling Exhibition: Rockford, Ill.; Beloit, Wis.; Raleigh,
N.C.; Cheltenham, Pa.; Abilene, Tex.; Lawrence, Kan.;
Baltimore, Md.; Waterbury, Conn. 20 paintings

1948 May 25–June 12
Thirty Paintings by Grandma Moses
The American British Art Center, New York. Catalogue
includes Introduction by Archibald MacLeish

September 20–through October
Grandma Moses
California Palace of the Legion of Honor, San Francisco. 22
paintings

October 18–November 12
*Exhibition of Recent Paintings by the Senior of American Primitive
Painters, America's Beloved Grandma Moses*
James Vigeveno Galleries, Los Angeles, Calif. 34 paintings.
Catalogue

Thanksgiving–Christmas
Ten Years–Grandma Moses
Galerie St. Etienne, New York. 42 paintings. Catalogue
includes *I Remember* by Grandma Moses (facsimile of her
handwritten manuscript)

1948–49 *Grandma Moses*
Traveling Exhibition: Montgomery, Ala.; Charlotte, N
Memphis, Tenn.; Monmouth, Ill.; Grinnell, Iowa; Ra
Wis. 20 paintings

1949 January 9–30
Art in the United States, 1949
Museum of Fine Arts of Houston, Tex. Included 2 pain
by Grandma Moses. Catalogue includes Introduction
James Chillman, Jr.

May 8–31 (extended to June 9)
Paintings by Grandma Moses
The Phillips Gallery, Washington, D.C. 30 paintings

October 3–22
First Boston Exhibition of Paintings by Grandma Moses
Robert C. Vose Galleries, Boston, Mass. 19 paintings

November 6
St. Mark's Episcopal Church, Hoosick Falls, N.Y. One-
show of 120 paintings and embroidered pictures

1950 January 30–February 18
Selected Paintings by Grandma Moses
The American British Art Gallery, New York. 20 paint
Catalogue includes Essay by Thomas Carr Howe, Jr.

September 7–October 15
*Grandma Moses: Exhibition Arranged on the Occasion of Her
Birthday*
Albany Institute of History and Art, Albany, N.Y
paintings and additional embroidered pictures. Catal

October 19–December 21
Pittsburgh International Exhibition of Paintings
Carnegie Institute, Pittsburgh, Pa. Included one paintin
Grandma Moses. Catalogue

June–December
Grandma Moses: 50 Paintings
Exhibition circulated in Europe under the auspices of
U.S. Information Service: Vienna, Munich, Salzb
Berne, The Hague, Paris. Catalogue published by
display center

December 10–January 15, 1951
Paintings by Grandma Moses
The Taft Museum, Cincinnati, Ohio. 32 paintings. C
logue

51 March–April
Grandma Moses: Twenty-Five Masterpieces of Primitive Art
Galerie St. Etienne, New York. Catalogue includes *My Tip-Up Table* by Grandma Moses; *About Grandma Moses* by Allen Eaton. Reviews and comments on the European Moses Exhibitions

April 9–28
Grandma Moses: Sixty of Her Masterpieces
The Dayton Company, Minneapolis, Minn. Catalogue

May 6–13
An Exhibition of Paintings by Grandma Moses
Brooks Memorial Art Gallery, Memphis, Tenn. 27 paintings. Catalogue

Grandma Moses
Traveling Exhibition: Kansas City, Mo.; Omaha, Neb.; Des Moines, Iowa; Tulsa, Okla. 26 paintings

52 January 11–March 2
Paintings by Grandma Moses
Art Gallery of Toronto, Canada

March 5–21
Twenty Famous Paintings by Grandma Moses
The American British Art Gallery, New York. Catalogue

May–June
Grandma Moses
Syracuse Museum of Fine Arts (now Everson Museum of Art), Syracuse, N.Y. 23 paintings. Catalogue

October
Grandma Moses
The Memorial Art Gallery, Rochester, N.Y. About 30 paintings, 2 embroidered pictures

53 *Grandma Moses*
Traveling Exhibition: Cedar Rapids, Iowa; Davenport, Iowa; Springfield, Mo.; Laguna Beach, Calif.; Windsor, Vt.; Wilmington, Del.; Houston, Tex.; New Orleans, La.; San Francisco, Calif.; Lafayette, Ind.; Terre Haute, Ind.; Birmingham, Ala.; Clearwater, Fla.; New London, Conn. 24 paintings

53 February–March
Grandma Moses
Santa Barbara Museum of Art, Santa Barbara, Calif.

March 14–22
Art Exhibition: Grandma Moses
Part of the California International Flower Show under the auspices of the Los Angeles Municipal Art Commission Hollywood Park, Inglewood, Calif. 57 paintings

April–May
"A Grandma Moses Album": Exhibition of Recent Paintings
Galerie St. Etienne, New York. 26 paintings. Catalogue

December 18–early September 1954
American Painting, 1754–1954
Metropolitan Museum of Art, New York. Included one painting by Grandma Moses

1954 February 14–28
Grandma Moses
Buffalo Historical Society, Buffalo, N.Y. 29 paintings

October 19–November 21
Man and His Years
The Baltimore Museum of Art, Baltimore, Md. Included 2 paintings by Grandma Moses. Catalogue

1954–55 *American Primitive Paintings from the 17th Century to the Present*
Circulated in Europe by the Smithsonian Institution for U.S. Information Agency: Lucerne, Vienna, Munich, Dortmund, Stockholm, Oslo, Manchester, London, Trier. Included 5 paintings by Grandma Moses. Catalogue published by each display center

1954–56 *Grandma Moses*
Traveling Exhibition: Coshocton, Ohio; Rockford, Ill.; Davenport, Iowa; Seattle, Wash.; Duluth, Minn.; Oakland, Calif.; San Diego, Calif.; San Jose, Calif.; Elmira, N.Y.; Pittsburgh, Pa.; Fort Dodge, Iowa; St. Paul, Minn.; Clearwater, Fla.; Greenville, S.C. 20 paintings

1955 November 29–through December
A Tribute to Grandma Moses
Loan exhibition of paintings presented by Thomas J. Watson and the Fine Arts Department of the International Business Machines Corp. IBM Gallery, New York. 42 paintings. Catalogue includes Tribute by Thomas J. Watson; *Work and Happiness* and *My Tip-Up Table* by Grandma Moses

1955–57 *Grandma Moses*
Traveling Exhibition in Europe: Bremen, Stuttgart, Cologne, Hamburg, London, Oslo, Aberdeen, Edinburgh, Glasgow. 35 paintings. Catalogue published by each display center

1957 May 6–June 4
Grandma Moses: New York Showing of an Exhibition of Paintings Presented in Europe During 1955–1957
Galerie St. Etienne, New York. 33 paintings. Catalogue includes *Grandma Moses* by Hubertus, Prince zu Löwenstein; excerpts from European reviews

August 31–October 13
Grandma Moses: A Selection of Thirty-Four Paintings from Public and Private Collections
California Palace of the Legion of Honor, San Francisco. Catalogue

1958 October 4–November 2
Famous Paintings and Famous Painters
Dallas Museum of Fine Arts, Dallas, Tex. Included 5 paintings by Grandma Moses. Catalogue

1958–59 *American Primitive Paintings*
Circulated by the Smithsonian Institution: Southampton, N.Y.; Shreveport, La.; Indianapolis, Ind.; Chattanooga, Tenn.; Birmingham, Ala.; Davenport, Iowa; San Diego, Calif.; Louisville, Ky. Included 12 paintings by Grandma Moses. Catalogue includes notes on 20 artists

1960 July 30–August 14
Grandma Moses: 100th Birthday Loan Exhibition
Southern Vermont Art Center, Manchester. 20 paintings

Fall
100th Birthday Celebration Exhibition
Webb Art Gallery, The Shelburne Museum, Shelburne, Vt. 17 paintings. Catalogue

September 12–October 6
My Life's History: A Loan Exhibition of Paintings by Grandma Moses
Assembled on the occasion of the artist's hundredth birthday. IBM Gallery of Arts and Sciences, New York. 44 paintings and one embroidered picture. Catalogue includes Tributes by Governor Nelson A. Rockefeller, Otto Kallir,

Jean Cassou. Autobiographical notes accompany the [pic]tures; all works illustrated. This exhibition, with the s[ame] catalogue, was subsequently circulated by the Smithson[ian] Institution to the following cities: Milwaukee, Wis.; W[ash]ington, D.C.; Chattanooga, Tenn.; Baton Rouge, La.; S[eat]tle, Wash.; Laguna Beach, Fla.; Fort Worth, Tex.; Wi[nni]peg, Canada; Chicago, Ill.

1962 April 28–29
Grandma Moses' Original Paintings
Hoosick Falls Central School, Hoosick Falls, N.Y. 95 pa[int]ings and embroidered pictures

November–December
Grandma Moses: Memorial Exhibition
Galerie St. Etienne, New York. 54 paintings. Catalo[gue] includes *On the Style and Technique of Grandma Moses* by [Otto] Kallir

1962–64 *A Life's History in 40 Pictures*
Traveling Exhibition circulated in Europe: Vienna, P[rague,] Bremen, Hamburg, Hameln, Fulda, Düsseldorf, Darmst[adt,] Mannheim, Berlin, Frankfort, Oslo, Stockholm, Helsi[nki,] Gothenburg, Copenhagen, Moscow. 39 paintings and [one] embroidered picture. Catalogue published by each dis[play] center

1963 June 29–October 22
The Home Country of Grandma Moses: Twenty of Her Best Pain[tings] of Local Areas and Activities
The Bennington Museum, Bennington, Vt.

December 5–8
The Original Paintings of "The Night Before Christmas" [by] Grandma Moses
Rensselaer County Historical Society, Troy, N.Y. 10 pa[int]ings

1964 July–September
Die Welt der naïven Malerei
Salzburger Residenzgalerie, Salzburg. Included 4 paint[ings] by Grandma Moses

July–October
De Lusthof der Naïeven. Le Monde des Naïfs
Museum Boymans–Van Beuningen, Rotterdam; M[usée] National d'Art Moderne, Paris. Included 2 paintings

Grandma Moses. Catalogue includes essays by Jean Cassou, J.C. Ebbinge Wubben, and Oto Bihalji-Merin. Biographical notes

5 December 14–January 9, 1965
My Life's History: Paintings by Grandma Moses
Forty paintings which toured seventeen European cities; in addition, 25 pictures never previously shown. Hammer Galleries, New York. Two Catalogues

65 July 17–31
Grandma Moses Art Festival: A Loan Exhibition
The Buck Hill Art Association, Buck Hill Falls, Pa. 35 paintings. Catalogue

December 7–24
Forty Grandma Moses Paintings Never Shown Before
Hammer Galleries, New York. Catalogue

66 July 26–October 2
1st Triennial of Insitic Art
Slovenska Národná Galéria, Bratislava, Czechoslovakia. Included 11 paintings by Grandma Moses. Catalogue

72 *An Exhibition of Mementos*
Grandma Moses Schoolhouse, Eagle Bridge, N.Y.

67 June 9–October 24
Paintings by Grandma Moses: Twenty-Three of Her Best Paintings of Local Areas and Activities
The Bennington Museum, Bennington, Vt.

December 5–30
Paintings by Grandma Moses
Hammer Galleries, New York. 28 paintings. Catalogue includes *An Appreciation* by John Canaday

68 May 1968–December 1972
The Grandma Moses Gallery
The Bennington Museum, Bennington, Vermont. 81 paintings, the "tip-up" table, documentary material on the artist's life and career

The Grandma Moses Schoolhouse was transferred from Eagle Bridge to the Bennington Museum, where a continuing Grandma Moses exhibition takes place.

1969 February 20–March 30
Art and Life of Grandma Moses
Paintings from American museums and private collections; in addition, *The Grandma Moses Gallery* of the Bennington Museum. The Gallery of Modern Art, New York (now New York Cultural Center). 151 paintings, the "tip-up" table, documentary material. Catalogue: Edited by Otto Kallir. Includes documentary material and previously published writings by and about Grandma Moses. Published by The Gallery of Modern Art, New York; A.S. Barnes & Co., South Brunswick and New York; Thomas Yoseloff, Ltd., London

December 2–30
Grandma Moses
Hammer Galleries, New York. 43 paintings. Catalogue

1971 December 6–31
Grandma Moses
Hammer Galleries, New York. 28 paintings. Catalogue

1972 February 22–March 11
Four American Primitives: Edward Hicks, John Kane, Anna Mary Robertson Moses, Horace Pippin
ACA Galleries, New York. Included 15 paintings by Grandma Moses. Catalogue

April 21–May 7
Paintings by Grandma Moses
Old Capitol Museum, Jackson, Miss. 15 paintings. Catalogue

1974 November 17–December 24
Christmas in the Country
10 paintings by Grandma Moses re-created three-dimensionally by James Bakkom of the Guthrie Theatre. Also an exhibition of 26 pictures by Grandma Moses and documentary material. Dayton's, Minneapolis, Minn.

1974–75 November–March
"Die Kunst der Naïven"
Haus der Kunst, Munich; Kunsthaus, Zurich. Included 5 paintings by Grandma Moses. Catalogue

Index

The titles of works by the artist are in Roman type. References to documentary photographs are in italics. The numbers refer to plates; colorplates are indicated by an asterisk*.

PMS / Premenstrual Syndrome

PMS /*Premenstrual Syndrome*

Ronald V. Norris, M.D.
with
Colleen Sullivan

RAWSON ASSOCIATES: NEW YORK

Rawson Associates
597 Fifth Avenue
New York, N.Y. 10017
Published simultaneously in Canada by McClelland and Stewart Ltd.

Library of Congress Cataloging in Publication Data

Norris, Ronald V.
    PMS/Premenstrual Syndrome

    Bibliography: p.
    Includes index.
    1. Premenstrual syndrome   I. Sullivan, Colleen   II. Title

RG165.N67   1983   618.1'72   82-42700

ISBN 0-89256-238-2

10   9   8   7   6   5   4   3   2   1

Printed in the United States of America

Composition by Weber & Stevens Inc.
Manufactured by Arcata Graphics Group Inc.
Designed by Robert Eisner

First Edition

To / Judy and all the women who suffer from
/ PMS, and to my children: Valerie, Valian,
/ Thane, Lance, Joshua, and angel Sigrid.

Contents

Before You Begin This Book

Contents

(continued)

Acknowledgments

Like most books, this one is the product of the efforts and cooperation of many people. For working so imaginatively and diligently to develop this book, we would like to thank our agent, Susan Cohen.

Orchestrating the many elements of such a wide-ranging project on a very tight deadline was an awesome job, ably undertaken by Lisbeth Bensley, our primary researcher. Alice Weil patiently helped edit the manuscript and added some sorely needed perspective and humor as we struggled toward the finish. To Lis and Alice and a wonderful band of researchers and aides who contributed to the book from London, New York, Boston, and Los Angeles, our gratitude: Barbara Czelusniak, Carole Gould, Eden Graber, Bruce Hager, Sonia Kudla, Sherill Leonard, Valerie and Valian Norris, Robert Rivkin, David Sanger, Stacy Schiff, Fatima Shaik, Kate Stout, Elisa Tinsley, and Christine Ziegler.

This book would not have been possible without the exceptional teachers, mentors, and colleagues who have taught the art and science of medicine and nurtured the belief that the quality of care and the quality of caring are both important in health services: Drs. Arthur Rempel, Fredric Santler, George Ball, at Whitman; Drs. Ray Bunge, Len Heston, Chase Hunter, at Iowa; Drs. David Rogers and Tom Brittingham, at Vanderbilt; Drs. Leon Eisenberg, Seymour Kety, Gerry Klerman, Tom Hackett, and Michael Murphy at Harvard and Massachusetts General Hospital. Drs. Jane Shaw and Peter Ramwell taught the skills and techniques of basic laboratory research at the Worcester Foundation for Experimental Biology. Dr. Charles Lloyd, also of the Worcester Foundation, provided the first introduction to PMS and exposure to clinical research in endocrinology.

Many other physicians, scientists, and other professionals also assisted us by providing material and consenting to interviews. We owe a particular debt to Drs. Willard Allen and William Keye. For their assistance in helping to gather the stories of women coping with PMS, we want to thank Patty Cannon and Lindsey Leckie, co-founders of the National PMS Society, and Virginia Cassara of PMS Action. Most importantly, we owe a very special thanks to the patients evaluated at the Premenstrual Syndrome Program offices and to the hundreds of women with PMS who agreed to be interviewed for this book, freely sharing their experiences and insights so that other women might benefit.

Before You Begin This Book

This book is a celebration of women. It is about women who cope, who have active lives, who juggle responsibilities of work and home, who raise children, who run businesses, who are warm and loving mates cherished by their families and friends. It is also a book about pain, a cyclical kind of physical and psychological pain that intrudes into the lives and consciousness of millions of women around the globe. Five to ten percent of all women — nearly seven million Americans and more than one hundred million women worldwide — find themselves struggling every month, for a few days or as long as three weeks, to deal with a menstrually-related illness known as premenstrual syndrome, or PMS. This book is for these women, their families, and friends.

We first became aware of the existence of premenstrual syndrome about fourteen years ago while completing a fellowship with Dr. Charles Lloyd, a well-known reproductive endocrinologist, at the Worcester Foundation for Experimental Biology in Massachusetts, where the birth control pill was initially developed. A number of women seen in the Endocrine Clinic of the foundation suffered from PMS. Further, while carrying out a study of aggression in women, we found that six women imprisoned for murder all had committed the murders the day before or the first day of their menstrual period. The connection seemed too solid to be mere coincidence. In subsequent years we also saw the symptoms of premenstrual syndrome in women we knew personally, in some women with whom we worked, as well as in patients we were treating for other problems. We diagnosed the conditions as best we could at the time and treated them with varying degrees of success. It was only after my wife developed PMS and I became aware of its deleterious impact upon her, our relationship, and our family that I recognized the significance of the disorder. I began to study the statistics and scientific literature, and came to appreciate how little understanding American women and their physicians had of this disorder. Our interest in the syndrome resulted in a decision to open the first center in the United States specializing in PMS diagnosis and treatment in 1981 and to establish a foundation to foster research in and education about PMS and similar disorders. Since 1981, more than two thousand women have been evaluated for the condition at our centers.

Based on the findings from our practice, we developed this book. Its purpose is not only to educate and inform the public about premenstrual syndrome as a treatable medical condition, but also to describe the wide-ranging impact of PMS on the home, family, and friends, in the workplace and in social situations. We've also examined the profound legal and social implications of the condition — our rebuttal to the debate that has developed over PMS as a legal defense and as a possible obstacle to the equal rights movement for women.

With the cooperation and assistance of many of our patients, we have gathered the stories of those who know what it's like to live with PMS. We asked the women we interviewed to speak freely about their experiences and the effect the disorder has had on their personal and professional lives and relationships — and they did. Unfortunately, most women feel that a stigma attaches to the PMS condition; they're probably right. We hope that as information about PMS and its treatment becomes available, PMS will be no more onerous a burden than the common cold. Today, however, most women do not want to be identified as suffering from the syndrome. Thus to preserve their privacy, we have changed the names and in many cases the occupations and geographic locations of the women we interviewed.

The identities of physicians and other experts cited throughout the book have not been changed, however.

For those readers who think they may have premenstrual syndrome, we suggest that you read this book carefully, especially Section VI on diagnosis and lifestyle changes. But we urge you to consult your own physician before undertaking a self-diagnosis. While too few physicians evaluate and treat PMS in this country now, the growing demand for such care will undoubtedly result in more and more physicians recognizing and treating the syndrome in the months and years to come. By reading this book and becoming informed health-care consumers, women can help their physicians become educated about PMS, too. And that's a first step toward improving medical care for PMS sufferers.

SECTION I

The Basics

Chapter 1

*"But it's always interesting when one doesn't
see. If you don't see what a thing means,
you must be looking at it wrong way round."*

Agatha Christie

PMS: What It Is and
What It Isn't

Premenstrual syndrome, or PMS, is a defect of physiology, not of character. In extreme cases, its effects are so far-reaching that it may become difficult to separate the syndrome from the personality. Most women, perhaps eighty-five percent of the menstruating female population, have experienced symptoms of PMS in the days preceding their menstrual period, even if for some it might involve just one cycle out of twenty. About forty percent of all menstruating women — nearly twenty-seven million Americans — experience fairly regular symptoms of premenstrual syndrome. For the vast majority, PMS occurs as mild complaints — including irritability, bloating, and headaches — simply signalling that the menstrual flow will start within hours or days. It is a minor, if recurring, inconvenience. Five to ten percent of menstruating women, however, suffer from severe PMS. For these women — three million to seven million Americans — the days prior to the onset of menstruation are marked by a gamut of physiological and psychological symptoms that disrupt their personal and professional lives.

PMS is a complex disorder apparently linked to the cyclic activity of the hypothalamic-pituitary-ovarian axis. It is associated with a wide range of symptoms recurring regularly at the same phase of each menstrual cycle followed by a symptom-free phase in each cycle. The symptoms include irritability, tension, headache, depression, fatigue, breast swelling and tenderness, abdominal bloating, weight gain, increased thirst or appetite, cravings for sweet or salty foods, acne, asthma, and constipation. Other symptoms that may occur on a regular, cyclical basis include:

- *Boils, herpes, hives*
- *Epilepsy, migraines, dizziness*
- *Conjunctivitis, sties, uveitis*
- *Hoarseness, sore throat, sinusitis, rhinitis*
- *Cystitis, urethritis*
- *Child abuse, alcohol abuse, assaults, panic attacks, psychotic episodes, suicide attempts*

To women with PMS, confronted each month by the same pains, depression or feelings of being out of control, Edna St. Vincent Millay's aphorism is particularly apt: "It's not true that life is one damn thing after another — it's one damn thing over and over." For women with mild conditions, her flippancy is on target; but those with very severe cases endure an anguish and agony that more accurately parallel that of Hamlet's father's ghost:

> "Doomed for a certain term to walk the night,
> And for the day confined to fast in fires."

The PMS disorder was first described in a scientific paper published in 1931 by Dr. Robert Frank. Today medical textbooks ignore or barely mention the syndrome and its multiplicity of symptoms. As a result, most physicians — male doctors who haven't studied PMS in medical school and never experienced a menstrual cycle — either dismiss it as a psychosomatic phenomenon or misdiagnose it. Yet, quite clearly, the condition exists. Despite the prevailing attitude, more than one hundred research studies on premenstrual syndrome and cyclic disorders related to menstruation have been published over the years. More painfully, it has damaged millions of lives, and contributed to divorce, child abuse, alcoholism, and violence, hamstrung careers, and hindered personal development.

Why does the medical establishment keep the blinders on? Despite the recent and rapid increase in the number of women practicing medicine, the prevalent view of the female body remains male-oriented, in the male-dominated medical and psychiatric establishments. As Paula Weideger writes in *Menstruation and Menopause,* "Gynecology textbooks are riddled with statements about the psychological or sociological roots of menstrual and menopausal distress. Despite feelings of vulnerability and menstrual shame, women have repeatedly attempted to tell their physicians that the problems are not in their heads but in their bodies. The doctor, convinced his theory is the right one, pays little attention to what his patient has to say.''

To many gynecologists, pain is the most decisive evidence that a woman has failed to accept the female role. This has led to a vicious circle in which women suffer the most severe discomfort, go to a doctor for help, are told they are psychologically responsible for their pain, and leave the doctor's office in physical and mental agony.

Thousands, if not hundreds of thousands, of laypeople — especially the relatives, spouses and children of women who suffer from PMS, if not the women themselves — long ago linked certain recurring behavior and physical complaints to the menstrual cycle. It is such a common problem, in fact, that it has entered our popular literature, almost without notice or comment. Two authors of novels published in this country have woven their plots around the lives of women with severe PMS: *The Third Deadly Sin* by Lawrence Sanders, the best-selling murder mystery, and *I Am Mary Dunne,* a psychological study of insanity, by Canadian writer Brian Moore. It must be emphasized that the central characters of these works are tormented by the most extreme type of PMS, the depths of which only a very small percentage of women are likely to know. Both authors developed their characters because they had known women who suffered from the premenstrual syndrome. Lawrence Sanders researched PMS and the host of physical and psychological disorders of his protaganist for two years before writing his book. Brian Moore says he was in love with a woman who had PMS. ''For two weeks she was normal. But her personality changed very rapidly, to the day,'' he told us in an interview. ''If we ever had any dinner engagements during this time, we could never go. And it interfered with her work. She was a highly trained, highly educated woman who had a very responsible job. However, when the symptoms developed, she had to be out of the office. Consequently, she had to work nights during her normal time to compensate.''

The memories of that troubled existence led him to shape his character Mary Dunne in his friend's image. ''Almost every woman I know has some personality change'' (due to her menstrual cycle). ''We can't dismiss it. Premenstrual tension differs greatly (from one person to another) and women who suffer from it badly see it affect their jobs, their relationships, their lives.''

The Menstrual Cycle

To understand PMS, you first have to understand the most delicate and sophisticated function of the female body, the menstrual cycle.

The control center of a number of body systems, including the sex hormones, is the hypothalamus. Each month from menarche on, this walnut-sized unit buried deeply in the brain acts as elegant interpreter of the body's rhythms, transmitting messages to the pituitary gland that set the menstrual cycle in motion. The pituitary, in turn, responds by producing two critical hormones: the Follicle Stimulating Hormone, known as FSH, and the Luteinizing Hormone, or LH. From first menstrual cycle to menopause, the hypothalamus acts as the conductor of a highly trained orchestra. Once its baton signals the downbeat to the pituitary, the hypothalamus-pituitary-ovarian axis is united in purpose and begins to play its symphonic message, preparing a woman's body for conception and child-bearing.

There are two phases to the monthly cycle, identified by the dominance of the hormone during each part: the follicular phase and the luteal phase.

In the follicular phase, FSH is secreted into the bloodstream and reaches the ovary, where it does just what its name promises: it stimulates the development of the follicles of the ovary that contain egg cells. (Usually only one ovary and fifteen to twenty follicles are stimulated in a single cycle.) At the same time, the endometrium, or uterine lining, starts to develop and thicken in preparation for the potential implantation of a fertilized egg. The follicles start to develop, vying against each other for a dominant role, like violinists competing for the position of concertmaster. After the fifth day, a dominant follicle emerges, fated to grow into an egg. The others wither and die off, while FSH secretion stimulates the remaining follicle to manufacture estrogen, another sex hormone. On the 11th and 12th days, a burst of estrogen is emitted from the follicle like a clap of tympani; this is the signal to the pituitary that the follicle is about to produce an egg. The pituitary responds with an answering explosion of LH, which lasts for two or three days, overriding the influence of FSH and jolting the ovary into producing an egg. Within thirty-six hours the crescendo is heard: the ovary erupts with the egg.

Ovulation marks the beginning of the fourteen-day luteal phase. (The length of a menstrual cycle varies, but the luteal phase lasts fourteen days. In the textbook example of a twenty-eight-day cycle, the follicular and luteal phases are both fourteen days. In a forty-day cycle, the luteal phase is fourteen days and the follicular phase is twenty-six days. Ovulation would occur on the last day of the follicular phase or the twenty-sixth day, not at the midpoint, or the twentieth day.) The egg leaves the ovary, passing through the Fallopian tubes to the uterus, where it may or may not be fertilized by male sperm. The follicle, now empty, changes character in response to the secretion of LH and becomes the corpus luteum, or yellow body. The corpus luteum manufactures and secretes progesterone and estrogens. The subsequent high concentration of estrogen in the bloodstream and pituitary inhibits the secretion of any more FSH or LH, which prevents them from signalling the ovary to develop any new follicles during this cycle.

If the egg that has been released is fertilized and a fetus conceived in the cycle, the corpus luteum flourishes. Enormous amounts of progesterone will be secreted to nurture and sustain the development of the fetus until the placenta takes over. Most cycles, however, do not result in pregnancy. In these cycles, then, the production of progesterone continues until a critical level is reached. When the pituitary detects that enough progesterone is in the bloodstream, it slows the production of LH. As LH production declines, the corpus luteum is no longer being fueled and it begins to decay. As the corpus luteum wanes, the amount of progesterone and estrogen being produced decreases. When the production of progesterone and estrogen reach their nadirs, menstruation begins. The uterus is no longer stimulated by the hormones and the endometrium — the lining of the uterus — begins to slough off. After the first day or two of flow, the pituitary responds to the absence of estrogen and progesterone by making more FSH and preparing for the next cycle.

In some women, however, the delicate multi-system effort of the menstrual cycle is thrown out of balance. The result: not a symphonic serenade, but an atonal cacophony. In some women, an imbalance in one or many elements of the hypothalamic-pituitary-ovarian axis produces the premenstrual syndrome: a Rabelaisian nightmare, a dissonance "above the pitch, out of tune, and off the hinges."

Reproductive Hormones

The sex hormones, estrogen, progesterone and the androgens (of which testosterone is the dominant substance), are all derived from cholesterol; they serve as blood-borne messengers from the glands that secrete them to the target organs that utilize them. Hormones act upon their specific target organ by quickening the rate of internal cellular reactions. Estrogen and progesterone are believed to act as gene activators. Once inside the nucleus of the cell, the hormone activates the gene, initiating the synthesis of protein, and eventually influences all of the characteristic functions of that cell.

Estrogen is present in both males and females, secreted by the adrenal gland. In the female body it stimulates the development of breasts and the reproductive organs. It is also responsible for feminine curves, the fatty deposits necessary to support reproduction. It acts on both sexes in fat metabolism and the production of blood proteins as well as vascular and muscle tissue. Estrogen's primary function is in the menstrual cycle and the maintenance of the fetus. During the cycle, as follicles ripen in the ovary under the influence of FSH, they begin to secrete estrogen. The hormone travels back to the pituitary, and there activates the surge in LH which leads to ovulation. After ovulation the corpus luteum continues the follicle's job of producing estrogen, as well as progesterone. To facilitate the sperms' journey to the egg, estrogen also increases and thins out the cervical mucus, giving the sperm easier access to the uterus. And estrogen assists the egg's journey to the uterus by increasing the motility of the Fallopian tubes. The hormone further contributes to the reproductive process by nurturing the growth of the uterine endometrium that will eventually anchor and feed the fertilized egg.

In concert with its male analog, testosterone, estrogen halts bone development during adolescence by sealing the cartilage ends of the bones. A deficiency in estrogen leads to osteoporosis, a common disorder in post-menopausal women. Estrogen also accelerates the synthesis of the blood proteins and the metabolism of fatty acids which inhibits the production of cholesterol. It appears to protect women from heart disease and arteriosclerosis; women's incident rates of heart disease are much lower than men's but do increase in post-menopausal women. And estrogen also stimulates gland secretions in the skin and plays a role in normal vascular maintenance; estrogen deficiency, such as that experienced at menopause, is marked by hot flashes.

Progesterone helps ready the endometrium for the implantation of a fertilized egg and sustains the fetus during pregnancy. Progesterone is estrogen-dependent; it requires prior stimulation by estrogen to do its work. Estrogen initially stimulates the growth of the endometrium, then progesterone steps in to convert the tissue into active glands. Under the influence of progesterone, the glands fill with glycogen to feed the fetus, blood vessels proliferate, and enzymes accumulate, ready to aid in the fetus' growth. Like estrogen, progesterone is initially secreted by the ovary's corpus luteum, later by the placenta. One of its functions is to prevent another egg from being fertilized once one is in place in the uterus. After fertilization, it causes the cervical mucus to become thick and sticky, which locks sperm out and further protects the fertilized egg and uterus from bacteria. Progesterone also elevates the body temperature slightly, which is why we can determine the time of ovulation and peak fertility by tracking a woman's temperature.

In men, the principal sex hormone is testosterone, secreted by the testes. It is responsible for the production of sperm, the development and maintenance of male reproductive organs and secondary sex characteristics such as pubic hair, the deepened voice, coarser skin texture, thicker secretion of oil by the skin glands, and male muscle and fat distribution. It accounts for sex drive and growth — in both men and women; the adrenal glands produce small amounts of testosterone in women. This hormone also accounts for the greater aggressiveness of males.

Physical, emotional, and behavioral changes can be tied to the cyclical pattern of sex hormone activity and to the changes of hormone supply between one cycle of life and the next. The pattern of hormone production is different for males and females; this contributes to sexual differences in physical and emotional experience, as well as differences in behavior. While females have a distinct, observable cycle that makes changes in their behavior or temperament easy to mark in terms of the cycle, males also exhibit recurring patterns of behavior that some researchers believe correspond to a cycling of hormonal levels. In men, however, these shifts are often attributed to "moodiness." The ebb and flow of male hormones are not as dramatic as those in women but they are observable. In some men a stretch of good-neutral-bad temper occurs at regular intervals — thirty days, forty days, fifty-five days, or so on — that is observed by family, friends, and co-workers who adapt their own behavior toward and expectations of the men to account for the mood swings.

A 1970 study, reporting on sixteen years of data collected by Danish researchers, showed that men experience a definite thirty-day cycle of testosterone production. A 1969 study undertaken by the Omi Railway Company of Japan reported that male workers had predictable cycles that affected their work efficiency, decision-making, and proneness to accidents. The railroad revised its work schedules to remove employees from critical duties during their "bad" or unpredictable phases. Dr. Franz Halberg of the University of Minnesota is continuing his research into cyclical behavior in males; to date he has found evidence of cyclical surges and declines in grip strength and beard growth due to changes in hormonal levels. As Dr. Estelle Ramey, a professor of physiology at the Georgetown University School of Medicine, has observed, "In healthy maturity, the adult human changes with clocklike regularity during each day, just as he or she does during each month, or each life's season." If the hormonal shifts in males were as sharp as those in women and contributed to as many medical problems, one could be certain that the validity of the condition would not be in question.

Eleven Landmarks

Premenstrual syndrome can be difficult to identify and diagnose because its symptoms encompass so many systems of the body. With PMS, one size simply does not fit all. The landmarks of PMS that can aid women and their physicians in identifying the condition are:

• *Time of onset.* PMS tends to begin at puberty, after pregnancy, after termination of the birth control pill, or after an episode of amenorrhea (no periods).

• *Time of increased severity.* Mild symptoms of PMS may be present for a number of years but the woman notes a marked increase in her symptoms following the discontinuance of the birth control pill, following a pregnancy, after the cessation of breastfeeding, after a tubal ligation or hysterectomy, or after an episode of amenorrhea.

- *Painless menstruation.* Although pelvic discomfort or pain may occasionally be a part of the premenstrual syndrome, painful menstruation is not.
- *Weight fluctuations.* Many women with PMS experience monthly weight swings of six to nine pounds, and over the years experience weight ranges of twenty-eight pounds or more. The proper comparison is made between the highest-ever weight, excluding pregnancy, with the lowest-ever weight by history.
- *Food cravings.* Hunger and eating binges, especially involving sweet or salty foods, are often noted in the premenstruum. The onset of acute symptoms, violent episodes, panic attacks, and migraine headaches often occur after an absence of food intake exceeding four or five hours.
- *Intolerance for alcohol.* Women suffering from PMS may notice a decreased tolerance for alcohol during the premenstruum, accompanied by alcohol cravings.
- *Inability to tolerate the birth control pill.* Women with premenstrual syndrome often experience weight gain, depression, headaches, and exacerbation of the premenstrual syndrome symptoms with the use of birth control pills.
- *History of postpartum depression.* The depression must have been of sufficient severity to require psychiatric treatment or admission to a hospital. A study of one hundred women admitted to the hospital for severe premenstrual syndrome revealed that seventy-three percent of those who had been pregnant had suffered from significant postpartum depression.
- *History of threatened abortion.* Bleeding in the early months of pregnancy followed by a successful pregnancy is relatively common in PMS cases.
- *History of hypertension or toxemia during pregnancy.* Studies show that eighty-six percent of women who have had a pregnancy complicated by toxemia subsequently developed premenstrual syndrome.
- *Increased sex drive.* Women suffering from PMS may experience an increase in libido during the premenstrual phase. By contrast,

women suffering from PMS as well as depression may experience a decreased interest in sex.

Timing Is Critical

The key to the diagnosis of PMS is not so much the identifying of signs or symptoms as it is establishing the timing of the symptoms in relation to the menstrual cycle. Several typical patterns are symptoms that begin:

● *One to ten days prior* to menstruation and continue until the onset of menstruation.

● *At ovulation,* resolve in a day or two, and then reappear later in the premenstrual phase.

● *At ovulation,* resolve in a day or two and then reappear later in the premenstrual phase.

● *At ovulation,* continue steadily into the menstrual period, resolving only toward the end of the menstrual period. These women often complain that they only have one good week per month.

Each pattern must be followed by a symptom-free phase lasting at least seven days to constitute a diagnosis of PMS.

Signs of other chronic disorders, including depression, rheumatoid arthritis, ulcerative colitis, and asthma may be present throughout the month in varying degrees, but worsen in the days before menstrual flow. Such instances do NOT represent the premenstrual syndrome. But it is possible for a woman to have one of these conditions, in addition to others, AND premenstrual syndrome concurrently. This is not unusual in the more severe cases.

Other Menstrually-Related Disorders

Premenstrual syndrome is commonly misdiagnosed. Among the conditions it has been mistaken for are:

Dysmenorrhea — pelvic pain or menstrual cramping, generally beginning one day prior to the onset of menstruation and ending during or with the end of the flow.

Endometriosis — a painful condition marked by severe cramps and heavy bleeding that results when endometrial tissue (the lining of the uterus) appears and proliferates outside of the uterus, clinging to the ovaries, uterine ligaments, vagina, vulva, cervix, intestines, or pelvic lymph glands. In rare cases endometriosis may spread to the kidney, lungs, arms, hands, thighs, or spleen.

Pelvic Inflammatory Disease — an umbrella term for various types of infections of the uterus, Fallopian tubes, ovaries and adjacent tissues, marked by severe pelvic and abdominal pain or abdominal swelling, nausea, vomiting, and high fever.

Some psychological conditions are also confused with PMS. Among them are:

Cyclothymic Disorder — a condition characterized by numerous periods of depression and other symptoms over a period of at least two years, but not severe enough to meet the criteria of a major depressive episode.

Dysthymic Disorder — depressive neurosis, characterized by a chronic mood disturbance of about two year's duration and a loss of interest in most activities. Symptoms include social withdrawal, tearfulness, extreme pessimism, and decreased functioning at work, home, or school.

Major Depressive Episode — condition marked by loss of interest or pleasure in all activities. Symptoms are persistent depression, hopelessness, sadness, and/or irritability.

What Causes PMS?

Why do some women have severe premenstrual syndrome and others no symptoms at all? Why do some women have mild cases while others make the rounds of doctors' offices seeking help? As Dr. William Keye, a reproductive endocrinologist and assistant professor of obstetrics and gynecology at the University of Utah Medical Center, says, "The real problem is, we don't know."

We don't know, but we have suspicions. Many theories have been proposed as to the cause of premenstrual syndrome. The most frequently discussed is that advanced by Dr. Katharina Dalton, the British pioneer in the field, who suggests that a deficiency of progesterone in relation to the amount of estrogen present before menstruation triggers the syndrome. Others suggest that perhaps the ovaries in some women produce a substance that sets off a reaction or imbalance in the endocrine system, or that an aberrant estrogen is at the bottom of it all. We think it is much more complicated than that. First of all, premenstrual syndrome is now a catchall phrase encompassing more than one hundred fifty symptoms that occur cyclically in some women. That is a very strong indication that we are not talking about one syndrome, but several. They may be the red flags of several different malfunctions of the endocrine system; or they could result from a central malfunction that affects many systems of the body, producing different reactions — or symptoms — from more than one system.

We also know that the tools of scientific research make it possible to identify the causes of PMS if the proper questions are posed, if sufficient money is made available to support the studies, and if the research is undertaken by top medical investigators on a systematic basis. Research into PMS is not nearly as problematic as trying to find a cure for cancer. And while the research is being done, we know — from clinical experience — that PMS can be treated and eliminated. Women no longer have to suffer in silence. With proper screening procedures, an accurate diagnosis of PMS can be made, and the condition treated with a combination of lifestyle changes and, if necessary, progesterone.

Facing Up to PMS

Many women suffering from PMS have visited and been examined by more than one physician — usually three and sometimes as many as twenty specialists, including gynecologists, internists, psychiatrists, endocrinologists, neurologists, and neurosurgeons. Their dilemma is that expressed by Alexander Pope in his *Moral Essays:* "Who shall decide when doctors disagree?" Because the medical profession, outside of a handful of physicians, has failed to recognize that pain and problems do accompany the menstrual cycle, enormous numbers of women are suffering. They are not fantasizing or imagining their symptoms. Most women have been ignored, misdiagnosed, or mistreated for their condition.

Is it any wonder then that women are the dominant health care consumers in this country? Sixty percent of all patient visits to physicians are made by women. The difference in health-care-seeking behavior between men and women starts at puberty, studies show. Boys and girls see physicians roughly with the same degree of frequency. Younger males, in fact, take a slight lead in the number of visits. But after puberty, the picture shifts dramatically. There is a sharp increase on the part of females, and a decrease in the number of visits by males. This pattern will persist throughout adulthood.

A variety of medications have been tried in PMS cases. But most women report that the typical medications make their symptoms worse, have no effect at all, result in significant side effects, alleviate some of their symptoms, but not all, or work for a few months and then no longer help. Among the medications that do not appear to resolve PMS are: diuretics, oral contraceptives, tranquilizers, antidepressants, lithium, bromocriptine, prostaglandin inhibitors, and vitamin therapy.

To overcome the damage that this lack of proper diagnosis and treatment has caused, education is sorely needed. If you're one of the millions of women confronted by a confusing array of physical and psychological events each month, you need information about the condition and reassurance that the problems are part of a biological condition. It has a name; it is not psychosomatic; it is not your imagination playing tricks on you; you are not losing your grip on sanity; you are not lacking in discipline or will to overcome it. For many, just being told that the pain is real helps to allay the fears, the despair, and the blow to self-esteem.

Changes in lifestyle and other therapy may be necessary to treat PMS. Reduction of stress, exercise, and careful attention to diet and nutrition can all help. Some women with mild or moderate cases of PMS find that the lifestyle changes alone resolve their problems. For the most severe cases, though, these help but do not eliminate the PMS symptoms. For these cases, we use progesterone, a therapy that long clinical use has demonstrated to be the most effective treatment. Progesterone seems to alleviate the greatest number of symptoms with the fewest side effects of any of the medications used to treat the disorder.

Chapter 2

"Nothing could easily be found that is more
remarkable than the monthly flux of women.
Contact with it turns new wine sour, crops
touched by it become barren, grafts die,
seeds in gardens are dried up, the fruit of
trees fall off, the bright surface of mirrors
in which it is merely reflected is dimmed, the
edge of steel and gleam of ivory are dulled,
hives of bees die, even bronze and iron are at
once seized by rust, and a horrible smell fills
the air: to taste it drives dogs mad and effects
their bite with an incurable poison."

Pliny the Elder, **Natural History**

Eve's Curse

Primitive societies associated menstruation with ill fortune, disasters, and the supernatural. Aristotle asserted that the "glance of a menstrual woman takes the polish from a mirror and the person who next glances in it will be bewitched." Pliny indicated that uncovering the body of a woman during her menstrual flow empowered her to stop hailstorms, whirlwinds, and lightning. During her menstrual flow, a woman was in contact with the stars and capable of magic, Aelion believed. This connection of menstruation with the supernatural seemed logical enough to early cultures: how else did women continue to thrive each month after suffering inexplicable and recurring bleeding, bleeding that did not result in death or stem from bodily injury? Like the phoenix arising from the ashes, women were clearly special, endowed with powers unknown to mere males. But the males were in control, after all. Instead of according women special status and honors for their rejuvenative feats, the men scrutinized this monthly phenomenona and concluded that it was accompanied by strange and sometimes unacceptable behavior. From Hippocrates on, healers cited mental disturbances arising from the association of guilt and fear with menstruation. Women were flawed, not blessed, with this cycle of blood.

Some societies ensured a safe distance between menstruating women and others by banishing the women during their flow to special areas — tents, huts, a hillside — set aside for this purpose. This taboo was enforced to protect the group from damage to the crops and from the outbursts or behavior that were associated with menstruating women. Some of these cultures apparently thought there was a poison or "menotoxin" in the menstrual blood. In part, this idea was inferred from the dramatic changes in bodily functions, attitude, and behavior that some evinced each month just prior to the menstrual flow. As soon as the flow began, or within a few days of it, the women's behavior would return to a normal state. To primitive peoples, then, it was assumed that a toxic agent or spirit had caused the dramatic changes prior to menstruation and that once the menstrual flow began the toxin was eliminated or washed away in the menstrual blood.

Freud and others rejected these theories about menstrual taboos on various grounds. Freud felt the theory of man's fear and horror of blood was exaggerated since it did not suppress customs such as circumcision of boys or the cruel extirpation of the clitoris and labia minora of girls, a practice which continues in some parts of the Middle East and Africa even today. Instead, these critics created a view of their own, a view to which few, if any, women we've ever met subscribe. Freudian theory suggested that women's envy and desire for the male sex organ and their anger and frustration at not having one led them to act out, emotionally or with otherwise inexplicable episodes of "hysteria," temporary paralysis, and a gamut of psychosomatic diseases. The males, in turn, sought to distance themselves and the community from these episodes, which fostered the creation of taboos. This theory undoubtedly reinforced Freud's self-satisfaction but it has very little to do with how women today — and probably in the past — perceived themselves and their sexuality.

As Sheila MacLeod so eloquently stated in *The Art of Starvation,* describing her experience at menarche: "I'm sorry to disappoint orthodox Freudians, but I felt no penis envy, and I didn't think myself to be maimed in any way... I was horrified and disgusted by menstruation rather than by sexuality. I felt that some dreadful punishment had been visited upon me, punishment for a crime which I had never committed. But I think I knew unconsciously that the supposed crime was twofold: I was being punished for being female and for having grown up.'' As she noted, this sense of punishment is felt by girls, not boys, in adolescence because the physical changes of girls traditionally were not considered an appropriate topic for open discussion. The development of boys, on the other hand, was and is treated as a mark of manhood.

Despite the advances in science and education over time, the superstitions and peculiar notions surrounding menstruation stubbornly persisted into the 19th Century. As late as 1878 the *British Medical Journal* published lengthy, earnest correspondence as to whether a menstruating woman would contaminate the food she touches. One writer, opposed to medical education for women, exclaimed: ''If such bad results accrue curing dead meat while she is menstruating, what would result, under similar conditions, from her attempt to cure living flesh in her midwifery or surgical practice?''

S. Icard, a noted French physician, writing in 1890, stated that ''the psychical and physical state of women during the menstrual periods seems to me to constitute one of the chief reasons why she should not administer public affairs. Indeed, one cannot depend upon a health so fragile and so often disturbed; the errs of judgments and false evaluations so often made at that time prove that they [women] are unable to undertake comfortably and successfully that which should be the exclusive lot of the strong sex.''

To these sexist opinions came a slew of women's voices shooting down the specious theories. Dr. Mary Jacobi presented a rigorous defense in her book, *The Question of Rest for Women During Menstruation,* published in 1876. In 1914, Leta Hollingworth, in her book *Functional Periodicity: An Experimental Study of the Mental and Motor Abilities of Women During Menstruation,* noted that ''the tradition emanating from the mystic and romantic novelists, that woman is a mysterious being, half hysteric, half angel, has found its way into scientific writing. Through the centuries gone, those who wrote were men, and since the phenomenon of periodicity was foreign to them, they not unnaturally seized upon it as a probable source of the alleged 'mystery' and 'caprice' of womankind. The dogma once formulated has been quoted on authority from author to author until the present day. A more immediate source of error is to be noted in the fact that the greater part of the evidence quoted on this subject is clinical in character, the contribution of physicians [male]. But it should be obvious to the least critical mind that normal women do not come under the care and observation of physicians.''

Hollingworth went for the jugular in challenging the basis of the male argument: "Men to whom it would never have occurred to write authoritatively on any other subject regarding which they possessed no reliable or expert knowledge, have not hesitated to make the most positive statements regarding the mental and motor abilities of women as related to functional periodicity... It is positively asserted that women cannot successfully pursue professional and industrial life because they are incapacitated, and should rest for one-fifth of their time; yet it is not proposed that mothers, housekeepers, cooks, scrub women, and dancers should be relieved periodically from their labors and responsibilities.''

From the dawn of time until well into the 20th Century women have had to defend themselves against male attacks on their abilities, despite the myriad responsibilities and skills they juggled effortlessly day after day, generation to generation. Man's fears and awe of woman, especially of her generative powers, have probably played some part in the reluctance of society in general —and the male-dominated medical profession in particular — to recognize and deal with premenstrual syndrome.

Uncovering the Medical Evidence

We know, of course, how the feminist debate has turned out — up to a point. Women have seized an equal role in all aspects of society, proving that they can fight fires, graduate from West Point, win election to political office, or become lawyers, physicians, accountants, truck drivers, ministers, and rabbis — and still be wives and mothers, should they choose to do so. All things are not equal though: while more than half of all adult women are in the workforce, they earn on average fifty-nine cents for every one dollar a man makes. But all in all, women's progress has been rapid, forceful, and successful in almost every facet of life in this country. Every facet but one. Women's medical problems have always gotten short shrift in this country. A belated acknowledgment of this was made in 1982 with the release of a scientific study noting that women's pain and discomfort, especially during the morning sickness of pregnancy and at menstruation, has been significantly underestimated and downplayed by physicians. Since more than four hundred thousand physicians in this country are male and about sixty thousand are female, the underestimation could well be due to the fact that a man has never experienced the reproductive incidents that a woman goes through and cannot comprehend the extent of the trauma.

The shortsightedness is apparent in the medical profession's attitude toward premenstrual syndrome. A review of the medical literature reveals that a lot of doctors have seen PMS in their practices, some have treated it, some have written about it, and hundreds of thousands of practitioners have read about it in clinical journals. But that's where it was left until recently. Why? Well, it is a woman's complaint, after all. And, as Food and Drug Administration officials pointed out a few years ago, it isn't life-threatening. To some physicians, then, premenstrual syndrome is not a priority. Many doctors view any discomfort arising from menstruation as normal, simply part of the woman's burden. To be fair, we must emphasize that because the symptoms of PMS cut across so many systems of the body and thus so many medical specialties, many cases of PMS are not properly diagnosed because no single physician has observed or been told of the spectrum of symptoms the patient has. The emphasis on specialization in modern medicine thus contributes to the confusion over and lack of recognition of PMS.

There is a trove of scientific evidence and published papers citing the existence of a battery of health problems and behavioral changes in women prior to the onset of menstruation. The first paper to do so in this country dates back more than fifty years. The first paper to do so worldwide was published in 1842, more than one hundred forty years ago. A prominent endocrinologist, Dr. Robert T. Frank of New York, is credited with first describing the scope of the syndrome in a paper published in 1931, *"The Hormonal Causes of Premenstrual Tension."* In his book published in 1929, *The Female Sex Hormone,* he described the recurring premenstrual problems of breast swelling and tenderness, headaches, edema of the eyelids, cheeks and extremities, hives, herpes simplex, abdominal discomfort, and "uncontrollable irritation and depression which manifests itself in manic or melancholic crises." He also noted that the number of suicides among women was highest during the time immediately prior to menstruation.

Other scientists had connected the onset of menstruation with health complaints even before Frank published his works. A monograph by Brierrede Boismont was published in Paris in 1842 concerning the relationship of menstruation and the mental state. He noted that various "low grade psychotic tendencies" appeared at this time. Other researchers published clinical papers noting a relationship between menstruation and genital herpes, periodic jaundice, gall bladder attacks, skin disorders, metabolic changes, a range of ophthalmological disorders including conjunctivitis, scleritis, iritis, herpes, corneae, and retinitis, even detachment of the retina. From 1900 until the publication of Frank's work in 1931, more than twenty papers appeared in clinical publications linking regular, periodic occurrence of various disorders during the premenstrual phase. Among them: arthritis, epilepsy, edema, skin disorders, headaches, and psychoses.

Frank opened his paper thus: "My attention has been increasingly directed toward a large group of women who are handicapped by premenstrual disturbances of manifold nature. It is well known that normal women suffer varying degrees of discomfort preceding the onset of menstruation. Employers of laborers take cognizance of this fact and make provisions for the temporary care of their employees. These minor disturbances include increased fatiguability, irritability, lack of concentration, and attacks of pain. In another group of patients, symptoms complained of are of sufficient gravity to require rest in bed for one or two days. In this group, particularly, pain plays the predominant role. There is still another class of patients in whom grave systemic disorders manifest themselves predominantly during the premenstrual period." The latter, he said, "complain of unrest, irritability, 'like jumping out of their skin,' and a desire to find relief by foolish and ill-considered actions. Their personal suffering is intense and manifests itself in many reckless and sometimes reprehensible actions. Not only do they realize their own suffering, but they feel conscience-stricken toward their husband and family, knowing well that they are unbearable in their attitude and their actions. Within an hour or two after the onset of the menstrual flow complete relief from both physical and mental tension occurs." He treated mild cases with diuretics, which brought some relief to those who retained fluids. In the more severe cases, he treated the women with radiation to the ovaries.

After the landmark Frank paper, another spate of research was published about conditions that recurred premenstrually: weight gain, fluid retention, ulcerative vulvitis, stomatitis, allergies, acne and dermatitis, irritability, restlessness, crying spells, headache, dizziness, insomnia, and painful breasts. In 1938 in a major article in the *Journal of the American Medical Association,* Leon Israel published a comprehensive article on "The Premenstrual Tension," in which he detailed a spectrum of recurring symptoms, ascribed their cause to a deficiency of progesterone in relation to excess estrogen, and reported that progesterone was an effective therapy.

The following year, E.C. Hamblen, a prominent gynecologist at Duke University, published his textbook, *Endocrine Gynecology.* Omitting any mention of Frank's work and Israel's paper, Hamblen wrote, "Despite the fact that menstruation is a physiologic process, most women experience certain subjective symptoms during the cycle... These include moderate lower abdominal discomfort, localized particularly in the pelvis; some slight mental depression; lassitude; a tendency to be annoyed readily; mild gastrointestinal symptoms..." In a chapter on "Abnormal Symptomatology of the Menstrual Cycle," Hamblen briefly described some symptoms that trouble women before menses, including premenstrual headaches, allergies, edema and fluid retention, skin disorders, breast discomfort, and psychoses. He did not categorize them as part of a common syndrome though.

The stream of publications continued. Researchers reported treating premenstrual tension marked by fluid retention with diuretics, premenstrual nervousness with progesterone injections, premenstrual tension as a nutritional deficiency with Vitamin B complex, and as hypoglycemia with a change in diet. In 1947 in the *Journal of Industrial Medicine,* Billig and Spaulding wrote about a "frequent striking clinical syndrome in women consisting of a triad of symptoms: a burst of energy several days before menses (premenstrual tension, easy bruising, and lowered threshold to pain.) These patients, just prior to menses, feel the urge to do something such as cleaning the house, doing the laundry. They are hyper-irritable, crabby, and admit to being 'hard to live with.' Invariably, they will find black and blue marks on their bodies and often have no idea how they were incurred. Practically all of them are somewhat irritable and hypersensitive, and tend to flinch when someone touches them. There is usually a history of recurrent complaints of peripheral radicular pains, which is usually the presenting complaint. They will readily admit that they 'just can't stand pain.' In many, considerable domestic difficulties are present, and frequently, they are a serious problem. A fair percentage give a history of munching and nibbling in between meals, and of increased nervous tension when meals are missed or delayed. Yet a surprising number eat little breakfast, and it is primarily the noon meal and the afternoon snacks which they rely upon to 'make them feel better'...." Their study noted that glucose tolerance tests revealed these women were hypoglycemic prior to menstruation.

More articles followed. Again the researchers reported premenstrual hypoglycemia, fluid retention, edema, psychotic episodes, postpartum depression, and raised the possibility that the recurring premenstrual symptoms were linked to a deficiency of progesterone relative to estrogen. In 1953, Dr. Katharina Dalton, who was to come to the forefront in the diagnosis and treatment of premenstrual syndrome in England, published an article together with Raymond Greene entitled, "The Premenstrual Syndrome," in the *British Medical Journal*. They wrote, "The term 'premenstrual tension' is unsatisfactory, for tension is only one of the many components of the syndrome. Its use has commonly led to a failure to recognize the disorder when tension is absent or is overshadowed by a more serious complaint. We have preferred to use the term 'premenstrual syndrome' but as our investigation has progressed it has become clear that this term also is unsatisfactory. Though the syndrome most commonly occurs in the premenstrual phase, similar symptoms occasionally occur at the time of ovulation, in the early part of the menstrual phase, and even rarely in the first day or two after the flow has ceased. The term 'menstrual syndrome' though correct, for in each individual the symptoms recur at monthly intervals, may wrongly create the impression that they occur only at menstruation. We have finally decided to retain the term 'premenstrual syndrome' in the full realization of its imperfection. The full elucidation of its cause may later suggest a more appropriate and more accurate nomenclature."

The first symposium on premenstrual tension was published in November 1953 in the *International Record of Medicine,* edited by Joseph Morton. The articles covered the history, clinical pattern, psychological symptoms, treatment, impact on industry, and legal implications. The following year Katharina Dalton published an article in the *British Medical Journal* on PMS, toxemia in pregnancy, and progesterone therapy.

Unfortunately, most of the studies are flawed in some way, which makes it extremely difficult to draw conclusions about PMS. They lack the controls and the careful synchrony of standardized scientific research. Without such consistency, it is difficult to draw upon these studies to pinpoint the causes and patterns of the disorder. Many studies include heterogeneous groups of patients instead of patients grouped by similarity of symptoms. Patients whose only symptoms are profound depression with feelings of isolation, hopelessness, or suicidal intent should not be scrutinized alongside patients with no psychological symptoms. Some studies do not specify that the post-menstrual period must be symptom-free. Consequently, patients who have other disorders, such as clinical depression, which may worsen just prior to menstruation but appears throughout the cycle, may be mixed in with patients with PMS. Control groups should be matched for age, demographics, weight, and history of pregnancy.

The most exciting research theory about the cause of PMS is that proposed by Drs. Robert Reid and S.S.C. Yen, reported in an article in the *American Journal of Obstetrics and Gynecology* in 1981. They attribute the broad-based nature of premenstrual syndrome to the "abberrant release of, or sensitivity to" hormones in the hypothalamus — beta-endorphin and alpha-melanocyte stimulating hormones. This results in a cascade of changes in the neuro-endocrine systems — within the brain-hypothalamus-pituitary complex — that ultimately leading to the various manifestations of PMS. The regulation of neurotransmitters (biochemical messengers between cells in the brain) is controlled by neuropeptide hormones. (Beta-endorphin and alpha-melanocyte stimulating hormone are neuropeptide hormones.) When the normal balance of these hormones is disturbed, alterations in mood and behavior are produced. Also, the pituitary will release greater amounts of other hormones that may have a number of effects on the body, including changes in the estrogen/progesterone ratio, levels of prolactin, levels of vasopressin, and alterations in the effects of such substances as dopamine, epinephrine, and norepinephrine. Regulation of progesterone and estrogen in response to these changes differs from woman to woman and may account for the various clinical signs of PMS. Future research will tell us how accurate this sophisticated theory is.

SECTION II / *Shared Pain*

Chapter 3

"Migraine headaches were, as everyone who did not have them knew, imaginary. I fought migraine then, ignored the warnings it sent, went to school and later to work in spite of it, sat through lectures in Middle English and presentations to advertisers with involuntary tears running down the right side of my face, threw up in washrooms, stumbled home by instinct, emptied ice trays onto my bed and tried to freeze the pain in my right temple, wished only for a neurosurgeon who would do a lobotomy on house call, and cursed my imagination."

Joan Didion, **The White Album**

Migraine

"A razor blade embedded in the side of my head."

"A piercing, blinding weight, like a meteor that crashed down from the heavens directly onto my brain."

"An intense heat, as if all the blood vessels, veins, arteries in the right side of my head were engorged, slowly expanding over a matter of hours until my eye and the lobe of the brain behind it felt like they would explode. But the explosion never comes."

The migraine sensation intrudes into the consciousness in distinctive ways. It is unquestionably memorable, a kind of heinous torture that, once braved, finds its way into diaries, journals, letters to friends and families as if the victims pray to exorcise the migraine demon by extruding it in writing.

Menstrual migraine headaches are among the oldest recognized illnesses. First identified by Hippocrates, who attributed the symptoms to "agitated blood seeking a way of escape," they are severely disabling headaches that always recur at the same phase of the menstrual cycle. Migraine, whether associated with the menstrual cycle or not, is predominantly a women's illness. A study by a Scandinavian researcher, T. Dalsgaard-Nielsen, revealed that boys and girls aged seven to thirteen years had a similar incidence of migraine, but after the age of thirteen girls had a higher prevalence and more severe headaches than did boys; that suggests that the hormonal changes associated with menstruation increase susceptibility. Eighty percent of the migraine attacks are suffered by women. (Yet some of the most famous migraine victims are found in that remaining twenty percent: Thomas Jefferson and Ulysses S. Grant, among them.) Most women say that their headaches regularly strike at some point before or during their periods. Many women with premenstrual syndrome report menstrual migraine as one of their symptoms; about forty percent of our patients have a history of migraine.

The extensive research and literature about migraine has failed to isolate a single cause or develop a universal therapy for the blinding vascular headaches. What is known is that migraine, or the predisposition to it, is hereditary. For those who find no history of migraine in the family tree, the medical literature advises that there is a "migraine personality:" individuals who could be portrayed as ambitious, introverted, compulsive, highly organized, perfectionists intolerant of error. Type A workaholics have a disposition toward migraine. And a disparate range of incidents may act as catalysts: stress, fatigue, allergies, flashing lights, abrupt changes in pressure, humidity, or temperature, and of course, menstruation or ovulation.

The aura that precedes an actual migraine distracts and disrupts, results in clumsiness, accidents, oversights, incoherence. Migraine itself may be accompanied by nausea and vomiting, chills and bouts of sweating, exhaustion, distortion of vision or hearing, extreme sensitivity to all sensory stimuli. Many drugs and therapies are used to try to control migraine, but once an attack is under way, rarely does medication touch it.

Any or all of these symptoms and experiences may occur with a menstrual migraine. It most commonly appears just prior to the onset of the period or during the actual flow, but sometimes occurs mid-cycle at the time of ovulation. Very often the migraine seen with menses will disappear during pregnancy only to return following delivery; it often subsides with menopause. Like a bad penny that plagues the ill-starred, menstrual migraine tends to increase in frequency and intensity with age and multiple pregnancies. Many women who have had hysterectomies but still have their ovaries experience headaches every twenty-eight to thirty days or so, the kind of cyclical occurrence that women who have been sterilized report with other PMS symptoms.

Many of the women we've treated for PMS recall that their first migraine episodes were triggered by pregnancy. Vanessa Clayton is married and the mother of two children. After the birth of her first child nine years ago, she began to experience severe depression, irritability, outbursts of anger, and other symptoms. Her dominant symptom, however, was migraine so severe that the attacks lasted ten days at a time.

"I was in the hospital every month for a few days," she says. "The doctors did tests for a brain tumor and everything else. After not finding a brain tumor, they told me about the migraine personality and suggested that the stress of a new baby could cause it, and they sent me home with medication for migraine." Drugs had little effect on the migraine pain; after the birth of her second child, her attacks increased in frequency and severity.

"The headache always preceded my period by one day," she recalls. "I felt I was the opposite of catatonic. Catatonics don't respond to any stimulus. I responded to everything. Light bothered me. Noise drove me crazy. If someone touched me, I jumped. And smells made me nauseated. I needed a lot of salt and sugar to make things taste right. I remember lying on my bed, trying to be catatonic so the pain would stop. I would lie very still, wishing the pain away, trying to be the way I thought catatonics would be. Somehow it never made the pain go away." For nearly ten years, every month spelled a fresh migraine attack and an emergency trip to the university hospital for Vanessa Clayton. "Time didn't exist for me because I did nothing but lie in bed in pain for days on end. And then I would get up and would be functioning again.''

She tells a story of a typical incident that occurred after a migraine incident. "Once I got my migraine and had to be taken to the hospital the day after I had picked up the laundry and dry cleaning for the family. I had picked up seventeen shirts for my husband, almost every one he owned. After I got home from the hospital, my husband came to me one morning and asked where his clean shirts were. I gave him a lecture about his inability to find anything in the house and sent him back to look for them. Then he came back again after not finding them, and I insisted that there were seventeen clean shirts that I had picked up from the laundry. At that, my husband said, 'Van, that was two weeks ago.' I had been totally unaware of how much time had passed since my migraine attack.

''That happened all the time. A sort of amnesia sets in with women with PMS. It's how we keep going each month. If you remembered it all, the pain, the fights, the terrible things you say to those you care about, and had to face it happening again to you, you wouldn't choose to live. So you forget. Conveniently. It's a defense mechanism. I would forget the pain. The problem, at the end, was that the pain dominated my existence, and I had only a few days of normalcy a month.''

In the three years before she came to our office, Mrs. Clayton's migraine and other symptoms lasted three weeks of the month. Since she's been on progesterone, changed her diet, and started to exercise regularly, her headaches are gone.

Another of our patients, Susan Henshaw, thirty-nine, also started having severe migraine headaches after the birth of her first child. The headaches would begin the day she began to menstruate, and last from two to six days. During those days, she would lie on her bed in a dark room. She saw neurologists, who took brain scans and prescribed ''every drug in the book.'' None of the standard migraine drugs worked. She was finally given Midrin, a combination of Tylenol and a mild sedative which is thought to contract the blood vessels in the brain. The Midrin relieved her headaches. Mrs. Henshaw, who says she would classify herself as a Type A/migraine personality, now realizes that the tension headache that built up during the premenstrual period culminated in a migraine. In the eighteen months that she has been treated with progesterone, and followed our prescribed lifestyle program, she, too, has been free of migraine.

Menstrual Headache

Migraine is not the only headache with a menstrual connection. All types of headache strike more frequently at some time in the menstrual cycle, say many researchers, including Dr. Katharina Dalton. Forty percent of our patients experience premenstrual headaches that are not migraine. Muscle-contraction headaches, marked by stiffness in the neck and the feeling of a tight, constrictive band around the head, sometimes accompany cyclical feelings of anxiety and irritability. Premenstrual symptoms such as irritability, weight gain, abdominal distention, and breast swelling and tenderness seem to be more prevalent in women who also suffer from any type of menstrually-related headaches.

But migraine, with its crippling, lengthy attacks, is the headache for which patients are most likely to seek medical help. Some studies attribute the cause of these attacks to hypoglycemia, tension, or water retention. In one study, Dr. Katharina Dalton analyzed the incidence of migraine and the eating patterns of more than two thousand women, and found that three-quarters of the participants were stricken by the headaches within twenty-four hours after they had eaten either chocolate, cheese, citrus fruits, or alcohol. Two-thirds of the women reported that they had fasted during the twenty-four hours before the attacks, having gone without food for five hours in the daytime or thirteen hours overnight. Her study indicated that careful attention to a hypoglycemic diet, with frequent small meals and an avoidance of salt, sugar, and alcohol, could have some effect in limiting migraine attacks.

One popular theory about menstrual migraine is that fluid retention plays a major role, which is why many women with migraine are encouraged to take diuretics and eliminate salt from their diet. This therapy doesn't alleviate the headaches completely but may modify the severity of the symptoms; we now know that only about thirty percent of women with premenstrual syndrome actually retain fluids so the investigations citing water retention as a major cause of menstrual migraine need to be re-examined.

Most migraine sufferers have tried half a dozen medications in their mission to end the pain. One preventive that works for some people is old-fashioned ergotamine tartrate, which constricts the swelling blood vessels during the ''aura,'' the period of a few minutes or several hours that usually precedes the actual headache. Sometimes medications for migraine can be used intermittently at the time of menses in an effort to prevent the periodic occurrence of menstrual migraine. The most powerful weapons in the anti-migraine arsenal are methysergide, propranolol, and cyproheptadine, all of which may induce significant side effects for some people. (Methysergide is a derivative of lysergic acid; Sandoz Pharmaceuticals first synthesized LSD-25 while looking for a migraine cure.) But since the medications are used only intermittently for short periods of time in menstrual migraine, there is little need to fear using them.

Hormonal factors head the list of theories proposed about the cause of migraine, and are inextricably tied to the fluid retention theory. Water retention may be the result of an imbalance between estrogen and progesterone levels; falling estrogen levels in the premenstruum is probably the trigger mechanism in inducing menstrual migraine. Experiments have shown that it is possible to postpone the onset of migraine attack by introducing large amounts of estrogen into the bloodstream, by injection or oral intake. Migraine has occurred when researchers withdrew the estrogen support. Most women who suffer from premenstrual migraine notice that they are headache-free during pregnancy, especially during the last six months. Women who say their headaches are more severe during pregnancy are fewer in number. This strongly suggests that migraine is tied to the balance between estrogen and progesterone. Progesterone treatment is most effective in those women who suffer their headaches only at the time of the premenstrual phase of the cycle. It is next to most effective in those women who suffer from headaches at the time of premenstrual phase and during the time of their period. It is least effective with women who suffer headaches intermittently throughout the menstrual cycle but with increased frequency. Some women who take progesterone for PMS find that it is helpful for their headache during the time of the premenstrual phase; those who also have a history of headaches occuring during the menstrual period note that stopping the progesterone sometimes will cause a headache to occur during the ensuing menstrual period.

Premenstrual syndrome is not the cause of migraine, but migraine may be a symptom of the premenstrual condition. Progesterone is not a treatment for migraine per se, but may be helpful in treating premenstrual migraine, especially when the progesterone is taken in conjunction with an improvement in diet and exercise.

"Then suddenly it was as if a gulf opened before him, and an extraordinary inner light flooded his soul."

Fyodor Dostoevsky, **The Idiot**

Epilepsy

When ancient healers began to observe a regular, periodic increase in epileptic seizures in women they naturally attributed the phenomenon to the moon, linking the two most common cyclical events of their experience. Since epilepsy was then adjudged a sign of madness and it was believed that insanity was intermittent, intensified when the moon was full, this led to the branding of epileptics (among others) as "lunatic," from the Latin word for moon.

As Fyodor Dostoevsky observed in his 19th Century novel *The Idiot,* "The sight of ... an epileptic fit fills many with absolute and unbearable horror, which has even something mystical about it." The fear that surrounded these seizures, he pointed out, sprang from the frightful and apparently inexplicable changes in the victim's body, the distortion of the face and eyes, convulsions, and spasm that gripped the body vise-like and thrashed it mercilessly about, but most of all because "a terrible, incredible scream, unlike anything imaginable, breaks forth; and with this cry all resemblance to a human being seems suddenly to disappear."

Dostoevsky's powerful imagery emerged from an intimate knowledge of seizures; he himself was an epileptic.

The relationship between epilepsy and the menses was not explored scientifically until the last century, and even now medical researchers are just beginning to draw some conclusions about cyclical seizures. Perhaps the most important step for humankind that the scientists took was to cut all ties to the waxing and waning of the moon's phases. Instead of lunar seizures we have catamenial epilepsy, from the Greek word meaning monthly. Many researchers maintain that seizures are exacerbated by menstruation in about fifty percent of the women with epilepsy. In women with catamenial epilepsy, the seizures often begin, or pre-existing attacks recur or become worse at menarche. Menopause seems to have a significant depressant effect on the incidence of seizures. Catamenial seizures are not the only cyclical form of epilepsy. Rhythmic seizures in women, with a periodicity ranging from eight to forty-six days, were tracked in a 1955 study; other researchers have found monthly seizure patterns in men.

About ten percent of the patients we see have epilepsy or histories of seizures; practically all experience grand mal seizures marked by muscle spasms and lapses into unconsciousness. With the development of anticonvulsant drugs, scenes like those described by Dostoevsky are rare. Most of our patients are well-controlled with anticonvulsant drugs on a regular basis, but they frequently have disturbances just before their period. One of our patients responded well to Tegretol, an anticonvulsant, except that she noticed that if she had a seizure it was on the day of ovulation or the day her period started.

Britt Weston, a twenty-year-old college student, had the same kind of experience. Her cyclical symptoms began very early, when she was about eight, as she entered puberty, and continued through her teens. Four days a month she was fatigued, cranky, moody, and threw tantrums. "I'd be depressed and I wouldn't know why." She was examined by a neurologist, an internist, and an endocrinologist, none of whom could diagnose her disorder. They told her that it was all "in her head," and suggested that she see a psychiatrist. She wouldn't because "I knew that I wasn't crazy. I'd rather live with it than pay a doctor who won't cure it anyway. It would all disappear after four days." Weston had been treated for epilepsy, and was taking anticonvulsant medication. It prevented the attacks most of the time. If she were under unusual stress or became very excited or overtired, though, she sometimes had a grand mal seizure.

At the onset of menses her symptoms worsened. She saw a gynecologist who properly diagnosed her low blood-sugar level. Weston then went to see an internist, who put her in the hospital for further tests. The hospital's chief of medicine diagnosed her as "progesterone sensitive" and put her on birth control pills. She said that he called once a month to find out how the pills were working. Each month she told him that her symptoms were worse, not better, and he said, 'Just give it one more month.' " After five months, she just stopped taking them. "I'd have terrible mood swings and depression for about three or four days out of the month. I didn't know how it started, but once it did, I couldn't get out of it. I'd just have to wait, and ride it out. I could do just about everything that I had to if I didn't have a seizure. If I had a seizure, I'd get a terrible headache and I'd be too weak to do anything that day." Eventually she realized that the seizures occurred only when she was reacting to stress on the day of ovulation or three days before menstruation. During this time her family "just ignored it. Once they realized what it was, they'd just pretend it wasn't happening. It was the best thing to do. There's nothing they could have done for me anyway. No matter what they'd say, I'd scream and yell and cry. But only for four days." Progesterone has alleviated all of her symptoms.

"Every once in a while, if I forget to take the progesterone, I have problems. If I remember, I'm fine. I thought that I'd have to live with this for the rest of my life. It's a miracle."

Dr. Richard H. Mattson, professor of neurology at the Yale University School of Medicine and director of the Epilepsy Center at the Veterans' Administration Hospital in New Haven, Conn., is a leader in the field of epilepsy research. In a recently published study of fourteen women during three to six consecutive menstrual cycles, he concluded that seizures:

- *Correlate with the stages of the menstrual cycle.*
- *Are most frequent at menstruation.*
- *Are most common when progesterone levels are lowest.*
- *Can be caused by stress independent of the menstrual cycle.*

Until Dr. Mattson began his research, the studies done for catamenial epilepsy had been limited by insufficient controls and insufficient followup of the patients in the study. Other studies and clinical observations vary widely from Dr. Mattson's findings. This may in part be due to the lack of consistent definition of the catamenial phase. Some researchers consider it to be the last four premenstrual days and the first day of menstruation. Others limit it to the two days prior to the period and the entire duration of menstruation.

Hormonal Triggers

Estrogen and progesterone are at the center of the debate over the triggering mechanism of seizures. Both hormones have been used in experiments with animals and humans to determine their effect on seizure frequency. A 1976 Scandinavian study of seven women indicated a rise in the incidence of seizures when progesterone levels dropped — prior to menstruation — making estrogen more dominant. The study also showed a reduction in seizures when progesterone levels were higher. Laboratory tests using progesterone and some other related steroids produced anticonvulsive properties in animals. And a substance closely related to progesterone, desoxycorticosterone, exerts an anticonvulsant effect in epileptic persons. While the results are not conclusive, "estrogen seems to have some epileptic capacity and progesterone seems to have some anti-epileptic capacity," explains Dr. Allan Hauser, assistant professor of neurology and public health at Columbia University and assistant director of Columbia's Sergievsky Center for the study of epilepsy and cerebral palsy.

In a study of twenty-five women with epilepsy focusing on the role of estrogen in seizures, more than half were found to have menstrual problems — premenstrual syndrome or irregular menses. Their spells clustered during and immediately before menstruation. The study group were given Premarin, an estrogen, which activated their seizures. The predominance of estrogen in the body prior to menstruation suggests that it may cause catamenial epilepsy; that, in turn, suggests that progesterone, an antagonist of estrogen, could prevent attacks. We have found this to be true in the patients with a history of epilepsy whom we treat with progesterone for premenstrual syndrome.

Unfortunately most physicians and researchers do not seem to understand the distinction between progesterone and synthetic progestational agents. In our clinical practice we prescribe progesterone, a compound identical to the molecular structure of the progesterone produced by the ovaries, in treating PMS. This is the therapy that produces excellent results in treating PMS and its related symptoms. Most of the treatment and experiments in hormonal-related conditions in women involve the use of synthetic progestational agents (not progesterone) or oral contraceptives containing estrogen, which frequently exacerbate a range of PMS symptoms including epilepsy.

Epilepsy does not cause PMS, and PMS does not cause epilepsy. However, seizures may occur in some women premenstrually and may be part of the PMS spectrum of symptoms. We have seen some women who have been properly diagnosed and treated for their epilepsy whose seizures are controlled by medication — except during the premenstrual period. Progesterone has been an effective adjunct in the treatment of these premenstrual epileptic seizures.

Chapter 5

> *"Premenstrual tension produces this*
> *dichotomy, for while part of me feels*
> *lunatic, another me stands by appalled at*
> *what the premenstrual self is doing and*
> *saying. Or screaming, in this case..."*
>
> Brian Moore, I Am Mary Dunne

Mood Swings and Depression

On the morning of Caroline Lind's wedding day in 1970, she wandered about her parent's house, pausing over mementoes and photographs, saying farewell to the things of girlhood. In the playroom that had been her haven, she browsed among the toys and books shared among five brothers and sisters, finally reaching for a gently worn, well-thumbed copy of Hans Christian Andersen's *Fairy Tales*. She leafed through the volume until she came to her favorite story, "The Snow Queen," about two children, Gerda and Kay, and a demon's magic mirror. Central to the fable is "...that horrid mirror in which all good and great things reflected in it became small and mean, while the bad things were magnified and every flaw became very apparent." When the mirror breaks, grains of glass shower the earth, flying into people's eyes, and striking at their hearts. The little boy, Kay, is one of the unlucky victims who soon has no capacity for love, kindness, generosity, or the appreciation of beauty, and comes under the spell of the Snow Queen, who turns his heart to ice. As Caroline read, she recalls, "I realized that that was how I felt each month, as if the demon's mirror shattered and sent shards of glass into my eyes and my heart. I was two different people, the good person and the bad person. When I was feeling angry, irritable, depressed, and in pain, no one could do anything right, no one could say anything right to me, I couldn't accept kindness. I was belligerent, hostile, I'd throw things. I was just like little Kay.''

Caroline Lind is one of the many women whose premenstrual syndrome is marked by sharp mood swings and depression. More than half the women we treat indicate that they experience mood swings or depression in the phase between ovulation and menstrual flow as a PMS symptom; during the rest of their cycle, the behavior of these women is normal. Our patients quite spontaneously describe themselves as Dr. Jekyll and Mrs. Hyde, or as two opposite personalities inhabiting one body — the good person and the bad person, or the sane twin and the mad twin. These labels are not simply whimsical flights of fantasy. Dramatic changes in their behavior, moods, and personality are confirmed by husbands, children, close relatives, friends, roommates, and co-workers. While many of these women say they have an inward sense of being "out of control," most do, in fact, control their behavior but fear that if the symptoms worsen they might assault their husbands or children. Very few women actually become violent. Verbal abuse, however, is common enough.

In some PMS women mood swings and depression develop slowly over several days; in others, the onset is very rapid. Self-esteem disintegrates with the inability to control the drastic shifts in personality and temperament, and the recurring sense of emotional helplessness. Most of our patients say they spent years berating themselves, asking "what is wrong with me?" or "why don't I have the willpower to control this? or "why I am different from other women?" The only way to restore a woman's self-worth and confidence is to treat her premenstrual condition and any depressive disorder she may have, and reassure her that millions of other women share her feelings. Research studies also verify the preponderance of this type of behavior during the premenstrual phase, especially in the last four days prior to and the first four days of menstruation. It is manifested in the increase in female suicides, calls to psychiatric hotlines, appearances at psychiatric emergency facilities, admissions to hospitals for psychiatric and physical reasons, and crying spells.

Unhappiness vs. Depression

Like "love" and "happiness," depression is as hard to qualify as it is to quantify. Unhappiness over disappointments or frustrations in everyday life confront everyone. Just because you're unhappy over not getting a promotion or because the washing machine is broken does not mean you're depressed. Unhappiness is distinguished from depression by the duration and pervasiveness of the mood. Depression is a persistent inability to experience pleasure or interest in *all* facets of life. If a woman lawyer loses a major court case and is still able to enjoy a game of tennis or dinner with friends at her favorite restaurant, if the low mood generated by her professional setback does not overshadow the rest of her life, and dissipates in a matter of days, she isn't depressed, just unhappy. Natural levels of the blues or brief bouts of feeling low strike most individuals at some point, whether they're ending a love affair or they've been fired from their job. But if you can't pull yourself together after a time and are unable to enjoy any facet of personal or work situations, you're suffering from depression.

The earmarks of depression — mood swings, the blues, unprovoked crying jags, fatigue, a sense of being out of control, distraction or a lack of concentration, lack of or sudden spurts of energy, lack of coordination, decreased sex drive — are among the most universal heralds of ovulation and menstruation. For most women these episodes are brief and disappear once menstruation begins. However, about thirty percent of the women burdened by extreme cases of PMS develop severe clinical depressions apart from the premenstrual disorder. Like storm clouds that hover above the horizon in the dog days of summer, shrouding the landscape in oppressive torpor, these depressions tinge every facet of daily life; they do not lift once menstrual flow starts. Women with major depressions must be treated both for their PMS and for the depressive condition.

If asked to name the single most common medical complaint of American women, in fact, many physicians would not hesitate in their response. An insidious, inward-directed anger, depression affects perhaps eighty-five percent of the female adults in this country at one time or another, according to some researchers' estimates. Most women do not even know they are depressed and do not seek medical treatment for the disorder, according to a study by Dr. Myrna Weissman, director of the Yale Depression Unit. Instead, they admit to bouts of feeling down, lethargic, unhappy, sad, gloomy, or troubled, but stumble along on their own and try to cope. While depression can develop apart from PMS, it is highly likely that a substantial portion of these women exhibit depression as a symptom of premenstrual syndrome. Both are silent diseases whose victims tend to keep their pain to themselves, ashamed or afraid or unaware that normal life is not a series of days or weeks filled with gloom and despair.

Many of the women we treat have been examined by psychiatrists who either did not recognize the premenstrual syndrome and misdiagnosed them as having a severe depression, or did not recognize that the women were suffering simultaneously from premenstrual syndrome *and* a severe depression. Psychotherapy, tranquilizers, and antidepressant drugs, especially the tricyclic antidepressants, Sinequan, Tofranil, Elavil, and Triavil, are the most common treatments in these cases. But rarely do they have any effect on premenstrual syndrome. An indication of the frequency of these treatments was revealed in a 1972 study, which reported that seventy percent of all individuals treated with psychotropic drugs were female.

The frequency with which the diagnosis of depression is made for women was attacked by Phyllis Chesler in her polemic, *Women and Madness,* and by some other researchers who argue that the numbers lie. Chesler's view is that the medical profession practices social and sexual discrimination in labeling women "depressed" when their behavior doesn't conform with societal expectations of women's roles. Maggie Scarf, in her best-selling work about women and depression, *Unfinished Business,* rigorously rejected the "numbers do lie" theory. Scarf concluded, "Women simply are more depressed, in the aggregate, than are men, in the aggregate. Beyond the shadow of a doubt."

The cause of depression is disputed. Classic psychoanalysis suggests that women's envy of men and their masculinity is at the root. "Menstrual or menopausal depression may, of course, be symptomatic of a psychological conflict," Paula Weideger points out in *Menstruation and Menopause*. "Menstrual depression has been related to a failure to conceive," notes Constance Berry and Frederick L. McGuire, "... as a woman's rejection of her femininity." Like Freud, Karl Menninger asserts that "the envy of the male cannot be repressed and serves to direct her hostility in two directions: she resents the more favored and envied males while secretly trying to emulate them, and at the same time she hates and would deny her own femaleness." Both Menninger and Freud suggest that woman's rage and envy, inevitably unleashed when

46

she has "failed" to conceive, is uncontrollable at menstruation. Most women — and many men — reject this penis-envy argument.

Research into the causes of depression, however, has indicated that hormones may play a role in triggering the episodes. It may well be that the hormonal changes critical to the orchestration of the menstrual cycle spark the mood swings and depressed states.

Women who suffer from PMS and a major depression seem to respond best to drugs known as monoamine oxidase inhibitors, such as Nardil, or to lithium carbonate. Again, these two medications may ease the depression but they have little or no effect on the PMS. When depression is simply a manifestation of PMS, our usual treatment for PMS eliminates the depression. This treatment includes changes in nutrition, exercise, stress reduction techniques, vitamin therapy, and progesterone, which you will learn about later in this book.

Typical of the confusing combination of depression and PMS is the experience of Jennifer Anderson, a thirty-six-year-old probation officer. "I could handle the physical symptoms," she says. "But I couldn't handle the depression. About one day before my period I would flip out." Her symptoms progressively worsened, with the depression lasting more and more days each month. One gynecologist prescribed diuretics and told her that she was depressed because of fluid retention. She visited a nutritionist who put her on a hypoglycemic diet, and later tried acupuncture and hypnosis. Eventually she was examined by three psychiatrists, one of whom told her that "some of her depression was related to her period." The psychiatrists tried putting her on antidepressants, but the drugs made her feel worse. Finally, she says, "I went to a psychiatric hospital." She left work one Friday during lunch and committed herself. "I didn't even tell anyone where I was going." Her period started the next day and her depression lifted. "If only I could have held on for one more day," she says. She believes that a lot of the depression that women experience is suppressed rage. "Women aren't allowed to be enraged in our society. It isn't 'nice.' So women suppress a lot of their anger." Progesterone and improved nutrition have helped in her case. "I'm less depressed, fewer days, anyway. Now I feel that I can handle the depression."

Lori Weiner, the thirty-nine-year-old mother of two children who works as a customer service representative at a bank, had had mild PMS since puberty: irritability, depression, nervousness, backaches, headaches. After a tubal ligation three years ago, all the symptoms, particularly the depression, got much worse. Gynecologists prescribed Darvocet, birth control pills, and other drugs, none of which helped. Her doctors told her that she "had to live with it." She saw two psychiatrists, and the second told her that although the PMS wasn't the cause of her depression, it was a factor that probably increased its severity. She was hospitalized for depression for about three weeks. "I felt better, but not one hundred percent."

Women who suffer from PMS and a severe depression are the hardest to treat. While the two disorders may be interrelated, they must be treated separately. Some women won't accept that. They come to our office after having tried so many other treatments that they are frustrated and angry. By the time we see them, they are pinning all their hopes for a cure on PMS because they have heard it is treatable with progesterone. Progesterone is not a universal therapy; it can't solve all ills. We emphasize that in our evaluation sessions. Women with depression and severe premenstrual syndrome need progesterone, lifestyle changes, and psychotherapy or antidepressant drugs. Without the psychotherapy or antidepressants, progesterone won't ease the depression.

One patient, Sally Hunter, could not accept the fact that she had a severe depression rather than PMS. After nearly a year of discussions with Hunter and her husband, she finally agreed to at least see a psychiatrist. She insisted on visiting a biologically oriented psychiatrist because she put a lot of faith in biological causes of illness. When Hunter went for the initial evaluation she was skeptical. But she did agree to go for a second session, again, very skeptically. Finally Hunter accepted the diagnosis of depression and agreed to begin psychotherapy in earnest. We later got her children into family therapy, too, because they had begun to withdraw, apparently because of her frequent angry outbursts. We suspected that she had abused her daughter, although Hunter wouldn't discuss it. The girl was especially withdrawn and the mother felt extremely guilty about her. For months the children didn't believe her when she said "I'm better. It won't happen again." They needed a third party, the therapist, to convince them.

The pattern of premenstrual depression is so familiar that it is now part of the novelists' palette. Brian Moore, the author of *I Am Mary*

Dunne, a psychological study of insanity, says his recollections of the dramatic personality changes weathered by a close woman friend with PMS guided him in fashioning his novel about "a character on the brink of madness." He was searching for a protagonist with whom his audience would be able to "sympathize or identify. Then I thought about premenstrual tension. I decided to use premenstrual tension as my madness. . . I think that premenstrual depression is the most acceptable form of madness in our society."

Chapter 6

*"I opened the bag of chocolate chip cookies
and ate two, for pleasure, or the memory of
pleasure. I didn't like the taste; it made my
palate heavy and dull. But I went on eating.
It was a way of getting through this difficult
time, this difficult walk."*

Mary Gordon, **Final Payments**

Eating Disorders

Food is not merely one of life's necessities; like sex, food is a basic pleasure and comfort. Whether exultant and celebratory or frustrated, lonely, sad, or bored, we reach out — for companionship, friends, lovers, or if it's the best alternative, for food. A nation of immigrants, with memories of the privation and hunger that haunted our families in the old country a generation or two or three ago, America put plenty on a pedestal, along with truth, justice, and opportunity. We once considered a groaning table a right of citizenship, conferred upon us for having shrewdly chosen to live in the world's bread basket, the land of amber waves of grain and coast-to-coast herds of dairy cows and beef cattle. Despite the trend in the last decade toward fitness and dieting, Americans continue to use and abuse food daily to a degree almost unchallenged, with the possible exception of Henry VIII. Our obsession with food, and sweets, in particular, starts in childhood with heavily sugared baby foods. From there we gavotte to the playground, filling ourselves with empty calories and energy bursts from the candy store. As Alfred Kazin, in *A Walker in the City,* recalls his own Depression-era childhood in New York, "We never had a chance to know what hunger meant. At home we nibbled all day long as a matter of course. On the block we gorged ourselves continually on 'Nestles,' gumdrops, poppy seeds, nuts, chocolate-covered cherries, charlotte russe, and ice cream... The hunger for sweets, jellies, and soda water raged in us like a disease; during the grimmest punchball game, in the middle of a fist fight, we would dash to the candy store to get down two-cent blocks of chocolate and 'small' three-cent glasses of cherry soda; or calling 'upstairs' from the street, would have flung to us, or carefully hoisted down at the end of a clothesline, thick slices of rye bread smeared with chicken fat.''

These days there's little of the chicken fat smeared on rye. Instead there's fast-food roulette. The ticky-tacky vista of red roofs, orange tiles, and Golden Arches that stretches along highway after highway the length and breadth of this country offers eloquent testimony to the fact that Americans don't eat well, they eat a lot. Television commercials and supermarket aisles repeat the message, this time with a parade of sugared cereals, ice cream, pudding, cakes, pies, and candy, alongside boxes and cans of heavily salted, sugared, floured, virtually sedated foods that can be fixed in a jiffy. Thirty million Americans may jog or participate in sports, but not all thirty million of them are living on spinach salads and fresh vegetables. If they were, the market for some of these instant carbo-caloric wonders would dry up.

This environment is a mined and dangerous trail for those receiving hunger signals from their brain. We know that depression and obesity may be due in part to an over-release of certain chemicals that act on the brain's hunger response, distorting an individual's response to and perception of food, and sometimes triggering cravings. Depression and food cravings recur regularly in many women with premenstrual syndrome. This may be a result of the hormonal balance in the body, but more research remains to be done — on PMS, depression, and food disorders — before the answers are known.

Eating Binges

Dr. Hilde Bruch, in her book *Eating Disorders,* says binge eating — the sudden, compulsive ingestion of very large amounts of food in a very short time, sometimes furtive, sometimes public — is usually triggered by stress or by feelings of loneliness, frustration, anxiety, tension, or boredom, or is a symptom of an underlying emotional illness, such as depression. It is extremely common among women, a significant percentage of whom are also depressed. She writes, ''...eating binges, uncontrolled eating in response to the slightest insult or disappointment, have occurred at some time or another in practically all of my fat patients.'' And the binges are almost always followed by self-recriminations.

Food binges wreak havoc, however temporary, in the lives of millions of women who can't control their cravings or attitudes toward food. Not surprisingly, the drama and destruction of binges can be found in fictional characters, too. In Mary Gordon's novel, *Final Payments,* the heroine Isabel Moore, reaches out for food in the midst of a depression following her father's death and her own search for identity. ''I would eat later, secretly in my room. I hid a box of crackers under my bathrobe and went upstairs. I did not lift up the dark green shade. I put crackers in my mouth whole, and ate them silently, as if I were in a fever, as if I were being watched.'' In another instance: ''I took off my clothes and got into bed in my bra and underpants. I had kept two bars of candy in my handbag. I ate them now, under the gray blankets.'' The emotional and physical effects of the binges were devastating. After a humiliating shopping trip to a dress store, she says, ''Size sixteen, I kept saying to myself. But what did it mean? Ten, sixteen, my body had caused only damage... My thighs chafed against each other as I walked. I decided to go on a diet.''

Bruch observes that for many ''obesity has an important positive function; it is a compensatory mechanism in a frustrating and stressful life. In others, however, it is associated with, and directly related to, severe personality and developmental disturbances.'' Many people, she says, hide their emotional problems ''under a complacent facade... Instead of expressing anger, or even experiencing it, they become depressed and the overeating serves as a defense against deeper depression... Overeating may occur at times of such severe emotional stress that the question is not so much 'Why overeating?' but 'What would be the alternative?''' She notes that statistics show that obese people have a higher incidence of most diseases and a higher death rate, but their suicide rate is dramatically lower. ''I have often been impressed with the fact that the situations in reaction to which obesity developed were situations to which others might have reacted with despair,'' she notes. ''However much of a handicap obesity may become, as a defensive reaction it is less destructive than suicide or paralyzing deep depression.''

Cravings for food, but especially for chocolate, sweets, or salty foods, are frequently experienced by women with premenstrual syndrome — sometimes for an afternoon, sometimes for several days or more. When the cravings are strong, they result in binge eating. The women eat compulsively and are incapable of stopping themselves. It's not simply a matter of self-control; it's PMS. The physiology of the symptoms can't be controlled simply by wishful thinking. When women of normal weight and normal eating patterns binge briefly, they usually lose the extra four or five pounds once their period begins. Some women gain eight to fifteen pounds by binging and eventually have great difficulty losing this weight during their symptom-free portion of the month. It is not surprising to find then, that most women who have PMS are overweight, and at least seventy-five to eighty percent of these women binge. Women with PMS frequently have great fluctuations in weight during their adult years. Of the patients we see, about twenty percent are more than twenty-five pounds overweight; the majority are ten to fifteen pounds overweight. Many who binge as a result of PMS find that over time they can't control their eating patterns at all; they chronically overeat and may gain more than twenty-five pounds.

Lois Benson, one of our patients, remembers her experience with cravings before her period: "They would come about four or five days before. I would eat things that I wouldn't even look at ordinarily, and gain anywhere from ten to fifteen pounds. But I would lose ten of that a week after." Now treated with progesterone and following our nutritional program, she occasionally has one day of craving, but has lost ten pounds already and is continuing to lose weight.

Erin Gibson, forty-three, a journalist and mother of five, had regular, strong food cravings that led her to consume gallons of ice cream, bags of snack foods, and entire cakes over two or three days. Since starting progesterone therapy, her food cravings are reduced: "I'll eat a few handfuls of potato chips compulsively instead of the whole bag, half a pint of ice cream instead of a quart."

Marsha Coleman, thirty-seven, an investment counselor and mother of four, says her "abnormal craving for sweets started with ovulation. I used to put on five, six, seven pounds a month. My normal weight was about 130, but now I'm 120 and I don't lose from there, I don't gain from there. I have leveled off and I don't change weight at all, with or without my period. I had literally two sets of clothes. I always had to wear wraparound skirts at the end of the month."

Both Agnes Lazarus and her daughter, Deborah, were compulsive eaters until they began treatment for premenstrual syndrome. Mrs. Lazarus has lost fifteen pounds. She says the progesterone treatment has been important in improving her college-aged daughter's self-image. "Deb couldn't control her eating habits before. Now her depression is relieved and she has been able to stay on a diet for the first time in her life and lose weight."

Links between food cravings and menstruation, and cravings and depression have been studied by many scientific researchers. One study, by Stuart Smith and Cynthia Sauder, reported in *Psychomatic Medicine,* of three hundred nurses and a pilot study of thirty-seven hospitalized depressive patients, found that of the group of depressed patients, fifteen women, or more than forty percent, said they felt like eating compulsively prior to menstruation, and nine of those fifteen women, or twenty-four percent, reported experiencing premenstrual depression. Of the sixteen who said they craved sweets, twelve patients, or seventy-five percent, said they suffered from premenstrual depression. All nine who craved chocolate had premenstrual depression.

Sixty-six percent of the three hundred nurses studied said they were tense or depressed just before or at the start of their periods. The nurses' study also showed "a rather striking association between recurrent depression, premenstrual fluid retention, and a peculiar craving for sweets in the immediate predepressive and premenstrual period." Of the one hundred sixteen who reported a desire to eat compulsively at specific times, eighty-five, or seventy-three percent, said they had premenstrual tension or depression; of the sixty-four who said they craved sweets at specific times, forty-nine, or seventy-seven percent, said they had premenstrual tension or depression. Of the forty-two who craved chocolate at specific times, thirty-four, or eighty-one percent, reported premenstrual tension or depression. The premise of the Smith and Sauder study was their observation of three depressed female patients "who demonstrated a peculiar and characteristic craving for sweets" before their periods that was "not present under normal circumstances. These persons did not normally tend to eat compulsively nor were they obese. Just prior to a period of depression, however, they reported a very powerful craving for sweets and in particular for chocolate, which they went to great lengths to obtain." Later they examined two younger patients with a craving for sweets "during the onset of depression." These women had considerable feelings of tension or depression just prior to the onset of each menstrual period and tended to retain large amounts of fluids then. They often developed a peculiar craving for sweets in the premenstruum."

Another investigation studied forty-five women, including twenty-five with premenstrual symptoms, who reported symptoms of irritability, fatigue, depression, crying spells, impatience, and cravings for sweets. Still another researcher, Joseph Morton, reported an alteration in carbohydrate metabolism to permit increased sugar tolerance. "The hypoglycemia is a recent and striking finding in premenstrual tension. It is clinically manifested by increased appetite or a craving for sweets." In Morton's study, thirty-seven percent of the women with premenstrual syndrome had cravings for sweets, and twenty-three percent had increased appetite. Tests of the women with premenstrual tension showed that they were hypoglycemic prior to the onset of their periods.

Anorexia Nervosa

About ten percent of the patients we see who are in their twenties and thirties have recovered from adolescent episodes of anorexia nervosa or bulimia, two eating disorders. Anorexics sometimes start by dieting from a slightly overweight or normal level with a goal of ten or more pounds under what would be an ideal weight; when they reach that level, though, they keep on dieting, refusing meals, balking at their favorite foods until their weight plunges to 90, 80, sometimes 70 pounds or less. Estimates of the incidence of anorexia range from one in one hundred adolescent girls to one in two hundred. Bulimics appear normal in appearance, usually maintaining an ideal weight. But they accomplish this through a bizarre pattern of binges and purges, much like the elite of Rome during a ritual feast. It is much more difficult to estimate the incidence of bulimia because frequently there are no outward symptoms; it's extremely common among high school and college students.

Women and girls trapped by these conditions have a distorted view of their own self-image and of food itself. Dr. Hilde Bruch, in *Eating Disorders,* defines the underlying personal feelings of anorexics as a "disturbance of delusional proportions in the body image and body concept." The anorexic seems to be completely unaware of her actual weight and size, insisting to her parents and friends that she is fat when she is actually little more than a walking, talking bag of bones. Dr. Bruch says some anorexics pursue thinness ''in the struggle for an independent identity, delusional denial of thinness, preoccupation with food, hyperactivity, and striving for perfection.'' It is the ultimate, self-selected malady for a teenager unable to confront her emerging maturity. For an adolescent plagued by the pain and emotional turmoil of PMS on top of the identity crisis of youth, anorexia may be a comforting distraction, requiring concentration, willpower, and discipline; anorexic girls frequently come from an extremely close family and are ''the perfect'' daughters, who earn high grades in school and are usually very obedient. Anorexia is usually their only form of rebellion. Mara Selvini Palazzoli says a girl with this condition ''believes that her mind transcends her body and that it grants her unlimited power over her own behavior and that of others... The result... is the mistaken belief that the patient is engaged in a victorious battle on two fronts'' against her body and her family. In *The Art of Starvation,* Sheila MacLeod variously describes her schoolgirl experience with anorexia as ''a form of passive resistance,'' and ''my only weapon in my bid for autonomy.'' Her war was waged in response to the realization that ''What was happening to my body — not only the changes brought about by puberty, but the fact that the clothes it wore and the food it consumed were chosen for it by someone else — was a metaphor for what was happening to me as a whole person.''

When we see these women, food disorders are no longer a problem for them. Anorexics, whose percentage of body fat to body mass falls to a level below that necessary for menstruation, usually stop menstruating at some point in their weight loss or experience amenorrhea. Amenorrhea, we know, may act as a triggering event for premenstrual syndrome. Some of the former anorexics we see have recalled that they had cyclical symptoms prior to menstruation during their active anorexic phase. Others don't remember, but it appears that the PMS did not develop until after the anorexia was under control. The connection between premenstrual syndrome and the incidence of anorexia and bulimia needs to be explored in formal research.

Chapter 7

"I set some arbitrary rules for myself. I wouldn't drink until 5 p.m. I wouldn't drink before leaving the house to go shopping. I would drink only on alternate days. For months I made myself crazy, adhering to these self-imposed restrictions."

Joyce Rebeta-Burditt, **The Cracker Factory**

Problems With Alcohol and Drugs

Premenstrual syndrome gives many women more than enough reason to seek out liquor or other drugs to block out the pain, the depression, the memories of bizarre episodes with their families or at work. Compounding this cyclical tendency to reach for a drink, most women have a reduced tolerance for alcohol or drugs premenstrually — sometimes a dramatically lower threshold for these substances. Many women who normally consume two or three cocktails without incident find they become thoroughly intoxicated with one during the premenstrual phase. Like food binges, drinking sprees can be habit-forming. Once a woman starts drinking because of her PMS symptoms she may just keep on drinking all month long. Sandra Thomas, one of our patients, says, ''I drank a lot during my premenstrual time to alleviate the symptoms. The trouble with drinking heavily for half the month is that you get into the habit. I started to drink just as heavily when I felt good as when I felt bad.''

Women who drink or abuse drugs were, like women with PMS, once silent sufferers. No longer. Their problems and experiences have filled novels and autobiographies, movies, and television over the past decade. Perhaps the best story of the journey of a woman drinker from mental hospital to recovery is told in *The Cracker Factory,* the best-selling novel by Joyce Rebeta-Burditt. The heroine is Cassie Barrett, a woman with a history of major depressions and alcoholic episodes that have landed her in an institution twice. In the first eighteen pages and within just about as many days, we learn that Cassie:

- burns a dinner,
- has a car accident involving her children,
- throws another piping hot meal down the garbage disposal in the mistaken belief that she has already fed her family,
- is accused by her husband of being incompetent when she can't keep up with the laundry — forcing him to wear one brown and one black sock to work — and stashes the ironing overflow in shopping bags behind the furnace,
- and collapses in tears at a supermarket after staring blankly at the shelves, distracted and confused, not remembering what she came in to buy.

All of this has happened, we discover, because after a lengthy drying out period and stay in a hospital, Cassie has had it. "I grabbed my coat and the grocery money and was waiting at the liquor store when it opened... Once home I pulled the curtains, put on a stack of records and curled up in front of the stereo with a tumbler full of scotch. I sipped and listened and sipped some more, until the barbed wire dissolved and a soft, mellow fog replaced the ache behind my eyes. I must have fallen asleep because the next thing I knew the kids were home and Charlie was due. I knew I'd have to scramble frantically to get to the market and home again, get dinner started and some of the clutter cleared away before he walked in the door. But first I needed a drink."

It's a graphic, if nearly breathless, first chapter. But it does more than simply draw the reader into the book. It paints a picture of life for a lot of women, women who drink, women who are on pills, women who are depressed. Even women who have extreme cases of premenstrual syndrome. The one thing we don't know about Cassie is whether her problems are cyclical. Cassie does relate a brief family history in which she recalls the outbursts of Aunt Lily who threw the Thanksgiving turkey at Cassie's father because no one passed her the gravy, and set fire to the broom closet because the family didn't want to discuss Catherine the Great. PMS, like alcoholism and some psychological disorders, does run in families, as we explain in the following chapter.

Alcohol is a mood altering drug; it is a depressant, not a stimulant. For someone who is already depressed, alcohol fuels their despair and sense of hopelessness. In combination with any medication, alcohol's effects are magnified. Drugs and alcohol is a lethal combination. Yet after the age of forty, women rarely limit their abuse to alcohol alone, but tend to use a combination of drugs and drink.

Women and Alcohol

For as long as grape and grain have been fermented into potable liquids, some women as well as men have over-indulged. But society's traditional view of women did not leave room for weakness or illness; women were stuck on a plaster pedestal, expected to remain pure and prim, virgin or mother until they died. Reality, of course, never quite matched that portrait. Until fairly recently, though, women with drinking problems kept them hidden behind drawn curtains; for if the problem did become publicly known, they were shunned by the community. Women who drank were automatically thought to be "loose," or immoral, beyond the pale, Blanche DuBois in the flesh. Two developments helped millions of women leave the cooking sherry in the kitchen and seek help: the recognition in the 1960s that alcoholism is a disease, and the deluge of women into the workforce. At least one-third of the ten million alcoholics and problem drinkers in the United States, or 3.3 million, are women, according to *The Invisible Alcoholics* by Marian Sandmaier. Other estimates put the figure as high as one-half of problem drinkers, or five million women. The percentage of women in Alcoholics Anonymous has risen from twenty-two percent in 1968 to twenty-nine percent in 1977, with women comprising thirty-two percent of new members joining AA between 1974 and 1977. Sadly, the rise in the number of working women that made it impossible for many with drinking problems to ignore their weakness for liquor any longer, is also thought to have contributed to a further increase in women alcoholics. Stress is a critical factor in problem drinking, just as it is with premenstrual syndrome. The stress of a job, on top of the burden of maintaining home and family, can lead some women to liquor. "Women in the workforce drink more, and there are more women who work using drink and drugs than those who stay at home," says Dr. Michael Murphy, president of the Bay Area Comprehensive Alcoholic Program, which operates several treatment centers in the Boston area providing comprehensive alcoholic treatment to one thousand to two thousand outpatients a year. Sixty percent of those patients are women. In addition, BayCAP helps treat three hundred to four hundred women admitted to hospitals for treatment. Dr. Murphy says the danger signals for a chronic alcoholic, the stresses that trigger drinking, are feelings of anger, tiredness, loneliness, hunger, migraine headaches — all of which may be symptoms of premenstrual syndrome.

Of the patients we treat for premenstrual syndrome, about twenty percent abuse alcohol and fifteen percent belong to Alcoholics Anonymous, usually joining because we've referred them. About forty percent of our patients are on some sort of medication when they come to our office. Valium and amphetamines are the most common. Valium is a tranquilizer, a muscle relaxant that induces a mild euphoria and is prescribed for anxiety; some of our patients have used as much as thirty milligrams a day or more; amphetamines, or speed, are an appetite suppressant and energy booster that helps some people temporarily cope with fatigue or depression. And we've treated one woman who had been a heroin addict; that extreme is rare.

Rita Hirsh's story is typical. Hirsh, a thirty-nine-year-old real estate broker, is married and has two sons. She began to drink after her PMS symptoms appeared to try to blank them out. "For two weeks, I would drink at home, quietly and alone. I wouldn't drink much when I was out. I had a very high tolerance for alcohol. There is no occasion that I can remember, or anyone I know can recall, when I acted drunk. When I first began attending Alcoholics Anonymous, many of my friends were surprised." Eventually she lost her capacity and tolerance for alcohol and began to have blackouts. Her first blackout occurred at a friend's house, where she and her family went for dinner. "I remember helping prepare dinner — pork curry. We sat down for dinner at eight, and I have no recollection of what happened after that. I don't remember what we talked about, I don't remember leaving with my kids at ten, putting them to bed, putting myself to bed. It's time lost forever. I got up the next morning and I had no memory of what happened the night before." The second time, she was home with her children. Her usual pattern, she said, was: "I'd pour myself a large glass of wine when I got into the house at five or six, and I'd drink slowly and steadily until I went to bed."

Her husband, Kenneth, didn't confront her with her alcoholism, even though he recognized it, because he thought it would destroy their marriage. "Now it's all to her credit that she recognized her problem and cured herself," he says. He noticed that she was drinking, but "we've always lived in a drinking environment. Drinks can close off your mind. I'd say to myself 'she's trying to block out the fight we're having.' When we fight, I tend to stop drinking. I think I'm afraid that I'd lose my temper. I did twice, in sports, and I really hurt people." (He is 6'3" and 220 pounds. Rita is 5'6" and 110 pounds.)

Hirsh says she was never noticeably drunk. Her husband remembers otherwise, especially the night that she threw a platter of prime rib against the dining room wall during a dinner party. Another major episode that occurred shortly before she decided to join AA, he says, came after they had had a major argument and she was particularly tense and angry. She told him she was going to get "as drunk as humanly possible." When she stomped upstairs during the fight, Kenneth Hirsh cleared all the liquor out of the house, packed up the children, and left. But he didn't see a bottle of wine and a gallon of vodka that were sitting on a kitchen counter. He says that leaving the liquor on the counter was "the biggest accident of my life, because she felt that I wanted her to drink herself to death." When he came home, "she was crying to her mother on the phone like a baby, then she got on with her father and I listened to her accuse him of never loving her or supporting her. When her friend finally came over and nurtured her, I left. Else I knew we would have a royal battle." The Hirshes began seeing a marriage counselor once Rita started progesterone therapy at the clinic; she also continues to attend AA meetings. "I'm an alcoholic. That means that I can't have one or two drinks ever, anymore," she says.

When Hirsh attended her first AA meeting, "I saw people like me. I heard many of the women speak of menstrual problems. There's a high incidence of PMS among women alcoholics, and a high incidence of alcoholism among women with PMS." Hirsh hesitated to tell her children about her alcoholism. "I went to AA meetings for two months before I told them. They noticed that I didn't drink anymore." She didn't tell them that she had stopped drinking, but "I knew that they knew. My husband would have wine with dinner, and I'd have ginger ale. They didn't question me, but I felt uncomfortable because I'm generally very open with them." She finally told her sons that she had an "allergy to alcohol," something that she felt they could relate to. She was attending AA meetings two or three times a week. First she told the boys that she was going to a "getting better" group. Finally she told them what it was. She was afraid, she said, that they'd find out from someone else.

Family Ties and Drinking Problems

Alcoholism runs in families; studies in this country and in Denmark have revealed a very strong genetic disposition to problem drinking. But men are more likely to become alcoholics based on genetic disposition, while females are more likely to show it as an effect of stress-related illness, like PMS, Dr. Murphy says. Many of our patients say their mothers, sisters, grandmothers or other female relatives drank because of what seemed to be a cyclical, PMS problem. Sometimes even children start drinking in reaction to a mother with PMS.

Carmen Sanchez, thirty-one, is an administrative assistant; she's married and the mother of a toddler. She is emphatic in her attitude to liquor: she doesn't drink and doesn't permit liquor in her home. Sanchez has had the symptoms of premenstrual syndrome since she began menstruating. She believes that PMS is the reason for the heavy drinking of her mother, grandmother, and sister. "My mother would drink very heavily the week before her period and get violent; she would beat my brother and me. For two or three weeks my mother would be fine, and then one week we all instinctively knew as very young children that something was wrong with her. My father would always say that mother was having her change this week. We got to notice the pattern... I think my mother's mother also has it. And my sister, too. I think it runs in the family. I can see it in just about every female member of my family, especially with its relation to the alcohol abuse. That's why I never drank. My sister was in the hospital about two months ago for thirty days. She had overdosed on alcohol somehow and her period was due in two days. My grandmother still says she has symptoms of PMS. She's a recovered alcoholic and lives in a nursing home. They're forbidden to have any kind of alcohol at all. She would say that she would always drink before her period because she couldn't deal with it. She's very outspoken about it, she talks about it a lot. She's eighty-three and she's still here."

Another patient, Gerry Simpson, also abstains from alcohol. Her mother had PMS and both parents were alcoholics. "My mother suffered rather severely from PMS when I was growing up, at least I now believe that. As a result, her marriage to my father was rocky and tumultuous. They both began to drink a lot. I think it was really as a result of my father's horrendous experience in the war (World War II) and my mother's PMS. I think they had started drinking to kind of overcome what had become an empty life." Simpson remembers: "My father's response to being drunk was to become violent and the first stage of my mother's nighttime ritual was to be verbally abusive, and then she would fall into a stupor. I was the caretaker of my family as we were growing up. My parents went through these alcoholic nightmares every night, but my older sisters and brother and my two little brothers slept through the violence and the nightmare. My father used to beat my mother regularly. My response to that was to get out of my bed and go and try to intervene in the conflict. I always did and I always succeeded; I was only nine or ten years old. I remember literally saving my mother's life on many occasions and putting them both to bed. Sometimes they would be totally unclothed, things would be bashed and broken all over the house. I remember really hating my brother and sister for not helping me through that. Eighty-five percent of the physical violence in that house was PMS-related, I'm sure. My mother would give everyone terrible verbal thrashings. I used to think that she was a witch; I thought she might have been possessed. I almost felt responsible for her tantrums because I knew she didn't like me. What really frightened me was taking on the characteristics of my mother, later. Of course, when I learned about PMS, I knew why my parents had had problems. She had PMS. It was why they were violent. Why she was alcoholic. Probably why he was an alcoholic."

The pattern of both husband and wife becoming alcoholics is not uncommon; in a relationship where the woman has premenstrual syndrome, her cyclical irritability and outbursts may trigger his drinking. After we presented material about PMS to a group of alcohol abuse therapists, one of the counselors said he had been confounded by the behavior of several men he was treating but now he recognized a pattern. "They have really worked hard in AA but every four to six months they start drinking again. And I've never been able to figure out why; they can't either. I know some of these guys' wives well enough and it's clear they've got PMS. I think when things have built up between the two of them over four or five months, then the wife has a severe episode of PMS, that's a crisis situation and the man deals with it by drinking." Since that discussion the counselor and several of his colleagues have referred the wives of their patients to us for treatment. Their diagnosis in these instances has been on target: the women have severe premenstrual syndrome.

We refer our patients with these problems to drug and alcohol abuse programs, especially Alcoholics Anonymous. Lifestyle changes and progesterone therapy are important in treating their PMS, but will not go to the source of their problems with alcohol. Progesterone may make it easier for some women to respond to treatment for alcohol and drug abuse because it tends to eliminate cyclical depression, anxiety, irritability — the kinds of problems that led them to alcohol and pills in the first place.

Chapter 8

"The lines are fallen unto me in pleasant places; yea, I have a goodly heritage."

Psalms, 16:6

It Runs in Families

Just as a droll wit or stubborn streak may pass from generation to generation in some families as predictably as great-grandmother's silver, a lineal disposition to health conditions is extremely common. Premenstrual syndrome appears to be one more characteristic that transcends generations. But it's hardly a tie that binds; PMS is more like an ineluctable fetter. We know that it runs in families. Once women are diagnosed and begin to understand the pattern of PMS, they rush to tell us stories about the troubles of their mothers, grandmothers, sisters, cousins, and aunts; more than half of our patients report that another family member has PMS. Like sure-fingered veterans at a quilting bee, they piece together incidents that strained family life and relationships and find that what had seemed to be the erratic or hostile behavior of a relative was classic premenstrual syndrome.

What we don't know yet is whether PMS is hereditary, if a genetic code is stamped on a woman's cells like electronic circuits etched on a silicon chip, programming her female descendants with the hallmarks of the syndrome. We've gathered some strong evidence that it might be. Several sets of twins have been treated at our center; in these cases, both women have the same symptoms and both experienced the same time of onset, whether at puberty or later. We have yet to find a twin who has PMS with a twin sister who does not. Dr. Katharina Dalton in England has made the same observation about PMS and twins. Many of our patients are mothers of twins but in most instances the children are too young to have developed PMS.

Genetic predisposition to the illness may be one reason or the entire reason that many women exhibit PMS at puberty. Or there could be a genetic predisposition that must be magnified by risk factors before the time bomb of the syndrome explodes in the system. Let's say your mother, grandmother, and sister have the symptoms, but you have never used the Pill, become pregnant, undergone a tubal ligation or hysterectomy, and avoided other risk factors. You may never develop PMS because, while you have a genetic predisposition to it, you have avoided the risk factors that would activate the signal in your genes.

Some scientists might argue that premenstrual syndrome is not hereditary, that it appears in relatives and close friends unconsciously. If A has premenstrual syndrome, and A lives with her mother and sister, B and C, works with D and E, and is extremely close friends with F, does the fact that A, B and C exhibit the same symptoms mean that the condition is genetic? Not necessarily. And what if you find that all of them — A, B, C, D, E, and F — have premenstrual syndrome? If it's genetically transmitted, then what's the explanation for its appearance in unrelated women? Could all these women from unrelated families experience the same genetic trait? We concede that there could be a role-modeling or mimic factor with the syndrome. To some degree, at least. Nonetheless, the frequency of the condition within families seems too high to be merely a coincidence or a copycat phenomenon.

The question of genetics can be answered once researchers devote the time and effort necessary to identify the genetic markers of PMS and trace them through many generations of families.

Searching Through the Family Tree

Our patients sometimes combine the analytical skills of Nero Wolfe and the practiced eye of a jigsaw puzzle fanatic in their efforts to hang PMS on the appropriate limbs of their family trees.

Barbara Southern, forty-six, and her twenty-two-year-old daughter, Holly, both are being treated at our Massachusetts center; Mrs. Southern's sister also has PMS, and their mother may also have suffered from it. Mrs. Southern feels that she probably had it during her teen years, but didn't connect it with her menstrual cycle until she reached her twenties. Her symptoms have changed over the years, initially encompassing depression, irritability, joint pains, back pains, compulsive eating binges, and fluid retention. "Depression used to be one of my biggest problems," she says. "It's gotten worse as I've gotten older." For the past eight years she has had a "peculiar stomach problem," which starts as hunger and becomes severe pain. "I have been trying [to find medical help] for years," she says.

She, perhaps understandably, was much more willing to discuss the depressive aspect of her daughter's PMS than her own. She says Holly's symptoms are like her own when she was younger: hunger, compulsive eating, binging, and serious depression. "I've always noticed it. It was very obvious — to me, not to Holly — when the second half of her cycle was beginning." Holly has thought of suicide during PMS and can't control her eating habits. Mrs. Southern said the long-distance telephone bills from her daughter, who's away at college, are heavy from mid-month on. "It's very difficult. I've seen it in her since she started her periods. No one would agree with me. But what could I do? I didn't even know how to help myself." Mrs. Southern says Holly has responded well to the progesterone therapy and lifestyle changes. "I'm in touch with her constantly. The depression is relieved. And she has been able to stay on a diet and lose weight.

"My sister has it, too. It seems to have gotten worse since she had a baby and two miscarriages. Of course, it's not as devastating for her. But she does report the fatigue, depression, and mood swings.Now my mother thinks she may have had symptoms of it, too."

Holly remembers that during her childhood her mother was frequently ill. "When I was a little girl, I remember my mother crying all the time and being depressed." She also recalls her mother suffering hunger and irritability. Holly's own case began with "depressions as far back as the beginning of high school. Severe, severe depression. It was like I couldn't find a solution for what was wrong at the time. I just wanted to die." It got worse when she started taking the pill at age nineteen. That's when she sought out a psychiatrist. "I have been in therapy for three or four years. Up until this point, I thought it might be psychological. That maybe I was mimicking my mother who was sick all those years." She always charted her mood swings and saw the menstrual connection, but still "doubted myself." She is clearly very grateful for the difference treatment has made: "Oh, my God. I have seen such a difference. I have been happy." The successful treatment also demonstrates to her that her complaints weren't symptoms of a psychodynamic problem with her mother.

We are also treating identical twins, Carla Mills and Sharon Cartwright, who were separated as children and given up for adoption. They have similar cases of PMS, marked by depression, anger, outbursts; both attribute their divorces to PMS. Carla was divorced once; Sharon twice. After locating each other in adulthood, they eventually found their natural mother and discussed PMS with her. Their mother and maternal grandmother had similar symptoms: depression, tension, headaches. Their mother said that she never felt well unless she was pregnant. Sharon remembers her mother as "always pregnant."

Many of our patients who have daughters, especially those in or approaching their teens, are fearful that the girls will develop premenstrual syndrome. Brenda Morgan has six children, including three daughters. "I'm watching them very closely because I just want to see that they are protected from this," she says. "If my daughters do develop it, there's no reason that they have to spend the major portion of their lives like I did, suffering. I spent most of my life thinking that I was probably insane and that I would wind up in an asylum sooner or later. That's an awful way to live. I hope the next generation would be spared this because of the growing understanding of PMS."

That view is echoed by Lauren Holloway, who has three children, including two girls, and whose mother also had premenstrual syndrome. Mrs. Holloway's condition grew from irritability and headaches that began when she started taking the birth control pill to extreme postpartum depression. "I think a lot about my own two daughters [and PMS]; this treatment is so wonderful that I want to go up on top of a mountain and shout to the world about it and help other women. I never understood what my mother's problem was when we were growing up," she says. "Mother was constantly going through different things. I've talked to my father about it. They divorced after thirty-six years of marriage. He just couldn't tolerate it anymore. We'd talk about what happened to her, and how she had her cravings and would go from doctor to doctor looking for an answer. They never found an answer but they always sent her home with something. That's the same thing they did with me. I found myself falling into the same pit. When I started crying and getting emotional and saying 'what is wrong with me?' my husband would call me Charlotte — that's my mother's name."

The disorder, like many genetic conditions, may skip a generation or two. Valerie Lawrence says her sisters and grandmothers have it, but her mother doesn't. Both grandmothers had multiple miscarriages and were treated with progesterone to help them carry a fetus to term. One of her sisters has "a peculiar case:" a life-threatening allergy to extreme changes of temperature, but only premenstrually. "If she's really hot and dives into a cool swimming pool or has been in the snow and is cold and comes in to sit by a fire, she'll 'blow up,' " Mrs. Lawrence says. "Her whole body turns red and she gets white welts — hives — all over and they itch like crazy. Twice she's been rushed to the hospital with her eyes, nose, and throat swollen shut; once her heart stopped."

Complications of Menstrual Synchrony

When both mother and daughter must face up to PMS each month, the tension in a household crackles, like an electric appliance threatening to short-circuit. Menstrual synchrony, a phenomenon as common as snow in Minnesota, usually plays a role in drawing the battle lines; women who live together or work together or spend inordinate amounts of time together often undergo subtle shifts in the timing of their menstrual cycles until all members of the circle experience the flow simultaneously. The pattern once was attributed to lunar phases, along with epileptic seizures and the birthing of babies. Whatever the cause, mutual cycles are a source of minor annoyance to some, especially to college students sharing bathrooms and tampon-dispensing machines, and a catalyst for violence in others. Some of our mother/daughter patients say they have come to blows over seemingly innocuous issues during a shared premenstrual phase. It's a potent situation when two women are locked in confrontation; it's near chaos when three or more women with PMS must negotiate turf and temper in the same home, the same office, the same locker room. When we interview patients, a frequent response to our questions about mood swings and other PMS behavior is "it's hard to figure out where my mother's symptoms left off and mine started."

Janice Feniman's story is a case in point. Her late mother had a severe case of premenstrual syndrome marked by tumultuous, violent behavior and drinking; her sisters also are burdened by it. "All of my sisters have mood swings. My oldest sister is on her third marriage and I think PMS was the cause of her divorces; she's also had a kind of hit or miss career life and that's because of her moods and depressions and outbursts. Our mother had a severe case. But I know that our maternal grandmother probably did not have it.

"My mother had difficulty with pregnancy and childbearing. Unfortunately she didn't know or care about birth control so she had five children and about four additional miscarriages and didn't enjoy being a mother," she recalls. "As I look back on it now, I am sure she had PMS because she was alternately a monster and a quiet, confused woman who just sort of muddled through life. She was not physically abusive to us, the children, thank heaven, but she was verbally abusive. She and my father were physically violent toward each other.

"I looked a lot like her and personality-wise I seemed like her. I was rather sensitive, easily hurt. So everyone said I was like my mother. That used to concern me a great deal. I just decided that I was going to survive. She apparently saw me as a threat to her; she always denied the good things that happened to me. There was nothing I could do to please her." After enduring for fifteen years one of the most complex cases of premenstrual syndrome that we have seen, Feniman was properly diagnosed and began progesterone therapy.

For many mothers and daughters, or sisters, or other women in close relationships with each other, the diagnosis is merely the starting point of a much more difficult stage: renegotiating the relationship. The women we treat frequently realize that their stormy travails with mothers or sisters were not due only to their premenstrual disorder, but were compounded by the other woman's case of PMS. They may have fueled a hostility to their mother over the years because of her outbursts and inexplicable reigns of terror over the family, labeling her a "witch" or worse. Erratic behavior and tantrums that seemed so vicious, unfair, and unloving to a child or adolescent are reinterpreted in light of the PMS pattern; now the daughter sees the mother as having suffered from an illness, and she's willing — sometimes eager — to accord the illness a sympathetic heart. Reconciliation is hardly simple, however. Mere mortals can't simply erase emotional damage inflicted over many years and redub the audio; there's a lot of static and garbling that has to be dealt with first. In most of these situations the women may need a third party to walk them through the initial awkward phase of establishing communication and pouring oil on still-turbulent waters. Counseling or psychotherapy can make the process easier for many.

Janice Feniman is one daughter who successfully bridged the gap with her mother. Once she began progesterone treatment at the clinic, she visited her mother and told her that she thought she had suffered from the condition all her life, that this hydra-headed disorder was the catalyst for the violence, the drinking, the temper tantrums. "We had a reconciliation of sorts; it wasn't easy. She didn't accept it at first," Feniman says. "But I just told her that knowing that her pain was like my pain made it okay; it just wiped the slate clean. She died last year but we had one full year of being a mother and daughter who came close to understanding each other."

SECTION III

Living With PMS

"All happy families are like one another; each unhappy family is unhappy in its own way."

Leo Tolstoy, **Anna Karenina**

Strains on Relationships

"PMS is the woman's physiological problem but it is also a family problem. The family is tortured just as surely and constantly as the woman," commented one of our patients, a thirty-seven-year-old mother of four. Premenstrual syndrome is not just a painful and debilitating illness; its pattern of pendulum-like swings of mood and unpredictability burdens personal relationships and family life with an emotional load that would hobble a team of Clydesdales. The syndrome has been implicated in a host of family-oriented problems, from general discord to separation, divorce, and child abuse. The stormy personal relations in turn produce guilt and shame in the victim, a loss of self-esteem, and sense of being "bad." Ultimately women may become profoundly depressed and even suicidal.

In a PMS relationship, the husband of one of our patients says, "Your vulnerability has been violated. You learn that it's not really safe to be vulnerable to her because when she's in pain she'll use it against you. After several good days, though, you begin to be freer and open up, only to find that the cycle will begin again and you're vulnerable to her again. I remember going for days without saying anything — that's PMS baggage."

The slide from mild symptoms to the extreme can happen slowly, over a decade or more in some women, in a matter of months in others. It is difficult to halt the progressive decline and downward spiral. PMS women can't control their feelings or pain once the symptoms start, a moment our patients variously describe as a black cloud descending over them, an alien being seizing their body, an incubus that possesses them.

77

Single women often say that they limit their social life, particularly dating and intimacy with men, to the days of the month they are symptom-free. One management consultant told us that in the four years before she found treatment for her condition she saw two serious relationships disintegrate because the men couldn't understand why she wouldn't see them more than two weeks a month. One of them told her that he wanted more than an affair, he wanted a commitment. She was so confused and guilt-ridden by her PMS behavior that she didn't explain to him why she couldn't spend more time with him.

Another of our patients had managed to hide her problem from the man she dated for two years by making excuses, being unavailable, "out-of-town," or overworked during the five days each month that she felt unstable. During that time she refused to accept the fact that her condition was related to menstruation; rather she thought it was psychological and would go away. Eventually this couple married, and her husband became exposed to PMS for the first time. He told us that he thought at first that her outbursts and irritability were just part of the normal adaptation to married life, that she was finding the change from a single to a shared lifestyle stressful. As her physical complaints worsened, the strain on the marriage came close to tearing it apart. Compounding her physical problems was the guilt she felt over not disclosing her illness before the marriage. She ultimately sought treatment and saved her health and her relationship.

The most damaging symptoms to a relationship are irritability, anger, verbal and physical assaults, impulsiveness, loss of trust, suspicion or paranoia. Initially when the symptoms are mild and brief, the relationship returns to normal once they disappear. As the condition worsens and the cranky spouse becomes a raging tergament, the effect is disastrous. Gradually the man grows less tolerant and begins to react. Most men echo the voice of one husband who told us: "You don't know what's going on, yet you have a feeling that it's a biological thing. But you can't say anything or else she will accuse you of being a male chauvinist. But eventually you begin to strike back and say things you don't mean. Then she reacts to your anger and the relationship changes."

Guilt builds rapidly and continuously under this stress. During their symptom-free times, these women don emotional hair-shirts in their desperate efforts to rid themselves of a shrewish image and to compensate for the trouble they stirred up premenstrually. Apologies mount. Anticipation of the next cycle of symptoms fills their good days; they start to compress their life into the healthy period. They tell us that's when they cook, clean, spend time with their husband and children, and attend parties. Lydia Aarons, mother of two, lived with premenstrual syndrome for ten years. During the two years before she was properly treated, she was bedridden with blinding migraine headaches and depression. Aarons remembers those times vividly: "Sometimes we'd be with people and the women were all talking about little daily things, like wondering when they should change their baby's clothes from spring to summer weight, and I would be thinking about how I could cook twenty dinners by Friday. My reality was so much harsher than theirs. I had to do all my housework and cooking and everything during the one week I could function or else my husband or family would have to do it."

That pressure to do it all, even if they only have one week or two weeks a month in which they can fulfill their obligations, produces a great internal stress. Combined with the bewilderment the women feel over the source of their strife, their self-image starts to crumble like the facade of a building throttled by earth tremors. They think, "I should be able to control myself." They grit their teeth and say, "This month it will not happen." Their husband may say it. Their friends may say it. The next month, when the inevitable strikes, they feel violated, their will thwarted. After a few months, their self-esteem is destroyed. It's the natural reaction of any individual who has set herself — or himself, this is not a feminine phenomenon — up for repeated failure. When the sense of self worth is shaken, coping becomes a Sisyphean task; productivity and efficiency vanish. At this stage, depression descends.

Some men view their wife's freshly developed lack of self-esteem as an enemy that must be routed from the relationship. These men say they've lost respect for their mates, and they attack them verbally for giving up, for having grown unconfident, uncertain, indecisive. Premenstrual sufferers who can't cope with normal life can't cope with this flanking maneuver either; the result is always even more dissonance in the relationship, bringing it a few steps closer to destruction.

These are formidable obstacles to overcome for any couple. But as Karl Berman, a husband whose wife suffered with PMS for fifteen years, observes: "A PMS marriage that has endured is going to be a good marriage. Because if there are cracks and flaws in it to start with, it'll fall apart. Once they've found out what PMS is, they've had to weather some of the most hostile stress imaginable. Once you've handled a bad case of PMS, you can handle anything."

Husbands and Wives

The stories told by the couples who have lived with PMS are poignant and revealing. We've spent thousands of hours listening to their experiences; while the patterns are similar, the details are not.

Karen and Dan Shelton were high school and college sweethearts in Salt Lake City, the arid Western settlement founded by the followers of Joseph Smith, known as "Happy Valley" to the Mormon families who live in sight of the rose- and lavender-veined mountains. Married for sixteen years, they have five children. Karen Shelton recalls being distraught at one point in their courtship because "Dan had very seriously considered not marrying me because of my moodiness. I do remember being scared then. At the time I chalked up that part of me to coming from a verbally and sometimes physically abusive family." But they talked about it and decided to go ahead with the wedding.

Dan: "I always had a suspicion that there was something wrong. It's like buying a car. You drive it home and find a problem. You either make a decision to trade it in or have it repaired. I never liked it [the PMS episodes] but I thought, 'okay I will do what I have to do to make the marriage work, to make the car run again.' If good times weren't there, they would eventually return, a window of warmth was always there. There was an indication that there was something organically wrong. At worst, it could have been a form of mental illness. When she first found out about it being a hormonal thing, I felt a tremendous sense of relief that suspended judgment, that she wasn't to blame for this thing. That was a tremendous help. It was no fun. It's as horrible an experience for me now as it was then. Once you discover the cause of it, there's a target for your anger other than the person. Recognizing that kind of directed my anger. That discovery is a psychological release and relief. It doesn't do a great deal for the times you're caught up in it. I've given her a hard time about it. I've told her she's a hypochondriac. Lots of times when she says she can't help it, in the back of my mind I'd say 'sure, straighten up and fly right; control it.' Even now, when she flies off the handle, it's still difficult to deal with."

Communications are strong in the Shelton household, a factor that both say helped preserve their marriage.

Dan: "We're a very verbal couple. We don't hold a lot inside. I'm sure a lot of fears I had we were able to talk about and work out. Recognizing PMS doesn't make it any easier for the victim or the family. You still feel horrible. You still have trouble handling it." After one violent argument the two had, he told Karen, 'You're so good when you're good. You're so wonderful when you're well.'

Karen: "When I'm having an outburst, most human beings would have taken a swipe at me. But not Dan." He is, in fact, "usually non-combative. That was aggravating to me."

Dan: "If I'd hit her every time I had thought about it, she wouldn't be here now... I recognized that there were times when something would seem to burst inside her and she would come apart. She always felt so sorry afterward. She'd always apologize and she was so rational then. One of the aspects of my character is that I'm very forgiving. I'm incapable of carrying a grudge very long. In fact, I don't carry grudges. That's been a real blessing. If we hadn't been able to get beyond that, we'd be carrying around some pretty heavy baggage that could only be destructive to our relationship."

Identifying the Pattern

Many mates of women with PMS observed the relationship between the outbursts and health problems and the menstrual cycle long before the women themselves.

Richard Paton kept a diary of the behavior and outbursts of his wife, Ann, for three years before she was diagnosed as a PMS victim; he had been aware of their cyclical occurrence for many years before that. "I became aware that her angry and depressed times were related to her periods about nine years ago," he says. "Every time we'd have a fight I'd go running upstairs and look at her package of birth control pills. There were always two or three pink ones left. I came to recognize that when there were two or three left, it was family battle time again. I was very aware of a group of signs that said 'Here it comes again.' Sometimes I could see her going like a whirlwind, cleaning the house, generally at absurd times of the day, and I knew that it was coming."

Ann says of her husband: "He caught on to PMS before I did." Once she caught him marking the calendar for the new year on the days that he thought would be one week before her period. "I got very angry. I thought it was sneaky, notetaking behind my back. He wouldn't bring it up in conversation, and when I tried to bring it up, he wouldn't be interested. But he saw the pattern, and he saw an enormous change in me the first month that I took the progesterone."

Why did Richard track her cycles? "I don't like to fight. I don't receive well. I get angry and lash out as much as she does, which, of course, makes the arguments worse. Keeping track helped me to modify my reactions. I knew I had to treat her very lightly and very warily during those times. The most terrible times between us always happened then."

Timing was also important because he travels regularly on business and tried to arrange to stay home when he knew that she was premenstrual. "I didn't think that the kids needed it. She had to lash out and it was better me than them. Sometimes I wanted to be away during the worst two or three days. Then she'd use the phone instead of the kids. I'd be in a hotel room somewhere, and I'd put the phone down on the bed and go to the bathroom or read a book. She wouldn't even notice. It was that type of haranguing."

Ann says, "Almost always, the fights would be over my criticism of his behavior. I could hear myself, a crazy woman saying 'I know you didn't go down to the village to buy stamps, you went down to call someone.' [He had an affair once, during her first pregnancy.] I'd be very suspicious and paranoid. I felt as if everyone were out to get me, especially him. I couldn't count on him and I couldn't trust him. No one could help me."

Her irrationality was confined to the two-week period before she began to menstruate. "I had control over myself during those other two weeks. When I'd have a crazy thought then I'd dismiss it. During the two weeks before my period, I'd obsess over it. The same crazy thought, over and over, like a broken record." When she behaved irrationally, "My husband would say 'Oh, Christ, here we go again,' and slam the door and leave, or sometimes he'd turn on me. We're still married and I love him very much. We have a good marriage. When something's going on, I try to remember how awful I must have been to live with then."

Her relationship with her husband became "extremely tenuous." During her premenstrual time, "If I didn't get too aggressive and I let him know that I needed him, everything would be all right. But if I turned my depression and anxiety into an attack, he'd back off. I used to feel that I was at his mercy, that he made a conscious decision to help me or not — now I see that it probably depended on how hostile I was. Sometimes I'd be able to see quite lucidly that the whole problem was mine, and that he was doing the best that he could. Other times, I'd blame how I was feeling on him.''

Distance didn't stem the outbursts, Richard says: ''Sometimes during a trip I'd sit in my hotel room fuming with anger: not reading, not watching television. Just angry. Every month she'd accuse me of being unfaithful. 'You're a bastard, look what you did to me.' And I'd think, 'God, won't she ever forget. Won't she ever stop bringing this up?' ''

They frequently battled over the telephone. ''One night I was in a hotel in Cincinnati, and she called and we began to argue. I hung up, and she called back. I hung up on her again and called the hotel desk to tell them not to put any more calls through. 'Not even calls from my office or from my wife.' '' When she called for the third time, the hotel operator wouldn't put her call through. When Ann threatened to call the hotel management and the police, the operator called Richard and told him *she'd* call the police. So he called his wife and said, ''The cops will come to our house, too, and take you to the funny farm.'' After hours of talking, he said, she finally hung up.

He reacted very strongly to their fights. ''The depression that I felt, I think I was as low as anyone could get. He realized that her problems were physical and cyclical, but ''I was terrified of breaking up our marriage and destroying our beautiful family.'' Richard said that to outsiders, ''We were the happiest couple alive.'' Some of their friends were aware that they had marital problems, but ''it didn't seem relevant to tell people that it was cyclical.'' Their marriage counselor, also a good friend, once told him, ''I don't understand how you two can be at each other's throats and still be a perfect host and hostess for eight people at dinner. We told each other that, even with everything, we probably had a better marriage than most people. Our lives were only difficult twenty-five percent of the time. But in the last three years, the stress period stretched to about two weeks of the month.''

Progesterone therapy has eliminated her symptoms, changing their lives considerably. ''If I had known what the cause was and that someone in the world was working on it, well, I would have been thrilled. Now I say 'This is the PMS reacting.' I try to be understanding. If she yells, I'm still angry, but later I tell myself that it's just the PMS.'' Since she began treatment, ''There's happiness in our family now.''

And Ann says she deals with her husband much differently now that the progesterone permits her to control her reactions. ''I realized that I can walk away from a potential fight by stating how I feel about the situation and being solution-oriented, instead of flipping out and getting irrational.''

Martin Schanberg, like Richard Paton, also saw the pattern of PMS long before his wife, Felicia, did. Her sharp mood swings and outbursts had led the couple to two gynecologists and four psychiatrists before she was properly diagnosed. The second psychiatrist wanted to put her in a psychiatric hospital. ''I thought there was something wrong with my brain,'' she recalls. But Martin Schanberg suggested that her moods were caused by a chemical imbalance. He told her that he could ''feel'' her cycles. She got angry and said, ''It has nothing to do with my period. It's just something the matter with me.'' Her husband told all the psychiatrists, ''She's not like this all the time, just before her period.'' But, she says, the doctors, ''shrugged it off.'' Her symptoms became aggravated after the birth of their first child. ''I noticed that she would get like that at the same time each month, about a week or two before her period. As time went on, I realized that it had to be physical.''

He said he'd lie awake in bed and try to analyze the problem. ''I'd ask myself how I could be such a terrible person. I don't drink or play around, and I'm home, helping around the house a lot. I didn't know how I could be hurting her so much.'' Martin found dealing with her during her premenstrual time disheartening and frustrating. ''Nothing I said was right. I couldn't help her.''

''During my bad times, I would be angry and irritable,'' Felicia says. ''And very clumsy. I would drop things and burn dinners. My husband used to say, 'You know dinner's ready when the smoke alarm goes off.' I'd burn toast and eggs all the time.'' Those jokes of Martin infuriated her because she couldn't seem to stop the episodes. ''I kept ruining things and dropping things and breaking things because my mind was somewhere else.''

The Schanbergs have an extensive collection of anecdotes about Felicia's lack of coordination. Martin recalls a Father's Day a few years ago when the family decided to go for a drive. ''She wanted to take our second car, because our boat and trailer were hooked up to the station wagon. We have a sloping driveway: you can't see the bottom of the driveway from the garage. I stood on the lawn and watched her back the car into the station wagon and the boat.'' He found it depressing at the time, but now he thinks the incidents are funny.

Martin: "I used to tell our friends that my wife had her priorities mixed up: she'd add too much water to the washing machine and too little to the potatoes. She was always burning vegetables.'' He says that he used to get upset but after a while he got used to it. "I saw how hard she tried to avoid accidents. She just couldn't help it. The clumsiness was part of the pattern. Two weeks she'd be fine and the other two she'd be awful. She'd trip over things. She sliced an onion for a salad one day and almost sliced off her finger.'' One day she smashed a glass on the counter, cut her hand, and watched the blood drip onto the floor. "I knew it was time to go to my room until it all passed.''

Sometimes her absentmindedness approached dangerous levels. On her husband's birthday Felicia made his favorite cake. After she put the cake into the oven, she saw a can of Raid on the counter and realized that she had sprayed the pans with insecticide instead of with Pam, the aerosol vegetable oil. As she threw the cake batter out, a friend walked in. "Where are you going?'' he asked. "I'm going to the store to buy more eggs,'' she said. "I have to make another cake because I used Raid instead of Pam on the pans.'' He laughed, she said, but she didn't find it particularly funny.

When she was diagnosed in our office, she felt exuberant. "Maybe I'll finally have a good Thanksgiving and Christmas.'' On progesterone therapy, her symptoms have completely disappeared. The difference, Martin says, is all internal. "No one knew what was going on. From the outside we're a model family, our friends and neighbors are probably envious of us.'' She has not convinced her family doctor or her sister, who is a nurse, that PMS was the cause of her problems. Her family doctor said, "It's rubbish. They've brainwashed you.'' The other people she talks to are also skeptical but, she says, "I know it's real.''

Social Tensions

Unpredictable, unpleasant, sometimes vicious or argumentative, women in the midst of the premenstrual torment are usually not capable of dealing with polite society. Stung by their penchant for verbal darts and gibes at the most inappropriate moments, friends and relatives grow alienated, spouses withdraw or refuse to accompany their mates anywhere that they think they might act out.

Kevin Larson, whose wife Marla had PMS for seventeen years, says: "I can't count the number of times we were invited to go places, when I'd say 'I'm not going with you anyplace like this.' We'd bow out. You begin to manufacture excuses very effectively. One woman at a PMS support group meeting said she used to tell people she had epilepsy so she could get out of social things without completely losing her friends. Marla would talk about her horrible back problems — which she really has — or that she was so tired or run down since the baby was born — which she was — or that her thyroid was acting up — which it was. They were legitimate bases for excuses but they were crutches for the real reason. That would precipitate a lot of guilt feelings. But it got to the point where it just didn't bother me anymore that we never went anywhere."

One husband terms his social adaptation to PMS "self-preservation maneuvers." He says, "You've got to drag your wife around when she doesn't feel good. At parties, you fill in, or you abandon her. I would find myself talking with people, having a great time, and Janet would be sitting across the room in a corner by herself or stuck talking to someone whom she couldn't cope with but couldn't seem to discourage from sitting with her. She'd say, 'Please don't ever leave me by myself at a party.' She couldn't handle it. You begin to think that your wife is damaged goods, that she's got a problem. So you accept it and say 'if that's what's got to be done, okay.' But it wasn't okay, and you knew that, you resented that."

Social strains lead many couples "to become kind of reclusive," according to another husband, Mark Halloran. "I'm not a real gregarious person, I don't have a lot of close friends. If people came over, it was kind of a hassle. It wasn't fun. Judy would plan things when she was feeling well — birthday parties, dinner parties. Then the day would come and she'd feel lousy."

Judy Halloran remembers: "When I'd plan them, I'd be fine. Then ten days later, I'd inevitably feel terrible. There I was, trapped by a decision I'd made. Women who have PMS tend not to know it or not to realize that every month the symptoms hit. They have convenient amnesia for the kind of suffering they go through each month and so when they're feeling well, they plan things as though they were always well."

Locked in a body they no longer understand, caught up in deeds and spewing out words they instantly regret, the women themselves soon have no interest in anything but coping with the syndrome. A common feeling, expressed by hundreds of women, is a dread of social get-togethers and parties during the premenstrual time. One of our patients, Roberta Carl, says, "Sometimes I felt as if I were a nebulous blob. I sat there mute. I couldn't talk or be social."

Ingrid Low, a forty-five-year-old mother of six, recalls: "My whole life used to be planned about what was going to happen those two weeks before my period. I couldn't go any place, I couldn't make any plans, I would literally crawl into a shell, or have to hide in my bedroom for four to five days. This is no longer the case; progesterone has really changed everything. I couldn't take stress at all in that period of time. I couldn't handle a holiday or a birthday; it would just be a total knockout time for me. It's an amazing, almost indescribable difference, considering that I'm forty-five and I've lived with this since I've been a teenager. I'm literally a new person (after being on progesterone therapy.). My husband and I have been married for twenty-five years and I think this is the first sane year the man has ever had. The difference is unbelievable."

The Last Phase: Divorce

Over time, premenstrual syndrome drives a wedge between husband and wife that leads them to discuss or threaten divorce; for many it actually leads to the courtroom. About twenty to twenty-five percent of our patients have been divorced; five to ten percent of the total have been divorced more than once. All of these women cite PMS as the primary cause of the split; the former spouses we've talked to confirm this. Most women we've treated have managed to save their marriages, but the damage done by their illness has left permanent scars.

Cynthia and Larry Wilson played out the same scenario hundreds of times. "Her bags would be packed, and she'd walk out the back door to the garage to leave," Larry says. "I'd race out the front door to catch her. I'd pick her up and carry her back inside. We'd fall on the kitchen floor and I'd hold onto her." When she felt better, she'd apologize. She would tell him that she didn't know how he could stand her, and asked him why he didn't leave. ''Because I love you,'' he told her. ''You know that in two weeks you'll be happy and enjoying things again.'' But when she was premenstrual, he couldn't reach her.

Sally Ziegler, a nurse and mother of two, says of her disintegrating relationship with her husband, Joe: ''Nothing he ever did or said to me was right when I was having my symptoms. When he was sweet and dear, I'd tell him he was patronizing and condescending. If he were angry or hostile, I said he was a son of a bitch and he didn't care and he wasn't good to me. If he tried to ignore me, I said he was too passive, which he wasn't. There was no behavior he could adopt that was right with me. I gave him an impossibly hard time. I did tell him he ought to leave me, that we should get a divorce. I'd say, 'if you can't take it, go. I can't bear the guilt.' We sat down and talked about it. I was crying and hysterical. He felt angry toward me. He's a very reserved, introverted, very proper, very closed type of person. Once he threw a plate on the floor in frustration over me. There was always a part of me that was still there, buried deep inside.'' Now Joe and Sally are going to a marriage counselor.

Another of the many couples who have stitched their marriage together with the help of marriage counseling or therapy is Lisa and Mike Ritter. Mike Ritter says that even during his wife's tirades, their two boys remained their priority. ''If she asked me for a divorce, I'd say 'Okay, but I'm not leaving.' I'd tell her that she had to be the one to leave.'' Only once, he said, did he leave. He stayed with friends for a week to ''cool off.'' Sometimes she'd say, ''I'll move out because you're a better father than I am a mother. The boys will be better off with you.'' Then he said, ''It would all blow over and we'd be there cuddling.''

Another husband, Steve Hart says: ''When Laura would offer to give me a divorce, of course I'd sometimes think 'You bet, let's do it.' But then I'd stop and think. We made a very strong commitment by getting married. But she's not offering a divorce to me, really. She's hitting herself over the head with guilt, just punishing herself for her bad behavior. You see through that very quickly. No. Why would I ever leave her? I love her. Love is more than just a passion. Love is a commitment. That's what holds it together. It's rock-hard cement. It's a commitment that lasts long after the passion has cooled down. That's love. Come hell or high water. I think after saying I love her for ten or twelve years, it's not a lie on my part. I do care about her. I do love her.''

For some, love is not strong enough mortar to fuse the fragments of the marriage together. The specter of the syndrome becomes too great a weight for the marriage to bear and divorce is inevitable.

Ariana Buren, a schoolteacher with three children, has been divorced twice. ''My husbands found it difficult to cope with me, the second one especially. It's a different situation. My children are from my first marriage. I was very much in love with my second husband, and still am. We had a lot of extraneous problems. We lived together before we were married, we both had children from prior marriages. It was very difficult. He was aware that something was going on with me that was cyclical. If I were premenstrual, I would drink a lot and become very argumentative and hysterically depressed. Certainly that was not an easy thing to cope with.''

Despite her return to health, she is still sorting out the emotional problems from her recent divorce and move into a new apartment and new job. ''It's a very different type of feeling that I have now. It's just all those things I have to cope with, and trying to get them straightened out.''

Catherine Rodriguez, thirty-two, a government lawyer and mother of a five-year old boy, also has been divorced twice. Her first divorce in 1970 ''may have been related to PMS.'' But her second divorce in 1980 after a two-year separation she feels was definitely attributable to PMS. ''I was an absolutely royal, unhappy bitch.'' Each month she felt out of control, angry, and depressed. She would sleep all weekend. When she wasn't sleeping she would abuse her husband, verbally and physically [throwing dishes at him]. When she first heard of progesterone therapy for PMS, she thought ''it was too easy a way out,'' and couldn't believe that her depressions were organically caused. Now, she says, she feels ''born again.'' She thought that life was something to be endured; now it's ''something to be enjoyed.'' Last New Year's she got back together with her ex-husband who was ''disbelieving, but hopeful.'' Their relationship is now solid, but she has decided for other reasons not to re-marry him.

Coping with Success

Once diagnosed and under treatment for premenstrual syndrome, most of our patients report a disappearance of virtually all of their symptoms within one to three cycles. Some women, who have difficulty identifying the correct day on which to start the progesterone therapy, or absorb the progesterone poorly, or who have extreme cases of depression or migraine, may have one or two "bad" days for the first few months of treatment. But even these days, they say, are never as severe as their symptoms were when the PMS was untreated. The relief, surprise, and joy at having the yoke of premenstrual syndrome lifted is a heady emotional experience. But successful treatment creates its own share of problems for many families. Any dramatic change in the circumstances of a relationship, even a turn for the better, upsets the equilibrium of the situation. We encourage our patients to join local support groups for PMS families that have sprung up around the country, or to seek family therapy or counseling if they need a third party to help them rebuild their bridges to each other.

As Lindsey Leckie, director of the National PMS Society, based in Durham, N.C., explained: "Couples often have a lot of 'scarring' and guilt overlay. It's hard just to go out and have a good time. There's about a two-month interval after a woman sees improvement when she expects the most support. But for most couples, it seems to be the most trying time. A lot of the husband's pent-up hostility and anger over the illness surfaces, especially the stuff he didn't vent before because his wife was vulnerable." The organization she heads, which she co-founded with Patty Cannon, is the catalyst of a national network of support groups; at this writing sixty-five groups were active nationally, providing help for PMS families and dozens more are started each month. "I don't think attending support group meetings is a lifelong thing. Some people cycle in and cycle out quite quickly. They're able to work through the problem they've got and then they get out of it. We want to offer temporary support. With less severe cases the need is of shorter duration. A lot of husbands and wives do stay for a long time, usually more severe cases of longer duration. The support group is an important way to reach out to the men in the lives of women with PMS. They need to forgive themselves for the anger they've felt and the guilt they feel. The husbands' reactions to meeting other men is amazing — instant relief, empathy."

One patient, a thirty-seven-year-old tax attorney in Atlanta, who is married and has a brood of eight children and stepchildren to raise, says, "PMS spreads out to the family. The family is not quick to forget. You go through your two weeks of pain and emotional depression. When you come out of it you feel so good that you expect them to say, 'Oh, she feels good now; that really wasn't her before.' But it doesn't work that way. The scars of the PMS time have to continuously be dealt with. Things were said during that period that you really didn't mean. Things were done during that period that you really didn't mean to do."

Cynthia Wilson says her children weren't as suspicious of her "cured" self as her husband Larry was. "In a romantic way and in a giving way, Larry had a hard time taking it. He was afraid that kind of giving would stop and the witch in me would come back. It hurt me that he wouldn't respond more overtly. I used to ask myself 'Has he stopped loving me?' We've had a lot of talks about it. Now when I reach out and everything's great, he'll accept it."

Dealing with the scars, the guilt, the painful memories and getting on to a new life is enormously difficult. The key, perhaps, is forgiveness. As Hannah Arendt wrote: "...no man can forgive himself and no one can be bound by a promise made only to himself... The possible redemption from the predicament of irreversibility — of being unable to undo what one has done — is the faculty of forgiving." Since one can't simply demand the forgiveness of the people who feel hurt, a women recovered from PMS needs to realize that understanding, patience, and time are her best tools in regaining her family's trust. Sometimes, of course, the wounds cut too deep to be bound by a Band-Aid. In these families, the best suggestion is to obtain psychological counseling.

In addition, the women newly rid of the syndrome finds that her family may have high expectations of her. Valerie Lawrence's experience was typical. "All of a sudden I'm okay, where once I was incapacitated three weeks out of every four. I've got two kids and a husband who's got great expectations. Unless I'm in bed with a migraine, I'm supposed to be wonder woman all the time. It's a sort of feeling that you've been Rip Van Winkle. It's very exciting and it's a great challenge. There's also an insecurity from a background of having not been well enough to do anything for ten years. Last year I had Christmas for the first time in a decade. I enjoyed it. But there are days when feeling good can also bring a daunting, overwhelming sense.

Don't misunderstand me, I feel wonderful and never, never would want to re-live the last ten years of my life."

Overall, the sentiment of women who have defeated the PMS rage inside them, with lifestyle changes and progesterone therapy, say they know they're at a new frontier. As Susan Pearson, a magazine editor and mother of three who is one of the survivors, put it: "Now's a time for healing, a time to explore new aspects of our relationship. It's still scary, but it's the most satisfying time of my whole marriage. I think we're lucky to be living now. All the other women with PMS lived and died without any help at all. We're pioneers."

The Children

The innocent victims of PMS are the children of mothers with the disorder. Children are very aware of and sensitive to any changes in their mother's personality, behavior, and emotional reactions, and how that translates into her treatment of and responses to them. Younger children will tend to withdraw, thinking her outbursts and illness are because of something they've done. But older children, especially adolescent girls, are more likely to respond in kind. This is a pattern of reaction also seen in children of divorce, and in children whose parent or sibling is extremely ill or has died. When the security of their home is jeopardized, when they sense they can't count on the all-encompassing, all-forgiving warmth of mother, they grow uncertain, suspicious, or hostile.

One woman, a bookkeeper in Delaware who is divorced and has two children, says, "My daughter took responsibility for my violent mood swings; she thought it was her fault. When I first found out that I wasn't crazy, that I had an illness, she said, 'Mom, it would be great if the doctor could help you, but what if your problem is caused by children?'" Not all children articulate their fears so directly, but most of them have similar feelings.

The mothers' views of their relationships with their children are a study in anger, verbal outbursts, occasional spankings that the women later regretted. In our experience the physical abuse of children is rare in women with PMS, except in the most extreme cases. Most women go to great lengths to avoid hitting or abusing their children; they'll leave the room, leave the house, send the child on an errand, anything that will put some distance between their children and their feelings of rage. Only one of our patients has ever said that her treatment of her children approached abuse. Monica Randolph, forty-six, is the mother of five children, three of whom are one year apart in age. When they were toddlers and she was also taking care of her mother's two youngest babies, she says "my kids were almost battered. I'm ashamed to say it, but it's probably true. I never wanted to lose my temper with them and god knows, I wouldn't have consciously abused them. But when I was taking care of five babies under the age of three at the same time and I would be in the premenstrual phase, I was like a keg of dynamite. I didn't know where these feelings of rage came from, but I couldn't control them. The oldest is twenty-six now and my kids don't seem to have any emotional scars. They spend a lot of time at home, we talk a lot, we have a good relationship. They know I would never intentionally hurt them. I love them more than I could ever say."

Many mothers develop enormous guilt over their failure to attend their children's music recitals, Little League baseball games, science fairs, and the like because of their condition. One mother's comment is an echo of hundreds we've heard: "On the day of my daughter's violin recital, I managed to drive her there, but I couldn't stay. Everyone else's mother was there, but I couldn't stay. My daughter didn't say anything to me, but I knew that she was disappointed. I felt so guilty."

Ronnie Albert still remembers how "I ruined my son's birthday outing." She and her husband were taking the boy to Broadway, to see the musical *Annie*. As they drove into Manhattan from their suburban home, she says, "I could feel that awful, heavy, painful feeling. I was so deadened with depression that I could hardly move. Fifteen minutes into the show, I went to the ladies room and stayed there, crying, during the entire performance."

The most universal experiences of these mothers are the day-to-day feelings of rage, the confrontations with their children.

Wilma Cohen: "I couldn't talk to my children. The physical feeling was that the inside of my body was going at one hundred miles an hour. If you could imagine that. Sometimes I couldn't cope with very minor things. If my husband walked through the door, I'd just announce that I was going to bed, 'take care of the kids.' I just had to walk away from everybody. Sometimes I would just storm out of the house, get into my car and drive, just to get that feeling out of my body. I felt like everyone at that time, my children especially, were suffering. I'd scream at them. I'd downgrade them. And you know, I consider myself a very good mother."

The outbursts and anger, the complete unpredictability of their mothers, makes younger children withdraw emotionally and physically, while children old enough to play anywhere out of their mother's striking range leave the room or the house. Teenagers tend to spend as little time as possible around their mothers, although adolescent girls may rebel and fight back once a confrontation starts.

Joan Wagner, a thirty-two-year-old secretary, is married and the mother of two children: "I would get up in the morning and scream at the kids because they tipped over a glass of milk. I tried to tell them what was happening, that my symptoms were physical, but I didn't really understand what was going on myself. My son would say, 'I can't stand you, Mother.' My husband didn't know what to do, so he'd say, 'Mom's sick now, so leave her alone.' "

Repairing the damage that premenstrual syndrome inflicts on the relationship between mother and child is a long and emotionally painful process. Most mothers with PMS spend a considerable amount of time explaining and apologizing to their children about their problem, emphasizing that the outbursts and erratic episodes are not directed at the children and do not mean that their mothers do not love them.

Penny Rhodes has six children, ranging from twelve to twenty-three. "The older ones, it really took a tremendous chunk out of their lives. They never knew how they'd find their mother. I'd be a lovely person for about two weeks, but when they came to the door they never knew what they were going to find. They don't seem to have any particular scars left on their life at this point that are very noticeable, but of course I've spent a lot of time talking to them and going through the whole process of explaining. They understand the illness and what caused it, so they've made very good adjustments. I would say in their younger years, they had a very difficult time. It basically colored their whole life at that point."

Carolyn Grant had migraine headaches so severely that she would lie in a dark room for two to six days because the pain was so severe. Her husband helped with the children and housework. "I have fantastic children. They were very responsible at a very early age. I'd get up in the morning and put cereal on the table, get them off to school, and go back to bed.'' Sometimes, she said, her children would bring her tea in bed. But, she said, the children noticed that she was different on certain days. She remembers that her younger son said to her, ''Mommy, you're really confused. I told you that three times already.''

Importance of Fathers' Role

Fathers can play a key role in helping the children cope with this stress in their lives.

Dan Shelton explains how he tried to help his children cope with their mother's illness: ''Any husband will feel assaulted, feel hurt, and sometimes hurt irreparably. But he realizes he's got to do something and help out. Ultimately, he has to be responsible for the children. In some cases, the kids may be abused. They're helpless at home with her all day. It's very difficult for him to keep saying to the kids, 'let's just leave her here to stew in her own juices.' It's very hard for kids not to take it personally. I take it personally. You respond to it in a human way. Kids haven't developed to that point. They probably ask themselves, 'Why does this lady hate me?' What it requires is a lot of overcompensation. Mothers are usually the all-loving parent and father is the taskmaster, whose love is more conditional. With PMS, in our family, we tried to overcompensate but to be very consistent with them so the kids would feel secure. If Karen's having a tough time, I'll take the kids into a room and read them a story or talk to them about school in a matter-of-fact, light way, as if nothing unusual was going on. I'd just say, 'Mom's hormones are out of whack today so just stay away from her.' There's an element of survival here. If it was really bad, I'd say, 'Hey, Tom, get on your bike. Go into the garden. Go play with a friend. Don't say anything. Don't make any sounds.' The kids learn that if they cut up too much, Karen would explode. Any PMS relationship is tainted with caution. Tom talks about it off the cuff even.''

Karen Shelton recalls the day her ten-year-old son asked, ''How can I be sure I don't marry somebody with PMS?'' It startled her, she says, but ''I didn't take offense at it. I'm sure he didn't mean that he didn't love me. But I told him, jokingly, to take a menstrual calendar with him on his dates to have the girl fill it out. Our daughter is very quiet and doesn't talk about anything much or ask me about PMS, but she's at a stage where she gets into snits occasionally and gets sassy, runs into her room. Her brother teases her when she does that by telling her she has PMS. She just can't handle that. Tom told her she would definitely have it because I have it and it runs in families. She just gets very upset when he says that.''

Robert Quint says, ''I'd tell the kids that we had to grin and bear it, not to argue with their mother because it was a difficult time for her.'' Generally, he said, the children never asked what was wrong. But sometimes their son would get frustrated when he couldn't understand why his mother was angry. Quint told him to put up with it, that there was nothing they could say or do that would please her when she felt like that. And he'd remind him how his mother was the other two weeks. She was a wonderful mother then, he said. But he adds, ''If I tried to discipline the kids when she was premenstrual, she'd jump in to defend them and we'd have a fight. The kids would watch from the sidelines. During the other two weeks, when she was fine, I'd be afraid to go near them.''

With her symptoms under control, their family situation has improved dramatically. ''The house is more carefree. My daughter doesn't hide in her room anymore, my son's grades have improved, and he's more involved in extracurricular activities at school.'' But, he says, the change is discernible only to the family. ''No one knew what was going on. From the outside we're a model family. Our friends and neighbors are probably envious of us.''

Paul Clinton shepherded his two sons around the explosions of their mother's temper. ''Most of the time,'' he says, ''the boys knew when to step aside. They're good friends and the older boy is very understanding. They'd go off into their bedroom or the family room, and I'd shuttle between them, trying to help her and telling them 'Mommy has a headache, just sit quietly and play.' Our older boy, who's ten, is a very enigmatic child. He just closed off his feelings. He'd play Dad with his younger brother. I heard him say, 'That's just Mom and Dad going at it again.' ''

Clinton remembers some ''nasty scenes'' when they were threatening each other with divorce and the children would be in bed with them. The younger one would cry and say, ''Don't do it.'' The older one wouldn't say anything. The older boy would comfort the younger boy. The early stages of their fights often were in front of the kids. Clinton adds, "How we have such super kids, I don't know." Two or three times, he took the children out to dinner to get them away from her. "But when we had our worst fights, her source of comfort would be the kids, and she'd take them out." He noticed that she took them to the zoo three times "to curry favor."

Initially he didn't want to discuss PMS with the boys. "I didn't want to set them up against their mother. But they've watched plenty of fights." According to him, she never threw anything at him in front of the children, "but they would hear the crash... Kids mature faster in this type of atmosphere. I finally explained to him (the oldest) that women get a period and that all women react differently. Some get cramps, some get grouchy. Mommy doesn't hate me as much as she seems to, it's just that time of month." He feels that the ten-year-old understood, but the seven-year-old didn't. The older child would say to him, "I understand Dad," but he didn't respond past that. "It's probably part of the loyalty thing that children have toward their parents," Clinton says.

Clinton knows the marital strife and PMS "has affected the boys to a certain extent. Children react when they watch their parents fighting and yelling at each other. They'd come down and see glass on the floor and hear me calling their mother drunken and crazy. There have to be scars. Now, though, "I feel they're very secure. I'm sure our youngest thinks of the past sometimes, but he's content. Sean, who's ten, is going through a stage. He's sure of those who love him; he's less sure of himself." He thinks the affection that he and Joanna show each other is the best thing for their children. "We're very demonstrative. We'd be hugging and kissing and working together in the kitchen when things were good. It was part of a reassurance program."

He says that now his son is older, he talks more, but he never brings up the past. He remembers once driving with him and saying, "You realize that things are much better in the house now that Mom has been treated." His son said, "Yes, I know. That's why she's in Boston [at our center] today."

Another couple also says their children adapted without much apparent difficulty to their disrupted home. But their mother makes a concerted effort to explain her illness to them and otherwise compensate if she's treated them unfairly. "I apologize to the kids if I'm having a PMS day," she says. Her husband adds, "I don't think there's any indication that they love her any less because she has PMS. They don't like PMS. They respond in their own way to it. Families recall incidents involving mothers and children that range from terrific battles to loving scenes of understanding.

Doug Richards, the eleven-year-old son of Martha Richards, relates an incident when his mother's anger cascaded over the household seemingly without reason. Doug had been playing outside in the yard. "Mom called me and I went into the house. She grabbed me and said, 'where've you been? I called you fifty times.' She chased me around the house with a flyswatter. Then she pushed me on the couch and hit me and said, 'Don't you ever do that again.' While she was chasing me around, the dinner burned. She threw all the food on the floor and when Dad came in there was food all over the kitchen. Sometimes I thought she was crazy. She'd yell and scream for no reason. But she was fine when she wasn't getting her period." Generally, he'd try to avoid her. His father would tell him, "Mom's in a bad mood, so don't upset her," and he'd stay in his room.

Claire Pettit tells of the night "when I had just put the baby to bed and my husband was giving our daughter, who was four, a bath. I had told my daughter about my problem and my cycle and everything. The two of them were laughing and playing in the bath. I just blew up at the noise and really fussed at them. I said if they woke up the baby they'd have to take care of him. At that, I saw my husband bend over to console Jennifer after my outburst. She just reached up and patted him on the leg and said, 'It's okay, Daddy. It's just her time of month.' "

When Ruth Watson, a thirty-five-year-old mother of two, explained to her son that "two weeks before I get my period, my body changes and I feel sad," he said, "Mommy, I wish I could help you." The children really notice the difference in her behavior now that she's been treated. "One day when I was getting nervous and irritable, my son said, 'Maybe you should take your medicine.' And it was past the time that I should have taken it."

Some parents, especially the mothers, say they find it hard not to overcompensate with their children for the pain they've introduced into their lives. For most PMS families, as with divorced couples, this may take the form of granting the children special privileges, easing up on normal discipline, taking them on special trips, to restaurants, or spending larger-than-normal sums of money on toys, games, and clothes. Cathy Berman, who has coped very well with her family in general, admits that her two children lack very little. "I have to admit to some kind of overindulgence with the kids because of the situation we have. I've been overindulging in clothing departments. They can have anything they want in clothes. I feel that I'm trying to compensate a lot for the outbursts and tension in the house. My mother [who also had PMS] did that. We were rather spoiled materially. There wasn't a lot we didn't have in the material sense. Christmas was a very elaborate time. The toy store would be in our living room on Christmas morning."

Advice to Husbands From the Spouse of a PMS Victim

At a seminar on PMS last year, the husband of a woman who has suffered from the disorder for fifteen years addressed a standing-room-only crowd that included more than one hundred husbands. He focused his attention on their concerns, telling them:

"Let me tell you what your life is like. The line between love and hate is very thin. You have accused your wife, your sweetheart, of hypochondria. You have unpaid medical bills sitting on the desk. You are tired of sending her in for tests because they don't work, they don't show anything. You're tired of her being on Valium, or tired of her being on painkillers. You're tired of doing the babysitting because there are times when she'll lock herself in her room. You're tired of getting the kids off to school in the morning because she can't get out of bed. Your social life is shot because you find that when you go to parties you can't stay very long sometimes during the difficult periods.

"You find that there are long periods of silence. You find that there are arguments at home. You find harsh words, you find fights. You find every now and again secret stores of chocolate; you find Coca-Cola in the refrigerator; you find little caches of food. These women are crazy for sweets or caffeine because it helps them.

"You suffer in silence. You discover that there may indeed be some violence, not intended, but spontaneous. Maybe you find paint peeling around the door frame where the door has been slammed so many times that the paint is falling off. Perhaps you find that your wife can't stand noise, she can't stand to watch the football game, she can't stand to see those things on TV that are violent and stressful because that upsets her. You've discovered that she doesn't exercise because exercise is painful. You discover her helplessness, and you find yourself being helpless alternately with being resolute and courageous and saying, 'I can cope with this.' And then alternately saying to yourself, 'I can't deal with this one more day, one more hour.' You find yourself mutually discussing divorce, thinking about it, or perhaps going even further and actually going through with it. I've talked to lots of husbands and they universally feel these things. And you don't know what's going to happen next.

"PMS is the most provocative of all diseases. It'd be nice to have cancer, it'd be nice to have heart disease, because then you could point to it and you could go to a hospital and they could do something about it. And somebody says, 'How come you feel so lousy?' You can say, 'Oh, I've got cancer.' That's so much infinitely easier to explain than to say, 'Well, I just feel like heck. I don't feel good. I don't behave well today.' What do you say?

"Well, for the women here, now you know you have PMS and suddenly you know you're not crazy, that this is a *physical* problem. It's a chemical problem, and you're not insane.

"For the husbands, it's difficult to deal with. If some guy rams your new car and you get out and you discover that the guy had an epileptic seizure while he was driving down the street and couldn't help himself, that's fine, that helps you understand the guy who rammed your car. But it doesn't do anything for your car. So the domestic discord is easier to understand if you've got a wife with PMS, but it doesn't make the suffering any easier. What I'm suggesting to you is that there are some ways that you can help, husbands.

"One is that you know that it's physical. Keep telling yourself that over and over again. Two is know that your wife can't help herself. No matter how much positive thinking you give her, no matter how many self-control pep talks you give her, she can't help it. There's nothing she can do. And so if she can't do it, you have to. And that, my friends, is tough. It's tough! Because dealing with these women is no simple thing. Remember, don't blame them, don't pass along the guilt because the guilt is deep enough and thick enough.

"Take the kids, if you can, when Mom's that way. Take the kids out to the car and say, 'Let's go to the zoo.' Or take them into their room and read them a story. Let her sleep in the morning, get the kids off to school in the morning, take care of them if you can. Better still, give the wife the key to the car and say, 'You go to the zoo.' Because she needs time away. If you have a cabin, a condominium, a grandmother with a spare room, a basement, give her the key to it, let her get out of your life for a little while, and say, 'Go away for a couple of days.' She can't deal with people, and especially she can't deal with people she loves because the guilt is more than she can handle. You've got to try to protect them."

Chapter 10

On the Job

Work defines us; we are what we do. Traditionally, women managed the household and raised the children. The homemaker, the housewife, the mother were the classic definitions of a woman. Today, nearly forty-eight million American women work outside the home in full-time jobs of every type and intensity. The definition of woman is now all-encompassing, whether blue-collar, pink-collar, or white-collar: clerk-typist or executive, lab technician or physician, assembly-line worker or factory owner, waitress or caterer, engineer, truck driver, television producer. Women can do everything. They prove it every day. Most of those forty-eight million American women are also married and the mothers of children. They're doing it all. But at great personal expense.

Economic survival has always been the primary reason that people work. That hasn't changed. Sheer necessity, not love of labor, created instant workforces for coal mines, oilfields, steel mills, textile plants, and auto factories. Despite the revolution in attitudes forced by the women's movement, in fact, the majority of American women work outside the home because they have to support themselves or children or because the family can't survive without two incomes.

But the beliefs that shape our approach to work have changed dramatically over the years. As William Faulkner once said: "You can't eat for eight hours a day nor drink for eight hours a day nor make love for eight hours a day — all you can do for eight hours is work. Which is the reason why man makes himself and everybody else so miserable and unhappy."

The work ethic on which this nation was founded no longer has much influence on how or why we work. The view that a man or woman becomes a better person by virtue of the act of working has been superseded by the more compelling thirst for ego satisfaction and personal recognition. It's a thirst that some women, especially those new to a career and eager to make their mark, seem unable to slake. As Studs Terkel wrote in the introduction to his book, *Working,* work is a search "for daily meaning as well as daily bread, for recognition as well as cash, for astonishment rather than torpor; for a sort of life rather than a Monday through Friday sort of dying." But he says, work is also "by its very nature, about violence — to the spirit as well as to the body... To survive the day is triumph enough for the walking wounded among the great many of us... The scars, psychic as well as physical, brought home to the supper table and the TV set, may have touched, malignantly, the soul of our society."

Women who work usually invest more of themselves, more of their identity, in a job or project than men do. They tend to care more, to take it all more personally than men. This is both an advantage and a disadvantage. It may bring women higher psychic rewards when they perform well and are recognized for their production. But their very personal stake in a job can magnify any disappointment or setback that might occur.

Women with severe premenstrual syndrome find their lives so disrupted by mood changes, depression, outbursts of temper, or physical discomfort that their work is affected. Stress exacerbates the syndrome, which is why women who are managing a household and raising children in addition to holding down a job, and high-achieving women in demanding professions tend to have the most extreme episodes of PMS. The pressure on today's women can reach inhuman levels. Expectations of women in our society, from hearth to boardroom, are three or four times higher than they are for men. To excel at everything, fulfill all responsibilities, personal and professional, and compete in a marketplace whose male-designed, but unwritten gameplans they've only recently begun to fathom — these are burdens that most men do not face. And if they did, men would probably refuse to assume them. Like sorority pledges and first-season rookies, women feel compelled to shoulder big loads without complaint while they "prove" themselves; they don't think they've earned the privilege, the luxury, of saying "enough."

This superwoman complex is a destructive phenomenon. No one can be all things to all people in all circumstances. By setting unattainable goals and marathon schedules, women set themselves up for failure: not because of inability but an overload of capacity. This is where stress comes in. Stress makes any health problem worse. It can cause infections to flare up and bring on headaches. During a stressful situation the body must mobilize so many of its systems to prepare for a crisis or attack or injury that any weak spot in the body breaks down. In women troubled by PMS, symptoms that might otherwise remain dormant or appear as mild warning signals suddenly rage out of control. When an episode of PMS affects a woman's work — if she loses her temper with a client or has a crying spell in front of her co-workers — the ramifications are far-reaching. Her behavior during a premenstrual phase can change the image of a woman in the eyes of her employer, manager, peers, or clients. Even more damaging is the impact of such incidents on the woman's self-esteem and sense of worth. I am what I do is not just a catch phrase. Most people, certainly most Americans, identify themselves with their work. To perform well bolsters self-image and self-confidence; it's a motivating force for even greater professional and personal accomplishment. To fail to live up to one's expectations on the job or to fall into disfavor with a boss or co-worker can be as devastating as rejection by a lover; it strikes at one's sense of self. When a woman's PMS symptoms emerge in the workplace, growing more frequent and more serious, she'll lose confidence in her abilities. She may become indecisive and unable to meet deadlines. Ultimately, untreated, she is likely to develop a major clinical depression.

About sixty percent of the more than two thousand patients we've evaluated work outside the home. Almost all of these women say that PMS has affected their work negatively; it would be surprising if it didn't. A major health problem will affect anyone's job performance, male or female. A man with severe arthritis couldn't juggle as many responsibilities as most women do who have serious PMS. But women afflicted with premenstrual syndrome adapt, sometimes with great ingenuity. The vast majority of our patients have managed successfully to work, maintain personal relationships, and raise their children, despite the presence in their lives each month of a debilitating illness. They have developed the most highly sophisticated coping mechanisms we have ever seen in any group of men or women. The media's image of women with PMS sometimes has been that of immature or incompetent women who fumble through life or can't control themselves. That's a highly inaccurate picture, bearing as much resemblance to reality as a sawhorse to a thoroughbred.

Women with PMS are experts at managing stress; they've done it with one hand tied behind their back for years.

Premenstrual syndrome raises different problems for different women. For some, it affects their memory and concentration, and makes it difficult for them to organize data or meet deadlines. For Roseanne Macri, a national sales director of a Los Angeles company, memory was the weak point. "Once a week every month, I would blank. I could not remember phone numbers. That would drive me up a wall because I'm capable of memorizing over two hundred companies and telling you exactly what was in their display at a show. I realize now that just before the final phase of the symptoms I'm not able to hear properly and I'm not able to grasp what people are saying. People I work with realize I'm that way at that time now, so they're more tolerant, they speak more slowly."

Val Peters, an office manager in Atlanta, recalls, "I couldn't concentrate or focus on things in the office. Getting a piece of paper out of the file would fluster me. I work with figures and budgets; it gets quite complicated. I remember when I first started, my boss would explain things to me and I'd realize that I had no idea what he was talking about. I couldn't concentrate. It was uncomfortable and frustrating. I'd also argue with my co-workers over trivial things. Normally I'm fairly mild-mannered, but before my period I'd get real irritable. Some days I would pass people in the hall and I wouldn't look them in the eye because I couldn't bring myself to say hello. It was like I'd become anti-people. Everyone irritated me. What's really shocking is that I could remember the exact moment that it would lift. That same afternoon I'd walk down the hall and greet the same people that I ignored that morning. I'd feel bad, like I should apologize for being unfriendly. There was such a strong contrast in the way I felt. I never asked whether anyone noticed the change in me because I was so ashamed of the way I felt. But when I asked one of the secretaries in the office to help me with my charting [she lives alone], she said, 'You've been very quiet during that week or so.' I hid the way I was feeling, I guess, but it was very strong internally.''

Dr. Glynis Morgan, forty-two, is the divorced mother of two college-age sons, who heads a major department of a large urban medical center. She had had mild symptoms since the birth of her first child, when she had postpartum depression for six months. Eight years ago she developed ''periodic paralysis,'' a profound muscle weakness that her physicians could not find explain. Her thighs actually became paralyzed about three times before her period; the paralysis lasted about twelve hours. After a tubal ligation in 1979, however, she began to experience irritability, breast pain, and depression, in addition to her other symptoms. Having PMS did affect her career, she says, but not as dramatically as it might have because her major health complaints did not begin until she had achieved a position of authority. ''I've done everything that I could have done, but it's been very difficult because of the physical symptoms. I didn't have the energy or the stamina that I should have had. I don't think that if I felt the whole time like I did those last three times that I could have done all that I did. I feel tremendous sympathy for young women who are starting out [in their careers] and have to deal with PMS, too.'' Progesterone makes her feel ''remarkably better. It's all the difference in the world.''

Our patients often say they were unable to produce a report on time because they couldn't synthesize the material or write a cohesive paragraph, or that they felt that their efficiency and productivity was sharply diminished during their symptom days. Nancy Winston, sales manager of a high-technology company in Silicon Valley, complained that she could only make sales calls three weeks a month; during the fourth week she went into the office, but limited her activity to administrative work and phone calls. Since she started treatment at the clinic, she's able to make outside sales calls all month long and has increased her sales commissions and productivity by more than twenty-five percent. Another woman, a key executive of a large Asian import business, had a similar problem; her employer was so concerned — and she was so valuable to his company — that he helped locate our center and bought her airline ticket to Boston to make certain she was treated.

Her symptoms have also been eliminated by progesterone therapy.

In some cases, colleagues and employers of the women who say their work quality varies cyclically disagree; they say these women are valued employees whose work is consistently of very high quality. We realize that some of the problems and fears our patients relate about their job performance are in fact just that. They feel less efficient, indecisive, confused, disoriented, unable to concentrate, but their boss or co-workers don't notice a drop in the quality of their performance. These women usually manage to control their symptoms until after they leave work. Still, that haunting sense of unease on the job is psychologically damaging; if untreated for too long, it inevitably results in actual problems at work.

A large number of our patients completed college and earned a bachelor's degree but were forced to withdraw from graduate school or decided not to enroll because PMS so affected their memory and concentration that they couldn't keep up with the more demanding work loads. A few women say they decided not to pursue medical careers because they knew they couldn't handle the demands of medical school and a hospital residency. Still others report that they have refused promotions because they didn't feel they could handle more responsibility and PMS, too. An attorney in Chicago says she changed law firms four times in nine years, at least twice because of PMS. The last move was to a firm that wanted to make her a partner. She finally convinced the managing partner that she was only interested in a commitment to the firm as a senior associate.

Some women say they grow suspicious or paranoid of others during their premenstrual phase. A producer of a major network television show says she spent most of her time in her office during her week of symptoms, with the excuse that she needed to catch up on paperwork. She wouldn't socialize with fellow employees, grew very distrustful of other people's motives, and agonized over imaginary errors. At one point, completely without reason or evidence, she believed her work was being criticized and that her boss was about to fire her. In talking to her co-workers, however, we were told she was and is a very valuable employee.

PMS women are the chameleons of the workplace; they are superb adapters. To cope with their symptoms and manage to get their jobs done, whenever possible, they schedule travel, difficult negotiations, critical contract discussions, and the start and completion of important projects for their good days. One literary agent confessed to handling book negotiations and sales only during her normal weeks and scheduling calls to publishers about overdue advance and royalty payments to her clients when she was "feeling bitchy." An attorney for a large Washington D.C. firm has a similar strategy. "I never make decisions or close deals on my premenstrual days. Those days I reserve for paperwork and thrashing out difficult points with difficult lawyers for the other side. Interestingly, I usually get my way."

PMS Leads to Absenteeism

Increased absenteeism is a byproduct of premenstrual syndrome. Many, but not all, of our patients say they occasionally or frequently stay home from work when they are unable to function or feel out of control. A typical history is that of Charity Evans, thirty-two, who teaches comparative literature at a Southern college. She says, "I miss one day of work about every other month. Every missed work day was because of cramps. I felt so bad that I couldn't go in. When I managed to make it in, I didn't do as good a job as I could have. Sometimes I felt as if I were going to lose control." She also experienced mild anxiety attacks; they were never so severe that she had to leave her classroom. "I just had to be strong and bear with the symptoms. I didn't want to give in to them."

Women have a forty-three percent higher absenteeism rate than men; PMS may be one factor but childcare and household responsibilities is known to be another. According to the Bureau of Labor Statistics, women were absent from their jobs because of illness or injury 4.3 percent of usual hours worked in 1981 compared with 3.0 percent for men. According to BLS, "The difference appears to be linked in part with family responsibilities of married women. The rate for single women was about the same as that for all men." A Labor Department study, "Absent Workers and Lost Hours," published in May 1978, noted, "Married women reported a higher proportion of time off for both illness and injury and miscellaneous personal reasons than did single women." One study reported that thirty-six percent of fifteen hundred women in one industrial plant sought sedation in the premenstrual week and may have lowered productivity as a result. A 1969 estimate put the cost to industry of absenteeism due to PMS at $5 billion; adjusting that estimate to 1982 dollars would raise the figure to nearly $10 billion.

Chronic absences exact a price; women may be reprimanded by their boss or fired. One woman's employer finally asked her for a letter from her physician about the causes of her frequent absences. Her physician gave her a lot of tests but told her she was normal and wouldn't support her claim of illness. She managed to negotiate a compromise with her employer by promising to miss no more days of work. Women in this situation, pressured to fulfill commitments they can't handle, begin to try to the hide their premenstrual problems. This adds to the stress, which worsens the symptoms.

Accident Rates Rise, Too

Studies show that more women have accidents in their premenstrual days than at other times. For some women, especially those in blue-collar or industrial jobs, this tendency can be downright dangerous. Patty Clemens, twenty-eight, a truck driver in Ohio, began experiencing a range of symptoms after undergoing a tubal ligation three years ago, including dizziness, cramps, confusion, anxiety, headaches, "funny" vision, spaciness, impairment of judgment and concentration. She's had several accidents and near-misses on the road during her premenstrual phase. "It would really get wild. Driving a large truck in city traffic is stressful to begin with. When I had my period, everything was magnified a hundred times. If someone cut me off three days before I got my period, I'd want to run him off the road." She said that she had accidents every Friday before her period for the three months before she came to our center for treatment. "I was so distracted, I couldn't think as quickly as I usually could. I'd lost my quickness of thought." She tore the side off a sports car on the first Friday. On the second, "a construction truck cut through my truck. It wasn't my fault, but I could have avoided it if I had been thinking more quickly." On the third Friday, a cab driver rounded a corner and rammed into her truck. "I felt so spaced out that I couldn't react."

Emotional outbursts are one of the most common reactions of women with premenstrual syndrome. Judy Firella, a microbiologist for a pharmaceutical company in New Jersey, had a classic case of depression and irritability that had gotten worse since the birth of her two children. "I felt as if I were on the top of a roller coaster, and I knew that I'd have to go all the way down to the bottom of the hill." She is troubled by the impact she feels PMS has had on her career: "I'd overreact. I'd get too emotional." She remembers one day when her boss brought a "filthy dirty desk, from a bar," into her pristine laboratory. She says she screamed at him for fifteen minutes, following him around the lab and into his office, complaining about the dirt and contamination the desk carried. Then she stalked out of his office, slamming the door behind her. He called after her, "Hey, you, come back." But she didn't. She says that she was always justifiably angry, but she didn't handle her anger "in a professional manner."

Cathie St. James, thirty-eight, single, no children, is a management consultant, whose work involves writing, organizing seminars and study projects. "I was so fatigued during those two weeks that I didn't have the mental ability to do my work, and I noticed that my production was dropping. I could do the reports that I had to do, but I had no mental energy for creative writing. I've never missed a seminar, or even an appointment, no matter how bad I felt. Other people may have been debilitated by my condition, but my upbringing and my conditioning wouldn't allow me to skip work." She says that her irritability sometimes spilled over into anger, but never at the office. "Sometimes when I got home from work, I'd lose control. I broke dishes, I broke a radio, but I always broke things instead of people." She feels that if she hadn't been so self-disciplined, she might have become violent. She has a very rigid physical routine for herself: She runs six to eight miles every day and lifts weights and does body building exercises every day as well. During those two weeks, however, she found it difficult to run even two miles, although she did force herself to do the two miles.

Claudia Sorano, a bank vice president in Chicago, handles major accounts and gets high ratings from her superiors. Except that they have noted that periodically she overreacts to stressful situations with anger and irritability. This has happened half a dozen times in the bank, but on at least two occasions that were memorable. Once she and several colleagues were out of town negotiating a major loan. The attorney for the client made a critical comment that she would normally have overlooked or diplomatically glossed over. Instead, she launched into a tirade against the man. Luckily one of her colleagues smoothed it over and the deal was completed. But later her colleague took her aside and reprimanded her, saying "You almost blew it for us." She felt terrible because she knew that she was premenstrual, that she should have kept her mouth shut, but she couldn't control herself.

Later she got promoted to another division and during one of the weekly meetings of vice presidents a similar thing happened. Another vice president made a seemingly innocuous comment and she took offense, letting loose verbally. Her boss noted it and later cautioned her that she couldn't behave that way. She knew her harangue was inappropriate. Soon after this she came to us for evaluation; she had known about PMS but had been denying it until the second incident.

Jill Morton, an architect for a large California design firm, first became aware of her PMS at work: "People who are close to you and personally involved with you tend to accept your problems more than people you work with." Several times, she says, her condition interfered with her nascent career. "In two specific incidents, my behavior became uncontrollable. Once with a customer, once with a person I worked for. I behaved very poorly. I lost my temper. I said a lot of things — that perhaps were true — that I would never have said under normal circumstances. I just said, 'Look, this is what is going to happen, buzz out of this situation, here I am and I'm taking over.' Mostly to superiors. This was interesting because I was in a program where I was evaluated very closely, in terms of advancement. One of my last evaluations was that I had very many strong points but that my inability was that I became so intense that I lost control of my temper. I lost control of the situation because I tend to overreact. Mostly I lashed out verbally. I've only thrown things at my husband, nobody else. Never at work. You don't throw things at guys who pay you."

Morton feels that her natural candor and aggressiveness is dramatically magnified when she is premenstrual. "I think that people recognize that I can do certain things, but they also feel that I am extremely volatile and that in certain circumstances they prefer to have someone else handle it if it's a very political type of situation, because I may lose my temper. I may tell the truth where they... I may be too painfully candid. What people think of me is that I'm very aggressive. In certain situations it's too much, in others, it's very good. I think it's hurt me in certain instances, but banking is a career that today accepts a certain amount of aggressiveness. Yet women who are aggressive are sometimes looked on as somewhat of a shocking element and they [men] don't know how to react.''

Problems in the Classroom

School teachers with premenstrual syndrome have classroom outbursts, and are less flexible and tolerant of the students' behavior. One patient even considered giving up teaching because she couldn't handle the stress, and felt she was being unfair to her classes. But she got treatment, eliminated her symptoms, and continued with her teaching career. Patty Montand, a thirty-nine-year-old high school teacher, says: ''When you teach, you need total control. The week before my period, I would feel as if I were going to explode. I was so irritable that I would take it out on the students.'' Twice parents came in for conferences after she verbally abused a student. ''All I could say was that I was sorry. I didn't know what was going on myself.'' Thinking back, she's amazed it didn't happen more often. ''I was never physically violent with the kids, but I was hostile and verbally abusive. It was always an overreaction on my part if they talked in class, or if they came in late.''

Lucy Romano, thirty-two, was a school principal until her problems with PMS made her decide to go back to graduate school and finish her doctorate. ''I'm very good with kids, but before I'd get my period I'd lose control and yell at them.'' When a student was sent to her office for disciplinary action during the wrong time of month, she would get irrationally angry. ''I would take it too seriously. If I had to do one more thing than I had planned to do that day, it would set me off.''She said, ''I'm bright, mature, responsible and all that. When I would react like this, I thought that I was losing my mind.'' One day she went to work feeling terrible. She remembers telling herself, ''Just stay calm. Walk into your office and control yourself.'' When she got in, she slammed her office door and broke down in tears. She went to see the superintendent of the school district, told him she had menstrually-related problems, and said, ''I can't do it. Just send me home for a week.'' She took the week off, but when she returned, the superintendent ''didn't trust me anymore. He didn't think that I could handle the job, and he kept me from proving myself by preventing me from handling all the responsibilities that I should have." She describes her job as stressful. "They replaced me with two and a half people."

For some reason, we've treated a relatively large number of professional singers over the past three years, especially opera singers. Sandra Condon, forty-one, is a part-time opera singer and administrative assistant. The PMS affected her singing. "It takes a lot of energy to sing," she says. "I'd be too tired, and too unmotivated. And I didn't sing well two weeks before my period, and the week of my period. I really could sing well only seven days of the month." When she felt well, she would sing some scales before dinner, and sing songs and exercises after dinner. She sings fifteen minutes out of every hour: Bellini and Handel arias, Italian art songs. She was offered the leading role in Gilbert and Sullivan's *Princess Ida,* but she took a secondary role instead because of her PMS. The performance was scheduled for the day her period would start. "I knew that I wouldn't be able to sing high Bs that night." When women menstruate, she said, their voices drop down a part of an octave. Her performance went well, but "I couldn't have sung the lead role." She remembers singing in a lieder class during the spring of 1980. "It was a couple of days before my period. I just had to get up and sing a couple of German songs; it was really no big deal. But I remember getting up and wishing that I wasn't there. I was very depressed. I got through the songs, but without the flair I normally would have."

Opting for Flexible Schedules

About half of our patients who work have changed their job circumstances or quit work or school to cope with PMS. Consulting and freelance work is one of the most common choices of working women with PMS because of the flexibility of schedules it offers. Many women decide to give up simply to avoid confrontations.

Marguerite Sorenson, thirty-nine, is an artist who lives in Maine with her husband and two teenage sons. She worked as a commercial artist for an advertising agency until five years ago when her health problems grew difficult. Sorenson is glad that she had the flexibility as an artist to work at home, but her illness jeopardized her career, making it tough for her to meet her commitments. But her painting helped her to cope with her pain and depression. Her specialty is representational work in watercolor — landscapes, flowers and nature scenes. Her work reflects her feelings and emotions. "When I was feeling terrible, I would use a lot of dark colors."

Amy Dorfman, thirty-eight, the mother of two sons, has quit three jobs in seven years because of PMS, as a market researcher, magazine advertising salesperson, and caterer. The first two jobs she left with "impulsive, emotional resignations" caused by incidents that occurred during her premenstrual phase. On the first job, she said she had been owed money for two or three months. When the office manager walked around distributing checks to her coworkers, but she was not paid, she lost her temper and screamed at the office manager. "I made an absolute fool of myself in front of four people who worked for me." Her boss took her aside and talked to her, telling her that she was disappointed in her reaction. Dorfman cried during the talk, and quit in anger. Her boss asked her to stay with the firm, and offered to double her salary but she refused. "I was so ashamed of myself, and I was afraid that I'd do the same thing again." While she was employed by the catering company, she didn't show up for work for one week. "I felt as if I couldn't cope. My husband was away, and I took the children and went to stay with a friend. I didn't call my boss or tell him that I was leaving. When I returned to the office the following week, he was very understanding, but again, I was so ashamed that I resigned." At her sales job, "I was a terrifically qualified, hard worker at times. And at other times, I just fell apart. There were days where I'd go in and pull lists of calls to make and they'd swim in front of me. I'd go in two hours early, because I knew that I had client appointments all day and I felt so disorganized. But I was so disoriented that the extra two hours really didn't help." Dorfman called in with the flu a lot, but "I'd force myself to go to work as much as I could because to stay home alone would be devastating. I'd be so depressed that I'd go to pieces. I'd get dressed, put on my makeup and try to hang in there, no matter how difficult it was." She never missed a client appointment when she was working, but in the summer of 1981 she took three weeks off. "I talked to my boss. Actually, I sat there and cried. She suggested that I take some time off and relax." She forced herself to do things. "I forced myself to go to work, and I forced myself to go to parties. I was more capable of forcing myself to get things done on the outside. The worst times were when I was home and I didn't have much to do.'' Dorfman eventually told the sales staff she worked with — all women — about PMS after an article about it ran in a leading newsmagazine and she felt that she could be treated. ''They were understanding,'' and allowed her to rearrange the days that she would work in the office. ''They told me that they could tell when it was a week or two before my period just by looking at me. I'd look extremely strained and white, as if I were under a lot of stress.''

Dealing With Anxiety Attacks

Some women report having panic attacks or incidents with phobias when PMS combines with the stress of a high-pressure job. One sales person for a computer company had panic attacks related to driving a car. As a sales person who made calls on clients, this interfered with her work. ''During those two weeks, I would experience an absolute terror of driving. I did drive, but I was scared to death that I'd have an accident. I'd stay off the parkways, and I couldn't drive in the city because I couldn't maintain anything near the average speed.''

Lola Scott, a real estate broker, relates an incident in the summer of 1981, ''that was my nightmare period, just before I got treatment. I was supposed to run an open house. That's where the listing sales person serves lunch for the other brokers in the area and shows them the house that is up for sale. There was a terrible thunderstorm the night before that woke me up at three in the morning. It poured with rain all day. I packed the food in the car and took the kids to drop them off at a friend's house. I was dressed in a pretty dress in the car with the food and the children, and the roads were flooded. There were stalled cars everywhere. I reacted totally irrationally. I saw myself stuck in a puddle forever. I got hysterical and said things like 'I'm never going to get there.' I knew that the open house wasn't that important, that if I were having trouble getting there, so was everyone else. The kids were great. 'No, Mom, everything's going to be okay,' my son said. 'Why don't you take this road instead?' And all I could do was see myself stuck in that puddle, in my pretty dress, with the kids and the food in the trunk of the car, forever.''

A magazine editor in New York had her first panic attack when stuck in a subway tunnel. She had been writing and making notes on manuscripts when the train suddenly got stuck in the tunnel; she was one day away from her period. Eventually the passengers had to leave the subway and walk out through the tunnel. Since then she hasn't been able to force herself to ride the subway, and has spent a small fortune on cabs. She subsequently had several other panic attacks and was treated with psychotherapy, but it didn't work. We first saw her as a patient for treatment of the panic attack. In checking her medical history, though, we saw that she had several other cyclical complaints, all of which had been getting worse in recent years. Since she's been treated with progesterone she has not experienced any cyclical symptoms in the premenstrual time. But she's still in therapy for her fear of subways and tunnels.

Keeping PMS Under Wraps

Few women in positions of authority have discussed their cyclical problem with anyone connected to their job, although a few of our patients in lower-level jobs say they have discussed PMS with co-workers. Very rarely a woman will have told a superior about her condition. Group leaders for the National PMS Society say women who call for referrals to support groups in their area frequently say they are afraid to mention PMS at work for fear of being fired or having their responsibilities diminished; they're also afraid to file claims for reimbursement of medical expenses with their employer's insurance company for fear that PMS will somehow reflect upon them or affect their job status.

Jill Morton, the architect, takes the majority view: "I think that probably the hardest thing is to admit, at least in a professional capacity, that you are afflicted with this thing. I would never say at work that I had PMS. I would feel my working associates, mostly men, would say, 'Aha. Raging hormones. We always knew.' It's the kind of thing that's like a closet sickness. I have to go to the doctor, and if I said it was for my toe, they would say, 'Oh, yeah. That's really bad.' But if you say I have this problem because I have a hormone imbalance and when I get my period it makes me really miserable. People are uncomfortable with that kind of a biological discussion while they're not if you broke your toe or your finger. I've not at all indicated my PMS in a professional capacity. Because I feel that people who are in the position of power right now are not in a position to understand something like that. It's something that's relatively new. The people for whom I work are from a generation that never spoke of those things."

Education about premenstrual syndrome, its physiological basis, and the availability of treatment should one day erase the stigma that many women feel attaches to their condition. The recent emergence of interest in premenstrual syndrome is a natural outgrowth of the dramatic rise in the number of women in the workforce. As women have moved out into careers, developing complex and demanding professional, political, and social roles, they have reached a stage where they can't and won't tolerate the illness and its interference in their lives any longer. Society's emphasis on health education and prevention, nutrition, exercise, and management of stress has made women more sensitive, aware, and demanding about their physical well-being. They're now vocal advocates for sensible, intelligent health care and refuse to be dictated to by physicians or anyone else who can't resolve their medical complaints.

Chapter 11

Violence is here,
In the world of the sane,
And violence is a symptom.

Jacob Bronowski, **The Face of Violence**

Striking Out

Lizzie Borden hated her stepmother with a steely white-hot intensity that had mounted without pause for five years. It was undoubtedly the profoundest emotion that Abby Durfee Borden had ever stirred in another. At sixty-five, Abby was dismal and uninteresting, a two-hundred-pound semi-recluse with few interests and less imagination. What she did have was a husband, Andrew J. Borden, Lizzie's seventy-year-old father and president of the local bank. Jealousy and greed fueled Lizzie's hatred and had ever since Andrew had purchased for Abby a half-interest in her sister's house for $1,500. The gift was Abby's only real asset; it was the only major sum of money transferred from husband to wife. And it detracted not one whit from Lizzie or her sister Emma. Both of them were well provided for by their father, both had their own checking and savings accounts, and income from real estate in their own names. Lizzie, Andrew's favorite despite her erratic nature, had at the time of her trial more than $3,000 in her own right, an enormous sum then for a thirty-two-year-old single woman. But Lizzie wanted more; most of all she wanted her father out of Abby's grasp. She certainly didn't want Abby to gain further from her father's wealth.

Sometime in the spring or summer of 1892 Lizzie Borden learned of a plan of her father's that outraged her. He intended to secretly transfer the ownership of his Swansea farm to Abby prior to letting John Morse, the brother of his deceased first wife, take over Swansea and its expenses as a kind of caretaker/boarder. The secrecy was intended to prevent Lizzie and Emma from finding out that Abby now owned two properties. Lizzie apparently never confronted her father with her discovery. Instead, by July, she was actively planning to kill Abby, to poison her with an untraceable substance. Lizzie made the rounds of Fall River's drugstores trying to buy prussic acid, to no avail. Pharmacists told her that prussic acid, a highly volatile and dangerous element, was not sold without a prescription. Later, a policeman noticed that the spine of the family's book of household hints was broken; its pages opened naturally to the section on prussic acid. Lizzie's lack of subtlety at the drug counters and with the household hints apparently alerted Abby to her plans; if Lizzie had known enough about poison to ask for arsenic she would have readily obtained it and would never have become an American legend.

After the tantrums and outcry Lizzie had kindled over the $1,500 house interest, Abby feared Lizzie intensely, terribly, and with good reason. Two days before the murders, after the Bordens en masse and their Irish maid Bridget Sullivan suffered bouts of nausea and vomiting, Abby ran to the home of a physician-neighbor telling him she had been threatened by poison and then poisoned in fact. She conveniently ignored the likely tie of the illness to a family meal of leftover fish following three days of mutton, probably tainted by the August weather. The physician, however, inquired into the Borden menus and assured her that the cause of the complaints was summer food poisoning. That night, Lizzie visited her friend Alice Russell, and described "this feeling as if something was hanging over me that I cannot shake off." The aura of temporal epilepsy was wafting over her; one of Lizzie's "peculiar spells" was coming on.

An Oppressive Dawn

By dawn of the following day, Thursday, August 4, 1892, an oppressive shroud of heat and humidity hung over Fall River; it was to be the hottest day in memory for several decades in a town distinguished by its wilting summers. It was also the first day of Lizzie Borden's menstrual flow. Despite the recent outbreak of unsettled stomachs, the household — Andrew and Abby Borden, Uncle John Morse, and Bridget — took a dining room breakfast of mutton, mutton broth, bananas, cookies, and johnnycakes. Lizzie, showing better sense, or perhaps preoccupied with her work at hand, chose coffee and cookies in the kitchen. After breakfast, Uncle John left on an errand; Bridget went outside to wash windows, following Abby's instructions; Andrew adjourned to the bank, where he planned to meet Abby and deed over the Swansea property to her. Abby went upstairs to the guest room, telling Lizzie she was going to put fresh slipcovers on the pillows on the bed that also served as a couch. The opportunity must have seemed heaven-sent. No one was in the house except Abby and Lizzie. But what happened next defied logic.

Lizzie slipped down to the cellar and grabbed a hatchet, bringing it up to the kitchen. The doorbell rang. A messenger delivered a note for Abby, probably a last minute exhortation and reassurance from Andrew that she should meet him at the bank, that Lizzie and Emma would not discover the transaction. Giddy with the realization that her plan was about to be set irrevocably in motion, Lizzie called up to Abby that a message had arrived for her and that she would carry it up with the wash. Arranging a pile of clean clothes to hide the ax, Lizzie clutched the linens, and ascended the staircase to the guestroom. As Abby Borden straightened up from smoothing the bedspread, Lizzie moved up behind her, and in one gesture, pulled the hatchet free as she flung the clothes away. With a single well-placed stroke, she laid Abby out unconscious, probably dead. Taking a moment to fasten the window's wooden shutters, she proceeded to bludgeon her stepmother nineteen more times — in what one physician termed "weak and ill-aimed blows for a man."

Without question, Lizzie had planned to kill Abby. But the murder itself and the subsequent murder of her father, whom she loved dearly, were probably committed in an episode of premenstrual syndrome. Her primary symptom was recurring epileptic seizures of the temporal lobe, probably marked by automatism — a period of automatic action in which the victim may remember only dimly or may forget completely her actions during the seizure, as Victoria Lincoln describes it in *A Private Disgrace — Lizzie Borden by Daylight*. Abby Durfee Borden was a murder target, but she was probably a victim of Lizzie's PMS and epilepsy. The conscious Lizzie had chosen a woman's means of killing — poison. She didn't want to create a mess. She didn't want to get caught. In the sleep-walker's motion that is automatism, Lizzie reached for a distinctly masculine weapon — an ax — that was at once too blatant, too obvious, too bloody a method for her nature. There's no question of the cause of death when a hatchet's involved; gashes and gaping wounds can't be blamed on rancid mutton. Victoria Lincoln believes that Lizzie's seizure ended "when that orgasm of hate was spent." After dealing death to Abby, she emerged from the haze of the epileptic automatism, saw the clothes still clean on the floor behind her, was stunned to find blood on her hands. Then she did what any pragmatic murderer would do: she cleaned herself up, stashed the ax in a tall slop pail nearby, and slipped downstairs as if everything were normal.

The Fatal Mistake

She had ample time to create a situation that could make it appear that an unknown intruder, maybe a burglar, had entered the house and killed Abby. But a second surprise awaited her, one that forced her to change strategies rapidly. Her father returned home, an hour and a half before his normal lunch time. He was looking for Abby, although he couldn't tell Lizzie why. That was his fatal mistake. Even though the automatism had passed, by depriving Lizzie of the time and circumstances she needed to set up the discovery of Abby's body, Andrew Borden would die at the hands of his favorite daughter. Lizzie told Andrew that Abby had left to visit a friend; while that excuse didn't make much sense given Abby's tendency to stay within the boundaries of the house and yard, Andrew apparently accepted it at face value and decided to relax before lunch in the sitting room. He, too, was killed with the ax, but this time Lizzie, now more sure of herself, spent only ten blows on him as he napped on the parlor sofa.

Despite the predominance of the evidence and Lizzie's transparent and contradictory lies about the events of August 4, a jury of twelve gentlemen of Fall River acquitted her of both crimes. The bizarre murders remained a *cause celebre* long after the acquittal. Her exploits were exaggerated, as Americans are wont to do, in folk song and legend telling of "forty whacks" for Abby and forty-one for her father.

Nearly a century later, Lawrence Sanders created another troubled and deadly woman, Zoe Kohler, in *The Third Deadly Sin*. Kohler, we learn, suffers from dysmenorrhea (extremely painful menstrual cramps), Addison's disease, premenstrual syndrome, and a number of psychoses that lead her to "act out" on the day before or the first day of menstruation. Not content to lose her temper or throw an ashtray against a wall, Kohler marks her monthly cycle by killing; she kills men. In scenes far more grisly than those of the Borden household, the novel details the murders, one by one, of six men lured to bloody deaths in their hotel rooms.

Women and Violence

Neither Lizzie Borden nor the fictional Zoe Kohler murdered because of premenstrual syndrome; but both killed during episodes of PMS. In widely publicized instances, three women in England diagnosed as having PMS, convicted of killings during premenstrual episodes, received lenient sentences because of their illness. Despite the media play given to those three cases, examples of women out of control during experiences of premenstrual syndrome are extremely rare. That's hardly surprising since, to begin with, women account for a minority of the arrests and convictions for violent crimes and represent only one out of thirty prison sentences in this country. Women have accounted for only about fifteen percent of all murders since records have been kept; premenstrual syndrome could account for just a fraction of the total. Yet some violent acts committed by women may be the result of a specially heightened mood. During a research project on aggressive behavior in women conducted at a Massachusetts prison some years ago, we interviewed six women who were sentenced for murder — three victims were husbands, two were children, one was a lover. Two things that were striking about all six cases were that the killings occurred on the day before or first day of menstruation, and that all six women could have been described as quiet, mild-mannered housewives. As Enid Bagnold observed, ''A murderess is only an ordinary woman in temper.'' That could be the temper of premenstrual syndrome.

Outbursts of anger, the throwing of objects, and on occasion even thoughts of murder are fairly common in women with PMS. A majority of women with PMS at some time or another, when under great stress or pain, say they have become angry, yelled, screamed, had a car accident, thrown something, or felt as if they wanted to throw something or act out against someone. Only ten to fifteen percent of the patients we have seen, however, have ever assaulted another person, their spouse or lover, or their children.

Links between menstruation and antisocial behavior were first made by criminologists in the 19th Century. The father of modern criminology, Italian scientist Cesare Lombroso and his son-in-law William Ferrero noted in their 1893 work *The Female Offender,* that of eighty women arrested for "resistance to public officials," seventy-one were menstruating. In 1890 S. Ikard cited a study of fifty-six Parisian shoplifters, of whom thirty-five were menstruating at the time of the offense. More than half a century later, another researcher quoted a French police prefect to the effect that eighty-four percent of female crimes of violence in Paris were perpetrated during the premenstrual and early menstrual phases of the cycle. Investigators who examined the behavior of women in prisons and special hospitals found they were more liable to aggressive behavior during the premenstrual and menstrual phases of their cycle. In 1953 Joseph Morton reported that the treatment of premenstrual tension in female prisoners resulted in improved behavior. In 1961 Dr. Katharina Dalton reported that forty-nine percent of one hundred fifty-six women convicted of theft, soliciting, and drunkenness committed the crimes just before or during menstruation. Of the forty-three women — twenty-seven percent — who complained of premenstrual symptoms, sixty-three percent committed their offenses at the time of their symptoms. The irascibility and tension that accompanies premenstrual symptoms makes some incidence of assaults and violence unavoidable, especially within families. As Jacob Bronowski wrote, "Violence is the sphinx by the fireside, and she has a human face."

Interviews with our patients yield hundreds of stories of incidents and outbursts, minor and major, related to PMS. "It was like being possessed," one woman remembers. "I'd fly at my husband, rip his jacket, smash his glasses. It was horrible and I was so ashamed."

With the cooperation of her husband and children, Carla Jones built up shelf upon shelf of glass jars and bottles in the family garage. When she felt a sense of rage rising and needed an outlet for it, she headed for the garage and smashed the glass against the floor, the wall, the driveway. Sometimes, she says, she'd stomp out to the garage in the wee hours of the morning, in robe and nightgown, and destroy a dozen or so jars. "It's the release of the urge to hit something that's important," Jones says. "It saves me the fear that I'll strike someone I love."

The Jones family concedes that the clean up is a little hazardous, and the glass is a danger to the tires on their two cars, but it's safer than any alternative.

Meg Newberry remembers being so upset one morning and feeling the aura of a migraine headache beginning that when her preschool daughter started to cry and wouldn't stop, she stalked into the child's bedroom to tell her to stop. "I was so furious and in such pain that I pushed the door incredibly hard and it bounced smack into the wall. I was so mad, I did it again and again. By the time I stopped I had punched a large hole in the plaster." She was chagrined later to discover that her daughter had a fever and the flu.

Incidents involving women with PMS and the men in their lives are fairly common, although few of them involve serious assaults or injuries. One patient, Tony Salazar, recalls her attempts to aggravate her husband, "I'd gun the car; I'd be so angry that he was afraid to let me drive. I'd bug him because I needed to do something with my anger." She threw pots, pans, dishes, glasses, "anything in reach." One day when she served dinner her husband looked at his plate and asked, "What is this garbage?" It was creamed corn, as he found out when she picked up his plate and threw it in his face.

While some women concede that they got physical with their mates or others they controlled their impulse for physical outbursts around their children. Nicole Maynard said her symptoms were so severe that she came close to hitting her three children, but never did. "I wouldn't touch them. I had enough control to stop myself. Although with my husband, he's a big guy, sometimes when I was really feeling bad, I'd start pounding on him."

Andrea Brixton, a thirty-six-year-old market researcher, is a soft-spoken divorced mother of three. She also found herself turning on other people. "I was violent toward others. My husband and I had marital problems for years, a lot of it because of my erratic behavior each month. Once I just decided I was going to kill myself with a kitchen knife, but I ended up stabbing him instead. He was in the hospital for a week with that. I had also slashed my wrists a few times before that."

Diana Robertson, thirty-nine, is a single schoolteacher. "I threw things," she says, "but only objects and never at a person, only around the room... Well, once I became terribly angry, explosive, and violent and I attacked my roommate with my fists. I didn't hurt her. But that kind of episode always happened in the two weeks prior to my period."

Leslie Talbot, twenty-eight, is a corporate benefits administrator; now divorced, she lives with a man and his three children. "I'm divorced because of PMS. I've been going through this for years. I don't want to get married again because of it. The first years my [current] friend and I were together, we could only live together half the month. Two weeks on and two weeks off. I've tried to kill him. I've tried to kill myself. More than once. It landed me in a sanitarium. Every time it was recorded that at the same time I had my period. The first two weeks of the month I'm an intelligent, reasonable person, and the second two I am a person completely out of control. Three weeks prior to my period — two weeks minimum — I become very over-anxious, depressed, and high-strung. It's as if all my emotions are pushed to the extreme. It's a constant mental battle to try to keep in control, and with all your effort going into that, it makes you understand what people say. It affects you physically. I broke glasses and bumped into things. I'm a freelance artist on weekends and in the evenings and I found I couldn't cut or draw a straight line during my symptoms. I didn't realize the clumsiness was a part of the syndrome. It's a complete physical change." She also has a hearing problem in the left ear that's worse in the premenstruum.

"There's another part of it. Because of the way you behave during PMS, people are mad at you, for having called them every name in the book. Since I've been treated, that part of it is gone. Things I used to neglect two weeks a month, I can now take care of steadily. I can maintain myself, so things around me are maintained. In my reactions, I have an opportunity to be normal. If I'm upset, I know it's for a reason, not because I'm suffering from PMS. And if I'm happy, it's not because I'm trying to be, it's real."

Debunking the Spouse Abuse Myth

Statistics on family assaults, between spouses or parent against child, are spotty at best. The attention paid in the late 1970s to the issue of battered husbands raised the possibility that spouse abuse by women may have been more frequent than attacks instigated by men, but men inflict the most serious physical damage.

Georganne Michaels focused her rage and depression on her husband, Peter, and sometimes their struggles escalated into violent brawls. Since Peter at 220 pounds is substantially larger and stronger than his wife, these encounters promised the most damage to Georganne. Peter Michaels recalls that "when the arguments started, they were over small, insignificant things... We'd have a small argument and she'd throw the wine in her glass at me. The argument would grow, and the glass would follow the wine." Once he locked her out of their bedroom. She took a hammer and tried "to bash down the bedroom door." In general, he says, "She'd be screaming and hysterical; I'd be trying to suppress this violent flailing animal.

"We'd have five-star, ocean-going rows and fights. I would be accused of things unjustly. I would try to fight back by sneering or walking around the house smiling — anything to reach the maximum boiling point in her. I'm a very big man, and I've played violent sports; I was afraid that I'd hit her. I cracked her ribs twice by holding her, when I was trying to restrain her and stop her struggling. Sometimes the difficulty of not picking up my fist and putting it into her face was an act of inhuman restraint."

Yet twice he lost such control. Once he came down to the kitchen and "she was bashing new Teflon frying pans against the counter. I thought they were coming at me next. When I held her, she struggled and when we moved next to the counter, I cracked her rib." When the second injury occurred, "I was lying in bed, and she jumped on top of me. I pulled her down, and my elbow went into her rib." Both times, he says, were accidents caused by "my considerable strength."

Certainly women with premenstrual syndrome may lash out at their husbands when angry and frustrated, but they are rarely the ones to inflict bodily harm. As Ann Jones points out in *Women Who Kill,* the contention of the main research paper on the subject, *The Battered Husband Syndrome* by Suzanne Steinmetz, that "husband-beating constitutes a sizeable proportion of marital violence" was not supported by the data; the Steinmetz study was subsequently roundly criticized by other scholars. The Steinmetz data actually showed roughly equal numbers of occasions when wives and husbands hit, pushed, and threw things. But, as Ann Jones notes, Steinmetz "overlooked the context of the events and left out altogether the types of physical attacks battered women most often experience... kicking, choking, cutting, bashing the head into a solid stationary object.'' In her work, Steinmetz cited criminologist Marvin Wolfgang's classic finding that wives killed their husbands almost as often as husbands killed their wives. She omitted Wolfgang's clarification that women were seven times more likely than the men to be acting in self-defense.

Rare Incidence of Child Abuse

Child abuse is another problem that remains largely hidden from public view. The true incidence of child abuse may never be known, but one assessment, extrapolated from the reporting rates of New York and Denver, is an average of two hundred fifty to three hundred cases a year per million residents. Others estimate that 0.2 percent of childhood injuries are caused by child abuse. In one study of hospitalizations of children, Dr. Dalton demonstrated a high rate of admissions of children for illness and accidents during the premenstrual phase of their mother's menstrual cycle. She has suggested that some cases of child abuse may be related to premenstrual tension but there have been no systematic studies. Among our patients, the incidence of child abuse is rare. But many of the women are extremely fearful that they might assault their children. Most incidents involving children that we hear of tend to be verbal. The mothers are hypercritical; a thirty-second scolding becomes a thirty-minute harangue. Usually when a woman feels a loss of control or an urge to strike a child, she'll walk away, out of the house, into the bedroom. It's the triumph of reason over emotion, requiring great restraint, that the women may not show with their husbands or lovers.

The kind of unexpected, apparently unprompted outbursts that Christina Crawford related about her mother, Joan Crawford, in *Mommie Dearest* go far beyond what most children with PMS mothers endure. But those graphic night raids, bursts of house cleaning and garden chores undertaken in the middle of the night, and unprovoked bouts of temper and imposition of punishments paint a picture of a woman with premenstrual syndrome. The most memorable scene from *Mommie Dearest* is, of course, the night raid involving the wire clothes hangers. ''Inside the closet my mother was in a rage. She was swearing a blue streak and muttering to herself... She grabbed me by the hair and dragged me into the closet. There before me I saw total devastation...

Shaking me by the hair she screamed in my ear, 'No wire hangers! No wire hangers!' With one hand she pulled me by the hair and with the other she pounded my ears until they rang and I could hardly hear her screaming.'' The loss of control and towering rage that Joan Crawford frequently exhibited are sensations shared by many women with PMS. Terry Wright, the mother of six children, is one of the rare women who admits that ''my first two kids were literally battered because I would just lose control.''

Lisa Santori, forty-three, describes the guilt she feels about the premenstrual violence that touched her three children, now grown and living on their own. ''I don't usually put my hands on my children. I'm not a person who normally hits children. I have and I will, but I do not believe in it. I was acting against my own beliefs but I couldn't control myself. Even now, they're twenty-five and twenty-six years old, and I realize that the things that I've done to them were probably at that time of the month. I just couldn't control myself, but I never related it to my period. I just thought they irritated me. As I learned about it, I realized that this is PMS and this is outside me. I mean I could tell the difference. I know the difference. After I'd do something I'd feel bad, and try to contain myself but that made me feel even worse. That sounds silly now. If I tried to contain myself it would be like trying to hold the flood back, the pressure would be a lot heavier. It was the same every month. The last three days before my flow, it was a nightmare for me.''

Doreen Trumbull's temper was more controlled but she remembers ''one spanking episode that was out of control'' and an incident in which ''I cuffed a stepchild around the face, which I shouldn't have done.'' In a large and boistrous household of two children belonging to both her husband and herself and five stepchildren from their previous marriages, strain and tension were a normal part of every weekend, she says. During one of those get-together Saturdays, Trumbull recalls, ''My husband and I ended up cuffing each other around'' over something minor, what a child had for dinner.

A frequent problem for these women are the feelings, the desire, to throttle or abuse a child. One women caller to a Phil Donahue television show about premenstrual syndrome said she often became enraged and out of control. Once she said she was about to throw her four-year-old through the living room picture window but she didn't because the phone rang — it was her husband — and she went to answer it. There's something to be said after all for the modern tyranny of the Bell System.

Two strategies developed by Veronica Minter, the mother of two preschoolers, redirected her anger. "I never got violent with the kids. I always kept myself back from them. But a few times, things would fly across the room. If I felt like I could really kill the kids, I would beat a pillow against the wall. I would never really hurt them. But there were times when I would grab the kids, throw them in the car, and go over to somebody's house, because if I didn't get out of our house, I would belt them. I didn't want to do that. I really tried to protect them from me."

Chapter 12

Dying
Is an art, like everything else.
I do it exceedingly well.

Sylvia Plath, **Lady Lazarus**

Suicide Attempts

Suicide, like bizarre murders and the sex lives of celebrities, holds a morbid fascination for even the most civilized among us. Incidents of suicide, however horrifying, tantalize the closet voyeur and taunt us with the possibility that we, too, could take our own life. Killing oneself because of unbearable pressures, in the most depressed of states, is the picture most readily evoked by the word "suicide," but it is sometimes the outcome of a final nose-thumbing challenge. Tempting fate, like moths that fly too near a flame, is as deliberate a contest for some as a chess match. At stake is not an intricately carved knight, nor a queen, nor a king, but oneself. For these individuals "life loses interest," Freud wrote, "when the highest stake in the game of living, life itself, may not be risked." Whatever the trigger mechanism, the fatal attraction of suicide has long been evident. Centuries ago suicide was recognized as part of human frailty by church and state, which took drastic steps to caution the populace from even considering the taking of their own lives. Suicide was decreed a crime, a felony that in England and some other jurisdictions carried the ironic penalty of death. Dare suicide, the state thundered, and you'll regret it but not live. Englishmen who tried and failed during the 18th and 19th Centuries were revived just long enough to see the state undertake the deed in a much more efficient manner. The Roman Catholic Church deems suicide or the attempt a mortal sin, again bearing the same stigma and penalty as murder. The Vatican's fiat is clear. Would-be suicides, take heed: you'll plunge straight to hell's fiery depths should you foil God's plan by taking yourself out of the game before the ninth inning. Yet neither label, of criminal nor sinner, daunts those intent on the act.

Leslie Farber, in *The Ways of the Will,* considered "the life of suicide," which he says "must not be seen as the situation or state of mind which leads to the act, but that situation in which the act-as-possibility, quite apart from whether it eventually occurs or not, has a life of its own." Suicide is a conscious act, despite the fact that it is considered or undertaken "when the balance of the mind is disturbed." For some women with PMS, life becomes a torturous existence in which the act-as-possibility haunts their thoughts.

Ursula Pappert, one of our patients, said she contemplated suicide. "It really scared me because it seemed at that point it was beginning to get more control of me. Luckily that happened just before I went to the clinic for the first time. PMS is such a severe up and down, and it doesn't just last for an hour or something, it lasts for days. You get to the point where you can't take it anymore, and you really start feeling guilty about your family and everything. 'I must be an awfully terrible person, and I think they'd be better off if I weren't around.' I can understand how people can contemplate or even try it. I never tried it but I thought about it just before I got diagnosed at the clinic."

Cesare Pavese observed that "no one ever lacks a good reason for suicide;" women with extremely severe cases of premenstrual syndrome of long duration usually have more than one. Their pain is magnified by the frustration and impotence of not understanding what is causing their illness and failing to find a treatment for it. Most women with PMS who have reached for a razor blade or a bottle of pills have done so because they were weary of the chronic illness, weary of being told by their families they were hypochondriacs or crazy, weary of being told by physicians that nothing was wrong with them or that a hysterectomy would fix it all — but it didn't. An overwhelming, all-encompassing sense of alienation, loneliness, and worthlessness, bred of ignorance and misunderstanding, cloaks them in a cocoon of despair that eventually becomes impossible for others to penetrate. They want relief of the most permanent kind.

Suicidal depression, which A. Alvarez calls "a kind of spiritual winter, frozen, sterile, unmoving" appears as a recurring theme in the poetry and fiction of Sylvia Plath. For the last twenty years, Plath has been the woman writer most identified with suicide and depression. She wrote of and from her own experiences. Obsessed with the memory of her father who killed himself when she was eight, she attempted suicide three times, succeeding on the fourth try although from the cues she left behind she apparently intended to fail yet again. Throughout her poetry and the autobiographical novel, *The Bell Jar*, the theme of suicide resonates. The heroine of *The Bell Jar* weeps at her father's grave just before she holes up in a cellar and swallows fifty sleeping pills. An introductory note Plath wrote to *Daddy* before a reading of the poem on the BBC said the poem's narrator "has to act out the awful little allegory once over before she is free of it." In *Daddy,* Plath rails:

> "At twenty I tried to die
> And get back, back, back to you.
> I thought even the bones would do."

From *Lady Lazarus:*

> "I have done it again.
> One year in every ten
> I manage it...
> A sort of walking miracle...
> I am only thirty.
> And like the cat I have nine times to die.
> This is Number Three..."

Her obsession with purity, blood images, and death are also given major expression in her poetry. In *The Munich Mannequins,* she wrote, "Perfection is terrible. It cannot have children." In *Tulips,* the poet is ill and in the hospital, the flowers brought as a gift "are too red in the first place, they hurt me," and the smiling faces of her husband and children in a family photograph "catch on to my skin, little smiling hooks... I am a nun now, I have never been so pure." She wants to flee from the blood (the red tulips), the pain and the entanglements of close relationships into death. In *Fever 103* she wrote,

> "I am too pure for you or anyone.
> Your body
> Hurts me as the world hurts God."

A. Alvarez writes in *The Savage God* that Plath, "spoke of suicide with a wry detachment, and without any mention of the suffering or drama of the act... She seemed to view death as a physical challenge she had, once again, overcome. It was an experience of much the same quality as mastering a bolting horse... Suicide, in short, was not a swoon into death, an attempt 'to cease upon the midnight with no pain,' it was something to be felt in the nerve ends and fought against, an initiation rite qualifying her for a life of her own.''

Plath committed suicide after a difficult two-year period in which she had given birth to a daughter, suffered a miscarriage, had been hospitalized with appendicitis, gave birth to a son, and separated from her husband. After failing to kill herself in a car accident in late 1961, she tried again and succeeded on a frigid Monday morning in February, 1962. Depression, illness, and the starkness of winter, combined with the demands of two small children, were too much for her; she turned on the gas oven one morning but apparently thought she'd be found and saved because she had made an appointment with a new au pair girl for 9 A.M. that day and had left a note with her physician's name and number. Alvarez, then the poetry editor of *The Observer* of London, wrote: "She lay down in front of the gas oven almost hopefully, almost with relief, as though she were saying, 'Perhaps this will set me free.' In part, I suppose, it was a 'cry for help' which fatally misfired. But it was also a last desperate attempt to exorcise the death she had summed up in her poems... when she and her husband separated, however mutual the arrangement, she again went through the same piercing grief and bereavement she had felt as a child when her father, by his death, seemed to abandon her.''

Despite the inexorable tie of depression, a women's disease, with suicide, women account for only slightly more than twenty-five percent of the suicides in this country each year, according to the U.S. Census Bureau, or about seven thousand of the twenty-seven thousand total. Researchers explain the discrepancy by noting that women are more likely to attempt suicide than men, but they succeed less often. The classic study, *Suicide and Attempted Suicide,* by Erwin Stengel in 1969 noted that ''the number of suicide attempts is six to ten times that of suicides;'' most data indicate that the ratio of men to women who attempt suicide is almost exactly the reverse of the ratio of men to women who complete suicide. Researchers also report that more women attempt suicide during the premenstrual phase than at other times in their cycle. Some of these attempts are made by women with premenstrual syndrome.

About ten percent of our patients have made a suicide attempt, and most of these women have made multiple attempts. About twenty percent of our patients, especially those who have PMS and a clinical depression, say they have had suicidal thoughts. Of the women who have PMS but do not have a pervasive clinical depression, some develop a profound depression on the second, third, fourth, or fifth day before their period; this is when the suicidal thoughts or attempts occur. These symptoms usually disappear after the period starts. But women who have PMS and a depression may have suicidal thoughts at any time during the month because they are suffering from two disorders.

Most common are the episodes of suicidal thoughts. Tracy Stevens, a mother of two, suffered from a postpartum depression so severe that she planned her entire life around the week and a half that she felt well. The rest of the time she spent in her room. She says she had planned her suicide in her mind. She didn't try to kill herself, although she desperately wanted to die, because "I couldn't leave my kids." The closest she came was just before she found out about the clinic, when she threw a glass against a kitchen cabinet and screamed at her husband, "You're not helping me. I need help!" Stephanie Lansing, twenty-four, also had severe depressions that eventually led to suicidal thoughts. "I talked a lot about not wanting to live," she said. "I just got so tired trying to get up the energy during my two good weeks to feel good enough to make it through the two bad weeks." Now symptom-free on progesterone therapy, she says, "When I think back on it, I just can't believe it."

Lynn Rousseau, the mother of three, also found she couldn't go through with suicide: "The big pain for me was the threat of losing this beautiful little family of mine. I never calculated how to do it or the cleanest way to go. I just thought about my car going off the mountainside. I know the embarrassment that comes from a suicide in the family. I would have chosen a way that looked like an accident. My death wish wasn't all selfish; I would have done it to prevent my family from living through this hell."

Thoughts of suicide and actual attempts have a complicated effect on the family. The murder of oneself is the ultimate violence, wreaked not only on the victim but on those closest to her. As Boris Pasternak wrote in *An Essay in Autobiography:* "...we have no conception of the inner torture which precedes suicide." A person "who decides to commit suicide puts a full stop to his being, he turns his back on his past, he declares himself a bankrupt and his memories to be unreal." But as Rollo May pointed out in *Power and Innocence,* when he writes of a patient, Priscilla, who remarked that a man she knew would not have committed suicide if "one person had known him" ... "I believe she was saying that this man had no person to whom he could open himself up, no one who was interested enough in him to listen, to pay attention to him.... he lacked someone who had compassion for him, a compassion which would be the basis of his self-esteem. If he had had such a person, he would have counted himself too valuable to wipe out."

At the same time that suicide and thoughts of suicide are a violence against the family, they can be a desperate cry for help and the recognition that might salvage self-esteem. The husband of thirty-seven-year-old Diana Marshall, who threatened to kill herself regularly, says, "She was angry, would cry incessantly, was shattered and debilitated. She'd run upstairs and lie on our bed, crying and talking about suicide. I'd tell her how much the children and I needed her. Sometimes, especially at the beginning, I thought that her threats were serious. But I'd been through it so many times — twelve times a year for ten years — and she always made it. I'd grit my teeth and bite my knuckles and say to myself, 'Here we go again.' I knew that nothing I said or did would improve the situation."

Maria Mancini, after suffering for ten years, started hoarding her painkillers and antidepressants prescribed for migraines and depression. Her parents, sisters, brother, and husband thought she was suicidal. "And I was. But I would never have committed suicide because I couldn't have left my two children. Yet death wasn't an enemy to me anymore. I think there are a lot more things worse than death. I think my brother [a physician] felt I needed to be committed. My parents didn't want to do that. My mother kept me at her house and put the medications away. She was afraid I would overdose."

When the trauma of premenstrual syndrome becomes too much for some women to handle, they actually try to take their own life. Fausta Martin, thirty-nine, married, two children, attempted suicide in the fall of 1977. "I swallowed a bottle of Valium about nine o'clock, after I had been drinking all evening. It was the culmination of two weeks of suicidal thoughts. I had been thinking about using razor blades, or crashing the car into a tree. I'd had suicidal thoughts for about two years, during those two weeks out of the month. But I was a fighter. I fought my symptoms all the way. I made myself go out no matter how difficult it was, because it was better than the isolated depression of staying home alone. By the fall of 1977 I had had enough. I just gave up. I felt that my husband and my children would be better off without me. I couldn't see getting better, and I couldn't live a nightmare anymore. By that time I didn't even have a two-week grace period. The two weeks were so terrible that the months just ran into each other.''

Her husband was downstairs. Her two children were asleep. ''I just couldn't live like that anymore. I'd fought it for so long. I'd tried so many different things and there wasn't a cure. I felt as if I had done everything that I could have done. My husband had stopped loving me and given up. I can't say that I blame him. I woke up the next morning and told my husband what I had done. I was lucky that I woke up. The Valium that I took was only two milligrams per tablet, although I didn't know that when I swallowed them. My husband took me to the emergency room. They didn't pump my stomach, but they kept me in the hospital for three days. My husband was shocked and angry. It was the last straw. His patience had run out. I vaguely remembered while I was driving around in my car that afternoon that he was supposed to go to a conference on the West Coast that evening. But I didn't get back until the early evening, so he missed his conference. I suppose I did it deliberately.'' Her children were four and seven at the time; she never told them about the incident.

Her husband Jack remembers the episode started after ''we had had an enormous battle. I was so angry and furious that I didn't care what she did. She told me that she was going to the car to commit suicide, and I told her to go ahead and do it. When she came back, I told myself that I knew she would. She came upstairs, and I had no idea of what she'd done until she told me the next morning. I called poison control and brought her to the hospital, but I was angry that she was destroying the family and my life. I felt like I wanted someone else to look after her for a while. I'd know that I had to take care of her, but I was still angry.''

In perhaps the most extreme case we have encountered, one woman, Phyllis Schwartz, was forced to sign away the custody of her children after she made a suicide attempt. (She is now involved in a court battle for their return). Schwartz says she took an overdose of many medications after "a hellish day and night in which I was out of control. I had overdosed on not one bottle of pills, but a multiple of all my medications. My heart stopped and my breathing stopped. I didn't call for anyone, they found me unconscious. But I know now that it will never happen to me again."

The extreme symptoms that push some women to the very brink of death are rare, but as these interviews reveal they are a real part of some women's lives. Most women with PMS choose a troublesome life over death, even though, as the Russian poet Mayakovsky wrote:

> "In this life it is not difficult to die
> It is more difficult to live."

Maybe, as Dorothy Parker told us in *Resumé,* suicide is really more trouble than it's worth:

> "Guns aren't lawful;
> Nooses give;
> Gas smells awful;
> You might as well live."

SECTION IV / *Female Complaints*

Chapter 13

"Women are growing honester, braver, stronger, more healthful and skillful and able and free..."

Charlotte Perkins Gilman, **Woman and Economics**

The Pill

Jogging and oral contraceptives probably represent the most common daily, shared experience of American women. Nearly forty million of them have taken oral contraceptives at some point in their life; nine million take them now. Despite a plethora of minor side effects and the potential for major ones, women continue to pop the Pill as acceptingly as they lace up their Nikes and jog around the park. They value the result even if it's accompanied by fluid retention or a case of shin splints. The Pill fulfills its promise: it's the safest form of contraception — about 99.5 percent effective. For three decades it has held sway as the magic bullet, a guarantee against unwanted pregnancy and a key to unprecedented sexual freedom. Some women with PMS — especially those whose symptoms started early and who have less severe cases — may find that they are more interested in sex during the premenstrual phase, contradicting research studies that report that most women have a decreased interest in sex just prior to menstruation. Many women trace the onset of PMS to their taking of oral contraceptives, and the Pill generally exacerbates all premenstrual symptoms, particularly weight gain, fluid retention, depression, and headaches. About sixty percent of our patients have taken the Pill at some time; only about ten percent currently use oral contraceptives.

Martine Hudson began taking the Pill one month before her wedding in 1970 and that triggered her premenstrual symptoms. "I became irritable and depressed. My parents and then-fiance became worried about me. On our way to our honeymoon I told my husband I wanted to come home," she remembers. "For the first six months I bled every day. I had constant migraines and depression which I didn't tell anybody about, as well as strange hair growth, swollen breasts. I told my doctor about the symptoms and she put me on *two* birth control pills a day. My symptoms just went crazy. I then told her that I was very depressed and didn't know why, that I cried all day. The bleeding had stopped though. She told me then that all those symptoms were because of the birth control pills. She said she hadn't told me this before so I wouldn't imagine symptoms that weren't there.'' Recalling the episode, Hudson paused and emphasized: ''I was *very* angry. If I had known what to look for, I would have been off those pills so fast. It took three months after stopping the pill for the symptoms to subside. But some of them didn't. It was then that I noticed a cyclical pattern to it all. I noticed weepiness and moods premenstrually. Then I became pregnant with my first daughter.'' What followed was a difficult pregnancy marked by migraine, bloating, weight gain, outbursts, and ten years of classic and devastating premenstrual syndrome.

Another patient, Carmen Estes also had an immediate reaction: ''There were definite symptoms from the first month I was married and started on the birth control pill: fatigue, weight gain, and immediate vision change. I required glasses and had a sense that it wasn't so much blurring as distortion in space. I gained fifteen pounds in one month. As a teenager, I had no acne, but from the time I took the birth control pill on, my face was extremely broken out. My doctor was smart enough to say that I never should have been put on the pill. After getting off the pill, I was still in a state of imbalance.'' Later Estes had toxemia with pregnancy, severe postpartum depression, and half a dozen other premenstrual complaints.

The Hormone Reaction

Hormones are the villains of these stories. The Pill prevents pregnancy by changing the body's hormonal balance. There are two types of oral contraceptives available: the ''combined'' estrogen-progestogen pill and the progestogen-only, or mini-pill. Until recently there was a third, called the ''sequential'' pill. Sequential contraceptives involved taking estrogen only pills for the first fifteen days of the cycle, then estrogen-progestogen pills for the remaining five days. Sequentials were removed from the market because they were unreliable and became associated with an increased risk of endometrial cancer.

The combined pill, the more popular type, contains an estrogen and a progestogen analog of testosterone — a substance with progestational properties. Two types of estrogens, which are very similar, are used, one of which is more potent than the other. Many different types of progestogens are used; each have slightly different effects on the other hormones in the body. Some progestogens antagonize the effects of estrogen and lead to the unpleasant side effects of breast swelling and tenderness, weight gain, fluid retention, even acne and headaches. When the Pill was first developed in 1951 it contained only progestogen; estrogen was thought to be carcinogenic. But the pure progestogen pill resulted in spotting — bleeding between menstruation — so estrogen was added. But the pharmaceutical makers overdid it. Estrogen was added so copiously that it was later found to be five times as much as needed, up to 100 micrograms in some brands. Today the pill contains between 20 and 30 micrograms of estrogen; in rare cases it is as high as 50 micrograms. The dosage was drastically slashed to alleviate the side effects caused by the large amounts of estrogen and as a safety measure because of fears that estrogen would lead to cervical, endometrial, or ovarian cancer. Despite the fact that estrogen has not been found to cause these cancers, the drug companies are continuing to research methods of producing a pill with still less estrogen.

The brand of combined pill and the amount of estrogen needed varies with the individual. Most gynecologists prefer to start a woman on a low dosage and scale upward if needed, to lessen possible side effects. If the dosage is too low, spotting will occur because the amount of estrogen is not sufficient to support the endometrial lining of the uterus. There's also a chance that ovulation will not be suppressed and pregnancy could occur. But if the dose is too high, it is more difficult to cut down because spotting will result once the uterus — which has come to rely on more estrogen than normal to bolster the endometrium — finds that the extra support is suddenly withdrawn. High amounts of estrogen also increase the risk of stroke or heart attacks. The combined pill is sold under a spectrum of brand names including Brevicon, Demulen, Enovid, Lo/Ovral, Loestrin, Modicon, Norinyl, Norlestrin, Ortho-Novum, Ovral, Ovulen, and Zorane. These are usually taken in cycles of three weeks on and one week off, beginning typically on the fifth day of the menstrual cycle. For those who have trouble adhering to this schedule, there is a brand that can be taken every day; the one week off is represented by seven hormone-less pills.

The progestogen-only or mini-pill, sold under the brand names Micronor and Ovrette, is less reliable than the combined pill because it does not prevent ovulation. Instead, it interferes with the permeability of the cervical mucus to sperm, preventing the sperm from reaching the egg, and by disturbing the growth of the endometrium, so that implantation of a fertilized egg cannot take place. The mini-pill is recommended for women who cannot tolerate the side effects of estrogen. Also, it's taken every day so its regimen is easier to follow. Nonetheless, women on the mini-pill may notice increased, frequently heavy spotting because progestogens halt the growth of the endometrium so it is constantly sloughing off. Progestogens also alter the motility of the Fallopian tubes with the result of an increased risk of ectopic, or tubal, pregnancies.

The primary function of the combined pill is to prevent ovulation. Initially, the combined estrogen-progestogen prevents the release of FSH by the hypothalamus-pituitary. Consequently, the egg follicles are not stimulated and no egg is produced. Menstruation, however, occurs because the estrogen-progestogen pill is stimulating endometrial growth and withdrawal. When the pill is stopped for one week, the growth of the endometrium halts and it sloughs off. This bleeding is commonly referred to as a "false period," because the bleeding occurs but for the wrong reasons. The mini-pill does not interfere with the release of FSH, nor with the FSH and LH surge that produces the release of the egg from the ovary. Thus, the body remains ready for fertilization. But the mini-pill thickens the cervical mucus, which then traps the sperm and prevents fertilization. Because ovulation does occur, there is a much greater risk of getting pregnant. In addition, the mini-pill carries greater risk of ectopic, or tubal, pregnancies, and of high blood pressure and increased blood clotting.

The Pill As Protector

Since its development thirty years ago, the Pill and its users have been carefully scrutinized because the drug was feared to be factor in endometrial, cervical, and ovarian cancers. However, over the past five years, studies have shown that the Pill, especially the combined pill, actually protects women from an array of disorders, including benign breast disease, ovarian cysts, iron deficiency anemia, pelvic inflammatory disease, and tubal pregnancies, and may also reduce the risk of rheumatoid arthritis, endometrial and ovarian cancer. Dr. Howard Ory of the Center for Disease Control in Atlanta, says the Pill saves women fifty thousand hospitalizations a year for these diseases.

The persistent problems that remain with the Pill of all types are an increased risk of developing blood clotting disorders which can lead to a stroke, and a suspicion that it can cause liver disease and tumors. Estrogen causes the walls of blood veins to dilate, which decreases blood flow. It also interferes with the normal clotting mechanism by making the blood platelets stickier, so that more and larger clots appear. This increased tendency toward clots may provoke heart attacks. But recent studies have shown that fatal clots, in women who are otherwise not predisposed to them, occur in about three out of one hundred thousand women taking the Pill. This incidence is minimal when compared with pregnancy and delivery mortality rates of twenty-five per one hundred thousand women. In women over thirty-five years of age, the Pill may lead to circulatory disorders; women who smoke should not use the Pill at all since it increases their risk of circulatory and blood clotting problems to dangerous levels.

While the reduced dosages of estrogen in the Pill may ease its side effects in many women, the Pill's triggering effect on women predisposed to premenstrual syndrome remains unchanged. In fact, we're likely to see a larger PMS population because of the Pill. Its popularity as a tool to control irregular and painful menstruation led gynecologists to prescribe it for large numbers of adolescent girls, beginning in the 1960s and continuing through the present. The exposure of these girls to the Pill at a much earlier age than their mothers or older sisters means they will have been on the Pill for more years by the time they move into their twenties and thirties and decide to stop taking it and start families. This group of women, then, are at extremely high risk to develop PMS. It is a large group, representing the tail end of the postwar baby boom. We expect that increased numbers of these women will develop PMS either as a reaction to the Pill itself or later, after a subsequent pregnancy, hysterectomy, or tubal ligation. Instead of demand for PMS treatment declining as more is known about it and more physicians treat it, the demand may actually climb because the pool of women at risk will be larger.

Chapter 14

*"That she bear children is not a woman's
significance.
But that she bear herself,
That is her supreme and risky fate."*

D.H. Lawrence, **Women in Love**

Pregnancy

Pregnancy imbues many women with a serenity of sorts, a sensation of physical well-being that is undoubtedly the source of the inner radiance and knowing glow that so many mothers-to-be are said to possess. Their birth experience meshes with that described by Sandra McPherson in her poem, *Pregnancy:*

"It is the best thing.
I should always like to be pregnant..."

Most of our patients who have been pregnant say they felt well, wonderful, terrific, even euphoric then. That's not surprising, since pregnancy is probably the only time they've received the most effective therapy for premenstrual syndrome — progesterone, in large doses. During the last two trimesters of pregnancy, a woman's body produces enormous amounts of progesterone to sustain the fetus. The word progesterone means just that: pro gestation, to aid pregnancy. For the vast majority of the women we see, pregnancy was the only time in their lives that they ever felt well. (Eighty percent of our patients are mothers.) They're not alone. A study by Drs. Raymond Greene and Katharina Dalton in 1953 noted that of fifty-nine women with PMS, ninety-three percent were symptom-free during the middle and last trimester of pregnancy and sixty-two percent remarked on their improved health and increased energy.

Women with severe premenstrual syndrome whose daily lives have been disrupted for one to three weeks a month for several years often choose pregnancy over PMS. One of our patients said she and her husband had planned to have four children but ended up having eight because the only time that she was comfortable and that her relationship with her husband was positive was when she was pregnant. Luckily they could afford a large family. No one is advocating that women should be or like to be kept barefoot and pregnant; but some women in extreme pain — physical or psychological — have developed a kind of primitive self-help program, opting to be bound to a large brood rather than trapped by PMS.

Some women with PMS have a difficult time in the first trimester when progesterone levels are still relatively low, but they begin to feel fine — often better than fine — in the second and third trimesters. About thirty percent of our patients have a history of miscarriages or threatened abortion during the first trimester. Some physicians suggest that's because of a deficiency of progesterone during the luteal phase of the menstrual cycle. A luteal phase deficiency would mean that these women don't have enough progesterone in their systems to sustain pregnancy. Many gynecologists treat women with a history of miscarriages in the first trimester because of a luteal phase deficiency with progesterone during the luteal phase, 25 to 50 milligrams twice a day.

Toxemia in Pregnancy

For some women pregnancy is not a pleasant experience; it can even be life-threatening to mother and child. Instead of having a sense of well-being or euphoria, they suffer from toxemia, a condition marked by severe hypertension, swelling of the ankles, feet, hands and face, dizziness and spots in front of the eyes, and dangerously high weight gain. The condition affects a surprisingly large number of women, about ten to fifteen percent of all pregnant women, particularly those in lower income groups, teenagers, and older women undergoing their first pregnancy. Severe toxemia can lead to convulsions or stroke, may cause liver or kidney damage, and occasionally requires the abortion of the fetus to save the life of the mother. Toxemia accounts for twenty percent of all maternal deaths in this country. The cause of the disorder is unknown but because it disappears after delivery some researchers suggest that the placenta is somehow involved in the massive retention of salt and water that leads to the physical signs of this condition. About ninety-six percent of the women who suffer toxemia in pregnancy will subsequently develop PMS.

Difficult births are common for women who experience toxemia during pregnancy. Whether this has anything to do with the premenstrual syndrome, however, is problematic. We know that most women with PMS or women who later develop PMS do not endure toxemic pregnancies. Rather they may feel well or even wonderful during their pregnancies, especially during the second and third trimesters. But we know from our own practice and from reports of case histories of other physicians that some women who have been treated for PMS experienced some kind of difficulty during the delivery of their babies. Not enough data is available to determine if this is a rare, infrequent, or common occurrence. It is not surprising, however, to encounter women with PMS who have had other reproductive-related health problems.

Several of our patients who have had abortions say that PMS symptoms started after the abortion. But we haven't seen enough patients with these experiences to determine if they have the same or different patterns from women who have never conceived or women who have carried a fetus to term. And some women develop PMS after a pregnancy; these women usually find that the symptoms worsen after each subsequent pregnancy.

It is extremely rare for a women to experience premenstrual symptoms during a pregnancy, but Mary Waters, a woman treated by a colleague in a Western state, says her problems developed with her third and last pregnancy four years ago. "I started the symptoms even before I knew I was pregnant; it lasted during the first three months of the term." The symptoms disappeared and then reappeared with great intensity about six months after the delivery of the baby. Her problems have been eliminated with progesterone therapy, diet changes, and Vitamin B_6.

Multiple pregnancies and the incidence of toxemia in pregnancy sharply increase the probability that a woman will develop premenstrual syndrome.

Chapter 15

Post-Partum Depression

Like nuggets of coal meanly tucked into a child's Christmas stocking, postpartum depression is an anti-climax. After months of excited anticipation of the most awesome mystery of life, birth, the baby blues arrive as an uninvited guest. It swaddles some mothers in a draining gloom, a psychological barrier to their enjoyment of the baby. Struggling to break out of the smothering gauze, they cry and rage, their frustration rises. Matty Quest, the protagonist of Doris Lessing's novel, *A Proper Marriage,* waddled through a discomfiting pregnancy and unexpectedly painful delivery of her first child, Caroline, only to find that her state of mind grows worse not better. At one point she tells the baby: "My poor unfortunate brat, what had you done to deserve a mother like me? ... You bore me to extinction, and that's the truth of it, and no doubt I bore you... you and I are just victims, my poor child, you can't help it, I can't help it, my mother couldn't help it, and her mother..." For some women, the depression is apocalyptic, a slap in the face from God; it shatters their daily existence, leading to rejection of the baby and withdrawal from family and society. In extreme cases, it may lead to suicidal thoughts or suicide attempts.

Twenty to forty percent of our patients have experienced postpartum depression, usually for long periods of seven to twelve months. (These are separate from the thirty percent of our patients who exhibit both a current depression as well as PMS.) It apparently accelerates or exacerbates the development of premenstrual syndrome or is part of the mechanism that produces PMS. Identifying this condition is not always easy; depression is a common disorder in women and depression is a symptom of premenstrual syndrome. A true postpartum depression is just what it sounds like: a woman becomes pregnant, delivers, and develops a depression that continues for a length of time. Some physicians say any depressed state that runs for at least two weeks qualifies; others require a longer episode before they'll make the diagnosis.

As one of our patients, Fran Harris, recalls: "It's just a very strong depression. You say to yourself, 'I should be happy. I have this beautiful brand new baby.' But you're not, you're just not happy. You're always rationalizing why you feel this way. You say to yourself, 'I haven't had much sleep lately because of the baby.' But I think that most people are just trying to find a reason why they're just sitting there and crying. You get to be like a recluse. You don't want to go out." After the birth of her second child, her depression was severe. "With the baby, I stayed in the house a lot. It was beautiful then, July. There was no good reason to stay in the house, but I stayed in the house a lot. I would cry, sit in the chair and cry. I felt the depression right after the birth of the child. I remember feeling bad in the hospital. I don't think a lot of women understand it and I know a lot of husbands don't. Mine was really skeptical."

Shirley deVereaux, forty-seven, has five children, thirteen to twenty-five, and had postpartum depression "with every child. It was worse with the second and third, probably because I had them in such rapid succession. I was bogged down, and more or less on my own. At that time my mother was still having children and was sickly, and I had two of hers all the time, so I had five little ones."

Agoraphobia and Other Fears

Lee Arnold went through "a really severe postpartum depression after the birth of my daughter. I think it was longer than usual from other women I've talked to. It seems that we all develop these awful depressions. Mine was so bad that I was starting to develop a fear of going out of the house, agoraphobia. Just getting on clothes and getting the baby dressed and getting in the car and going to the store was just too much trouble to imagine. I didn't blame it on anyone, I just thought it was me. I thought that I had to get myself out of this. I did notice after about two or three months that it was cyclical. I just wanted to lie in bed and not even get up on those days before my period. I think that's how I probably kept myself from becoming very angry."

Jackie Weber, the mother of three, came close to rejecting her baby completely. After the birth of her first child, "my husband recalls how surprised he was at the hospital that I was not drawn to this new little baby. He expected this motherly instinct to flow because it always had in his mother. She has eight children. I didn't have any idea that he saw this in me. I didn't have a real interest in the baby. I wanted to breast feed but that wasn't going well. The baby cried all the time and I thought that was normal. This is what motherhood is all about. The struggle began almost immediately. I was very nervous but, because of the expectations of everyone, I pretended that I was very happy about the whole thing and faked my way through it all as it turned out. I felt desperate. I didn't care, I was not drawn to the baby. I had really wanted the baby and I was overjoyed when I found out I was pregnant, and it was a boy and we wanted a boy. But I felt no emotional commitment. I was nervous anyway and shaky. I cried a lot. The baby allowed me no sleep and because the baby was so demanding I didn't feel well. I remember inwardly feeling like my life had ended, but I did not project that on the surface." She added, "My best friend had a baby the same month and we used to go everywhere together. Her little baby never cried and she felt so well. I remember trying to be lighthearted like her. She was calm, I wasn't. Her baby slept, mine cried."

After the birth of her second child, Weber suffered from postpartum depression for two years and was treated with Tofranil. "I responded well for five days and then it didn't work anymore." After her third delivery, the postpartum depression was severe but her doctor refused to prescribe Tofranil when she asked for it because he said it was addictive. After this third birth, "I suffered three weeks out each month. I was severely depressed. I felt like I was going to die. I was so depressed, so angry. And there was no way I could hide these feelings any longer, the way I did with the first two deliveries. I would often make excuses and stay home from church meetings and social events, or I'd go late or duck out early so I wouldn't erupt. I thought I was mentally ill. I screamed at the children, felt like throwing them out a window, wanted to divorce my husband, wanted to throw things, books, anything, across the room." After seeing dozens of doctors in three different cities in which they lived, she saw a physician who diagnosed her properly as having PMS. But his treatment was to do a hysterectomy followed by monthly estrogen implants, a painful process.

Psychiatric Problems Encountered

Postpartum depression is an extremely common disorder. The psychological or physiological stress of childbirth precipitates not only postpartum depression but other psychiatric problems as well. The ancient healers, Celsus, Galen, and Soranus, all recorded cases of postpartum psychosis. An English study reported that sixty-six percent of a random sample of women who delivered at one hospital later suffered from postpartum depression at least briefly. And many studies show that women are more likely to be admitted to a psychiatric hospital after delivery than at other times in their lives. A study of seventy-one women over seventeen years with post-delivery psychiatric admissions revealed that forty percent of the cases began within a week of delivery.

Another research project involving seven women with postpartum depression evidenced the link with the premenstrual syndrome. Typically, it noted, women suffer from a relatively mild postpartum depression in the thirties or late twenties, with an average age of onset of thirty. "Emotional stress or an infective illness may have coincided with postpartum time. She appears to recover but then relapses. Then for years she suffers from recurrent phases of depression, irritability, tension, with phobias, obsessive fears, or hypochondria. The severity of her symptoms is related to the menstrual cycle, usually the premenstrual phase. Her moodiness, unpredictability, and loss of temper are reacted to by the children and the husband, the family atmosphere becomes clouded and unstable, and the family ceases to function as a unified group." It's a profile that fits many of our patients.

After Andrea Neubecker's daughter was born, she was mildly depressed, with "no drastic emotional changes. Things started to get to the point where I knew they were wrong about five years later." Then, she said, each month she experienced "times of very unusual fatigue, a slight roller coaster effect. I'd be worn out by 7 P.M., I'd be laid out on the couch. Tests showed nothing. We moved that year, and I think that the stress and the change and the move probably aggravated it. It really became disabling by 1980. Things were really getting out of control as far as crying and feeling that I couldn't keep up with things, worthlessness. Almost everything was directed at myself, inward. I don't think other than a very rare occasion when I'd let it it out on my husband. I don't think I ever acted out toward the children. It was always inward. I avoided contact with people. You're not sure of yourself so you don't want to be around other people.''

Dr. Katharina Dalton investigated postpartum depression prospectively by focusing on a group of women without PMS and following them through pregnancy and afterward. She found that of the women who experienced postpartum depression, about seventy-six percent subsequently developed PMS. Unfortunately, most of the studies in this area have not distinguished women with postpartum depression who have never had a previous depressive episode from women who have had one or many depressions prior to the pregnancy. What seems to happens is this: women with postpartum depression are depressed steadily all month-long for a period of time; then they begin to feel better; then they get worse; then better and then worse, and on and on, creating a cycle. The postpartum depression and additional symptoms, like breast swelling and tenderness, eventually become confined to the premenstrual phase, resulting in PMS.

Grace Henson fits this cycle-creation pattern. Henson, a stockbroker with four children, remembers: ''After the last pregnancy (twins) I went through a very bad baby blues, and it just didn't seem that I came out of it. Once my period started, my first period was an ovulatory period, I just hemorrhaged and was rushed back to the hospital. After that, I'd be okay for a couple of weeks and then I'd slip back into it. I'd just be crying all the time. Naturally this especially affected the children. I never got to the point of taking it out on them or being overly angry with them. I took it out more on my husband. We fought constantly. Finally it got very difficult in April. But again my case is a little different. Twin births are extremely difficult for parents, especially when you have other children. To this day, they don't sleep through the night. When you have babies up all night long, and you're not getting any sleep on top of everything else that's going on, well, I'm just glad I didn't find a cliff and jump off it. As far as relating to the family, I just felt that nobody understood me, and that I couldn't understand myself, so I started counseling about two months after the baby was born. I have kept that up because I found that it was doing a terrific amount of good.''

The cause of postpartum depression isn't known, but there are many theories. Some researchers have suggested that an imbalance between the relative levels of estrogens and progesterone in the period immediately following delivery is the trigger; others say there may be a kind of rebound effect — an overproduction of hormones — following the loss of the placenta that the body can't handle. The view espoused by Dr. Dalton is based on a feast-and-famine analogy. The hormonal swings of the menstrual cycle are infinitesimal compared with the massive increase in placental steroid hormones, including progesterone, during pregnancy and the abrupt deprivation of these hormones following delivery. This zenith/nadir effect calls for a remarkable adjustment on the part of the woman. This dramatic shift in hormone levels results in many women experiencing what's tantamount to an addict going cold turkey: feeling the euphoric glow in late pregnancy, probably caused by the huge amounts of progesterone in the bloodstream, followed by the progesterone deprivation and depths of depression.

A forty-five-year-old mother of six children, Marty Eisner, experienced the depths of postpartum depression after the birth of each child. She recalls, "When I was pregnant, it was the only time in my whole life that I really felt terrific. Now I know that this is the way normal people feel all the time."

Progesterone is not a treatment for depression but it may help postpartum depression. Interestingly, our patients who have had postpartum depression usually require more progesterone to alleviate their symptoms than women who haven't had the baby blues.

Chapter 16

/*"Chaste to her husband, frank to all beside,
A teeming mistress, but a barren bride."*

Alexander Pope, **Moral Essays**

Sterilization

After the birth of her third child, and at the suggestion of her gynecologist, thirty-six-year-old Marlene Swift underwent a sterilization procedure known as a tubal ligation. "It seemed to make a lot of sense at the time," Swift says. "My husband and I weren't planning to have any more children and my physician recommended it as a permanent, safe, easy method of birth control." Tubal ligations involve the severing of the Fallopian tubes so an egg cannot reach the uterus. Unlike its sister procedure, hysterectomy, tubal ligation usually does not affect the ovaries, halt the production of progesterone and estrogen, or stop menstruation. What Swift was soon to discover is that there are many complications from this "safe, easy" procedure that about seven hundred thousand American women undergo each year. But painful menstruation and pelvic inflammation, or heavy and prolonged bleeding are frequent results. For some women, like Marlene Swift, premenstrual syndrome is another. About twenty percent of our patients have had tubal ligations; in almost every case the procedure seemed to trigger PMS or a worsening of pre-existing PMS.

Paula Thompson had a tubal ligation one month after the youngest of her two children was born. She, like many of our patients, found an array of problems soon developed, including irritability and temper tantrums, postpartum depression, suicidal thoughts, and some minor scuffles with her husband and children. The premenstrual symptoms continued to worsen until she began progesterone treatment and lifestyle changes; now she's symptom-free.

Eileen Alpert developed premenstrual syndrome at puberty. "After my second child was born four years ago, I started constant bleeding. I was given a D&C; that didn't stop it; I was given Provera. I also had my tubes tied. Right at that particular time I noticed there was a drastic change in me. It wasn't just minor, it was a complete change. An emotional change.'' Alpert was depressed, developed cyclical insomnia, acne, food cravings, colitis, and migraine headaches. All these complaints disappeared when she began treatment for PMS.

Hysterectomy is the surgical removal of the uterus and/or the removal of the ovaries; about six hundred fifty thousand women undergo hysterectomies in this country each year. It results in sterilization but good physicians do not perform this procedure merely as a permanent method of birth control. The most common reason for hysterectomy is to excise large, usually benign, fibroid tumors of the uterus that can cause severe menstrual bleeding, lead to anemia, and potentially to ovarian cancer. Fibroid tumors can reach the size of a ten- to twelve-week-old fetus, filling the pelvic cavity; three percent of women who develop fibroids die of ovarian cancer. In women under forty-five, surgeons now leave the ovaries intact unless there's irrevocable damage, such as a malignant tumor that doesn't respond to other therapy. Removing the ovaries induces early menopause and increases the threat of degenerative bone disease and heart disease. Estrogen replacement therapy is almost always prescribed for women following a hysterectomy, which in itself is risky; the use of estrogen increases the risk of endometrial cancer three to eight times. For these reasons, if one ovary is damaged or diseased, surgeons usually leave the other one in women who are still menstruating so they won't develop postmenopausal symptoms. Healthy ovaries may be removed with the uterus if a woman is near menopause, or if there is uterine cancer because cancer of the female reproductive organ may be hormone-stimulated.

Depression May Result

Another major postoperative complication of hysterectomy is depression. A study of more than seven hundred women who had undergone hysterectomy revealed that two and a half times as many psychiatric referrals were made for women who had had hysterectomies than those who hadn't: seven percent for the hysterectomy cases vs. three percent for the control group. The incidence of divorce and marital disruption after hysterectomy was also significantly higher than for the control group. Of the patients referred to a psychiatrist after the operation, eighty-five percent were suffering from depression, and sixty-six percent had also been referred to at least one other medical specialist for complaints ranging from nervousness to exhaustion, insomnia, and depression. Twenty-eight percent were admitted to a hospital for an overdose of drugs. Some of these diagnoses may have masked incidence of premenstrual syndrome.

About ten percent of our patients have undergone hysterectomies. Women who had premenstrual symptoms prior to the hysterectomy or tubal ligations usually experience a worsening of the PMS. Despite the fact that radical hysterectomy, the removal of the uterus and ovaries, induces menopause — and many women find that premenstrual syndrome symptoms end at menopause — some women who have had their ovaries removed continue to have cyclical symptoms. For a small number of women, the problems worsen. Dr. Katharina Dalton believes this is because their ovaries are no longer producing any progesterone. A typical pattern following hysterectomy is an end to the symptoms for six months to a year followed by a recurrence of premenstrual syndrome in a more severe form. A few women who say they did not have PMS prior to a hysterectomy trace the onset of their condition to the hysterectomy. Where cyclical symptoms continue or begin after this procedure, the timing tends to follow the pattern of the prior menstrual cycle. If the cycle was twenty-eight to thirty days prior to the hysterectomy, the PMS symptoms will recur every twenty-eight to thirty days. The most common cyclical symptoms following hysterectomy are headaches, depression, dizziness, fatigue, joint and muscle pain. We don't know why PMS occurs or worsens after a radical hysterectomy but it's probably tied to the mechanism for menstruation, the hypothalamus and pituitary. Some physicians recommend hysterectomies as a therapy for premenstrual syndrome and say their experience has shown that it relieves the symptoms; some theories about PMS say this might happen if the ovaries have been secreting a substance that produces the symptoms. In some women, hysterectomy produces no change in their symptoms at all.

More research needs to be undertaken into the function and effects of progesterone and estrogen, and the disposition and impact of hysterectomies in women with different symptoms and characteristics. The possibility that the sex hormones have functions beyond that of reproduction has not been fully explored; the predominance of premenstrual syndrome, however, could be an indication that the progesterone and estrogen do have more far-reaching functions than is now thought.

SECTION V / *Life Phases*

Chapter 17

"Things she had never noticed much before began to hurt her; home lights watched from the evening sidewalks, an unknown voice from an alley. She would stare at the lights and listen to the voice, and something inside her stiffened and waited. But the lights would darken, the voice fall silent, and though she waited, that was all. She was afraid of these things that made her suddenly wonder who she was, and what she was going to be in the world, and why she was standing at that minute, seeing a light, or listening, or staring up into the sky: alone. She was afraid, and there was a queer tightness in her chest... Because she could not break this tightness gathering within her, she would hurry to do something."

Carson McCullers, **The Member of the Wedding**

Adolescence

The tumult of adolescence is like being lost in a funhouse: the distortion of reality is brief but seemingly endless at the time; what's billed as a barrel of laughs is more typically a frustrating, frightening, panic-inducing run through a maze of booby traps and trick mirrors. When you're caught in that space and time, you just want out.

Teenage girls struggling to grow into their bodies and their emotions are perhaps those who suffer most from premenstrual syndrome. In most instances neither they nor their parents are able to distinguish a medically treatable problem as complex as PMS from the accepted traumas of adolescence. Extreme and bizarre behavior in teenagers that is neither socially acceptable nor part of any well-known illness has on a few occasions been diagnosed as a psychological disorder, periodic psychosis of puberty. We think that these cases are very likely premenstrual syndrome; the fact that an entirely new psychiatric category has been developed to describe it underscores the confusion about PMS in adolescents.

The forty or so teenagers we have treated have had severe cases; in a few instances they were brought in for evaluation because their mother or another relative also has premenstrual syndrome and was familiar with its pattern. As physicians and the public become educated about PMS, identifying it early will become easier. Puberty is one of the stages of life at which a significant percentage of women first experience the symptoms of PMS. Estimates of the incidence of the syndrome in adolescents vary from twenty to thirty percent of the teenagers who visit physicians for various complaints; few of these girls have been or are likely to be properly diagnosed and treated. One pediatrician in Boston, a patient of ours, says she has observed a great number of girls with PMS in her practice; since she's undergone the evaluation process herself she's been able to diagnose them and refer them for treatment.

A Loss of Identity

The crisis of adolescence, of course, is loss of identity as "the body changes its proportions radically, when genital puberty floods body and imagination with all manner of impulses, when intimacy with the other sex approaches and is, on occasion, forced on the young person, and when the immediate future confronts one with too many conflicting possibilities and choices," as Erik Erikson writes in *Identity Youth and Crisis*.

The sense of self that a girl may have gripped so confidently in childhood — I am me, my parents' child — seems to have evaporated without warning, like perfume in an unsealed flacon. Who am I? is the $64,000 question she poses. And she needs the answer fast, for "...in the social jungle of human existence there is no feeling of being alive without a sense of identity," Erikson says. No longer a child but not yet an adult, a teenager becomes frustrated and rebellious, poised for insolence or tears depending on which hormone surges first and fullest. It's a confusing phase, as voiced by Biff, in Arthur Miller's *Death of a Salesman:* "I just can't take hold, Mom. I can't take hold of some kind of life." For an adolescent girl, PMS intensifies the already formidable problems she faces in coming to terms with her emerging maturity, sexuality, sense of self, and relationship to family, authority, and peers.

Menstruation brings with it painful episodes of cramps to many teenagers, and irregular cycles to others. Those problems by and large are diagnosed and treated without much difficulty. But the presence of any or several of the symptoms of premenstrual syndrome can be far more crippling, physically and emotionally, than dysmenorrhea. PMS can even develop in a girl before menstruation begins. It sometimes takes hold at puberty, anytime from age eight to thirteen, but usually around eleven. Menarche, or the actual menstrual flow, may occur as much as two years later. In this age group, the syndrome is often marked by frequent, recurring attacks of asthma or epilepsy, striking just prior to menstruation or at menstruation. The attacks may occur at other times, as well, but are usually more frequent or more severe prior to menstruation. Girls whose episodes are usually well controlled with drugs may require more medication or find that it is less effective just prior to their period. Many of our patients, now in their twenties and thirties, whose asthma or epilepsy began in adolescence have been able to sharply reduce or discontinue their medications once they've been treated with progesterone. Anorexia nervosa may also appear in a teenager with premenstrual syndrome.

What parents usually fail to identify are the behavioral symptoms or the cyclicality of any symptoms, physical or psychological. If an otherwise well-behaved, normal girl periodically and regularly shows a marked change in mood or reaction a few days each month for several months at home or at school or both, and then reverts to her regular behavior, she may well have a mild form of premenstrual syndrome. It's more serious if she's rebellious or has difficulty concentrating, especially if it begins to affect her schoolwork or her ability to function. Dr. Katharina Dalton studied a group of English schoolgirls and concluded that premenstrual symptoms resulted in lower grades on examinations; attempts to duplicate her results on several occasions by a researcher at the University of California at Davis, however, were unsuccessful.

The usual response of parents to this type of behavior is to write it off to adolescence; teenagers are difficult. Even when parents do notice a cyclical phenomenon, they don't know what to do about it. Most physicians with whom they raise the issue dismiss it as normal.

Naomi Rath, eighteen, noticed a personality change with her periods when she was sixteen. "I was very moody. Bitchy, I guess you would say. I felt like I was a different person and I didn't like that person very much," she said. "Finally I was having maybe four good days a month." Her mother recalls, "She always had severe, painful periods. She's got every symptom, physical and mental. She'd do and say things she wouldn't ordinarily. She was irritable and angry. She basically is very easy to get along with; she kept it under wraps for a long time. And in between, she would be her own fantastic self. But finally, it was ruining her life. She lost a job over it. This extreme exhaustion would come over her and she couldn't work. And you know, those around you, who deal with you, suffer just as much." After being diagnosed and treated for PMS, Naomi says, "I felt like one hundred pounds had been taken off my shoulders." She was especially glad of the opportunity to meet other women at the center who also had PMS. "It helped a lot in the beginning to talk to the other women," despite the fact that most of them were ten or twenty years older than she. Friends her own age, she says, hadn't been supportive. "When you talk to your girl friends, they laugh and say, 'let's lock YOU up.'"

Her mother says of her daughter, "She doesn't *have* moods anymore. It's a dramatic change. Absolutely."

As the Raths can attest, if the symptoms are severe and last several days, they disrupt relationships with parents, peers, brothers and sisters, teachers. Whether they respond with empathy, anger, or authoritarian control, the girl may begin to act out further, in open rebellion, conflicts with the law, shoplifting, or sometimes by running away or engaging in sex. Some girls, though, become solemn, secretive, and withdraw, not only from their family but also from their friends. This is particularly destructive to self-image at a critical developmental stage.

It's a classic profile, epitomized by the characterization of Frankie Addams, the protagonist of Carson McCullers' *The Member of the Wedding,* a fifteen-year-old girl struggling to deal with her approaching womanhood: "And finally the troubles started. She did things and she got herself in trouble. She broke the law. And having once become a criminal, she broke the law again, and then again. She took the pistol from her father's bureau drawer and carried it all over town and shot up the cartridges in a vacant lot. She changed into a robber and stole a three-way knife from the Sears and Roebuck Store. One Saturday afternoon she committed a secret and unknown sin. In the MacKeans' garage, with Barney MacKean, they committed a queer sin, and how bad it was she did not know. The sin made a shriveling sickness in her stomach, and she dreaded the eyes of everyone. She hated Barney and wanted to kill him. Sometimes alone in the bed at night she planned to shoot him with the pistol or throw a knife between his eyes.''

Acting Out

Many adolescents may fantasize, dream, or act out petty rebellions but take their distress no further. Other adolescents with PMS may exhibit violent behavior, suicide attempts, alcohol and drug abuse. One of our patients — let's call her Mara — is a heroin addict. Her parents noticed monthly episodes of irritability and rebelliousness in her at puberty, in contrast to her normally happy and outgoing nature. Over time she withdrew from her friends and was difficult to deal with at home and at school. The mother kept a diary about her daughter, documenting the occurrence of these events about every thirty to thirty-six days. When Mara began to menstruate her periods occurred every thirty-two to thirty-five days; for several days prior to her period she was extremely difficult and irritable. At the age of sixteen she became involved with various types of drugs, rapidly moved on to heroin and became a heroin addict until we saw her at the age of twenty-six.

Mara told us that she became addicted to heroin for many reasons, but an important factor was that it was the only substance that satisfactorily controlled her severe premenstrual symptoms, including depression and irritability, breast swelling and tenderness, fluid retention with abdominal bloating. When she began to menstruate, she struggled to cope with these symptoms two weeks out of each month. After trying to block out the pain with a variety of drugs, including alcohol, she eventually found that heroin worked. Her addiction landed her in jail on several occasions, for drunk driving and driving while under the influence of drugs; many times she berated or attempted to challenge the police, which resulted in additional charges of resisting arrest. Both mother and daughter noted that within a few days of her arrests, the mother would have to bring Tampax to the jail for her daughter.

Mara said the only time she did not crave heroin was during her two pregnancies; she felt "the best I've ever felt," in the second and third trimesters, when enormous amounts of progesterone were floating in her bloodstream, inducing a surge of beta-endorphins that mimicked the heroin high.

PMS can be a nagging source of conflict between a girl and her parents, but particularly between a girl and her mother. The erratic, but cyclical behavior patterns create a bewildering situation, ripe for hostility and misinterpretation. A girl with PMS also may have a tremendously heightened sex drive in the premenstrual phase and may act out sexually or appear to compete with the mother on a sexual level. This is true whether or not the mother has PMS or whether the mother has realized that the daughter's problem rears its head on a monthly basis. If the mother also has the symptoms of PMS, the daughter's behavior compounds her problems and strains the relationship between them. A family with an adolescent suffering from PMS may need psychotherapy or counseling to help them resolve their problems.

Chapter 18

*"The time which we have at our disposal
every day is elastic; the passions that
we feel expand it, those that we inspire
contract it; and habit fills up what
remains."*

Marcel Proust, **Remembrance of Things Past**

The Twenties and Thirties

Time is what there's never enough of in our busy lives, but its constraints may be most bridling to those in their twenties and thirties.

The twenties is a decade of experimentation and experience, the period in which we emerge from our school years and ties to parents, ready to test our wings and shoot for the moon. But it's also a comforting stretch of time in which we are still allowed to make mistakes — in our personal lives or in our occupations — without placing our entire future in jeopardy. The twenties, in fact, is a luxurious span that can spell playtime for those of us who have trouble facing adulthood. And for the ambitious, it's a fertile period for out-achieving colleagues and slipping onto the fast track.

For women committed to a fast-track career course, this is a time of immersion in work and learning from mentors. While the work can be demanding and difficult, neophytes usually don't have to bear the brunt of responsibility for major projects or deals because they're still in training. Thus, there's some freedom and probably time to frolic on occasion.

For women who marry early or are settled into a solid relationship, this the early nesting time — a lot like playing house for some.

For those who choose to start families immediately, this may be a harried but enjoyable time as they grow into their new roles and adapt to the presence of children in their lives.

The clock is no longer a friend as we wind up our twenty-ninth year. Just a turn of the calendar page away is the thirties — the "deadline decade," as Gail Sheehy tells us in *Passages,* a time to climb the job ladder, settle down, raise a family, write that novel, star in a movie, seize center stage of Carnegie Hall or center field of Yankee Stadium, indulge whims and fantasies, accomplish all the dreams we've treasured from childhood — before it's too late, before we tumble headlong into an abyss marked "middle age " as helplessly as Alice cascaded through the rabbit hole. The greatest pressures and highest expectations emerge in our thirties, radiating from all sources — self, mate, children, employer, friends, and community.

For women focusing singlemindedly on a career, the thirties are the critical years for advancement.

For women in a marriage or serious relationship, it's a period requiring substantial attention to their mate.

For women who have young children, this is a nurturing phase when hours must be devoted to the hugging, loving, story-telling, teaching, feeding, washing, tending chores of little ones.

Superwoman's Dilemma

For the superwomen, doing it all simultaneously, the competing demands seem never to stop: mate, children, household, job. Oh, yes, and self. Finding time to read a book or soak in a hot tub is either impossible or the minutes are stolen away from essentials, like doing the laundry or answering a week's worth of mail.

The clock ticks on, a monotonous pressure building up second by second like steam rising in a cast-iron boiler on an icy morning. We become fixated by time as surely as the White Rabbit worried over his pocket watch. The experience is not unique to modern society. Thomas Hardy sounded the theme in *Jude the Obscure:* "As you got older, and felt yourself to be at the center of your time, and not at a point in its circumference as you felt when you were little, you were seized with a sort of shuddering."

 What if we can't accomplish it all? What if we face the bathroom mirror one day and look into the eyes of a thirty-five-year-old unhappy in love, unhappy in work, unhappy in the rat race, burnt-out, anxious, and insecure? Even Ralph Waldo Emerson knew that feeling, noting in his *Journals* that "after thirty, a man wakes up sad every morning, excepting perhaps five or six, until the day of his death." The pressures are undeniably real. But most are unrealistic or unnecessary. What begins to happen in the thirties is that the successful adapters approach the pressures in their lives like a cardplayer dealing a game of solitaire: match up the sequences that lead to a winning run and discard the ones that don't. We have to distinguish the pressures that are important and deserve a response from the ones that are unnecessary baggage. The latter are best jettisoned immediately if we're to reach our destination. For many, even the destination has been changed. When we hit the thirties, if we haven't made it past the audition, we have to reassess our goals. The goal should be a happy and fulfilling life. That's not a brass ring restricted to the best and the brightest. We can all find some joy and enjoyment if we're willing to accept our lives. Be good at what you do and be happy with your friends and family. Accept life for what it is, stop demanding the impossible. More importantly, let others know they can't demand the impossible from you.

For women who bear the added burden of premenstrual syndrome, the pressures mount and multiply tenfold because they are dealing with a chronic illness as well as dozens of conflicting demands. Few women in their twenties have severe cases of PMS — they probably haven't encountered as many of the incidents that magnify the risk and intensity of the disorder as women ten or fifteen years older. Many women in this age group who develop PMS may have mild or moderate conditions that can be alleviated by a change in diet, exercise, reduction of stress, and so on.

Highest Risk Group

Women in their thirties constitute the highest risk group for premenstrual syndrome simply because they have probably encountered more of the incidents that are known to contribute to PMS: they are more likely to have been on the birth control pill at some point, to have been pregnant or miscarried, to have had an abortion or tubal ligation or hysterectomy. Those that actually have PMS must decide how to deal with the pressures of job, home, and family. Pressure creates stress, and stress makes any illness worse because it strains the body's flight or fight response and immune system. Those with mild and moderate cases of PMS, which appear one to four days a month, may find that they can fulfill their commitments and juggle all demands merely by making lifestyle changes in diet and exercise and by learning how to relax. They might be able to schedule difficult duties or delicate projects into their symptom-free days. But women with severe PMS have a much more difficult time coping. For them, PMS is a chronic, almost crippling condition that affects one to three weeks of their life each month.

The career woman who is strongly affected by premenstrual syndrome is usually in her late twenties or early thirties. That is a crucial time for job development, the period in which one can make or break a reputation and win promotions. A working woman, whether married or single, is less willing to put up with the symptoms than a woman who doesn't work because she cannot afford to lose time to an illness. The careerist usually is much quicker to seek therapy; she usually searches out treatment before she reaches forty.

Women who are married, whether or not they work outside the home, have added pressures as well as added support systems because of the relationship. By the time a woman is in her thirties she may have been married for five or more years. That's a critical period in which many marriages run into problems requiring time and attention. Women without children are usually involved in a career and face the double load of marital and job pressures. Those who are mothers without jobs probably have young children, who have enormous needs for parental attention and love. The woman with one or two children who develops PMS after pregnancy is in for an especially difficult time. She'll become less joyous around the infant in the face of PMS and the difficulties she faces in meeting all of her responsibilities. Everyone depends on her and she feels that she can't let them down. The wife and mother who doesn't work outside the home, however, can sometimes tolerate PMS longer because she has more supports. She may not seek treatment as aggressively as a woman who works because, unconstrained by office deadlines, she recovers from her symptom days, and like a whirlwind accomplishes everything she left undone as well as the future jobs. Husband and children, even other relatives and friends, may pitch in and help out when she's ill or bedridden. She may develop a convenient amnesia that lets her forget during her good days how painful the symptom days were. As a result, it may take months or years to face up to the fact of recurring illness. The woman who is a wife and mother and maintains a job outside the home has to have a highly refined coping mechanism to manage it all. And many women do; many of them are our patients.

The range of reactions women have to their symptoms is as broad as their personality types. Those who have strong, supportive relationships and seek treatment tend to be able to follow the lifestyle changes and progesterone therapy plans and recover with alacrity. Those without a good support system and with lots of stress in their daily routine — due to marital problems, divorce, separation, or the single life — usually have a lowered tolerance for stress that interferes with their concentration, willpower and discipline. This makes it difficult or impossible for them to follow the diet and other lifestyle changes. Women with PMS need support and help as they approach their treatment: the love and understanding of mate and family, a compassionate and caring personal physician, the motivation and opportunity of a job, profession or school to further their development in this phase of life.

Chapter 19

The Forties

The middle passage of a journey may turn out to be as comfortingly calm as a cup of cocoa sipped by a fire, or mined with as many hazards as the desert sands of El Alamein. The middle years of life's trek bear the same double-edge. A certain confidence acquired along with the bruises of arduous travel is worn by women in their forties, at last settled into careers and personal relationships. After a few digressions of lifestyle, jobs, or mates, they finally know where they're headed. As Jung wrote of life's midpoint, "... we have achieved a real independence and with it, to be sure, a certain isolation. In a sense we are alone, for our 'inner freedom' means that a love relation can no longer fetter us; the other sex has lost its magic power over us, for we have come to know its essential traits in the depths of our own psyche. We shall not easily 'fall in love,' for we can no longer lose ourselves in someone else, but we shall be capable of a deeper love, a conscious devotion to the other." He concludes: "To be sure, it takes half a lifetime to arrive at this stage." Many women can vouch for the fact that it wasn't easy to get there. But having made their peace with the past, they fashion vital, albeit very different, lives.

Beth Davis, forty-six, and her husband, Dennis, the parents of six, have lived with PMS since their marriage began twenty-seven years ago. Davis was referred for treatment to us almost two years ago by a gynecologist who had read about premenstrual syndrome and thought her condition fit the criteria. Since she began responding to the progesterone and lifestyle program, Davis has started a small boutique in her community and joined in a range of social activities that she hadn't been well enough to enjoy in her twenties and thirties. "There's so much to do now, and I'm going to do it all. Dennis and I are having a wonderful time together, sharing our fun times and sharing our work. And our youngest daughter is having a much easier, less tense childhood than her older brothers and sisters had. Life does begin at forty — well, in my case, it was forty-four."

Approaching Menopause

The forties are an emotionally-loaded decade for many women because the decade marks the approach to menopause, the end of their reproductive years. The *angst* many women express over reaching the forties is not simply regret or dismay over the loss of youth but a virulent passion stemming from what some perceive to be an outrage unjustly handed down from Olympus, the threatened theft of their sexuality. The sensitivity of women to age is a cliche that has fed a thousand quips over the years. Perhaps the best of the worst is that of Ambrose Bierce who observed: "You are not permitted to kill a woman who has wronged you, but nothing forbids you to reflect that she is growing older every minute. You are avenged 1440 times a day." Cliches are born of reality, like it or not. That's really what the sensitivity of women to age is all about. It's not the years themselves that count so much, it's the significance of the aging process for women. Men remain capable of siring children until they are senile; women are deprived of their generative powers at an early age because nature deemed that their bodies wouldn't be able to support a fetus to term in the later years. Some women still fear the approach of the forties: as if a woman who is sensual and desirable woman at thirty-nine is somehow transformed a year or two or three or five later into a dried-up crone. The fears are ridiculous, but their presence cannot be ignored. Women in their fifth decade have developed strengths of emotion, mind, and character that enhance their desirability, rather than detract from it. For women with premenstrual syndrome, the forties is a time in which the extremes of their symptoms may lessen naturally, for physiological and social reasons. Women of this age may find the pressures on them from family and job easing: their children are probably older, in their teens or twenties, requiring less minute-to-minute supervision and making fewer demands for attention. These women are likely to be further along in their careers than a woman in her thirties, or alternatively, to be resuming a career now that the children are more independent. In either instance, they are unlikely to be precisely at that make-or-break stage, scrambling for promotions and projects as validation of their worth. Children and jobs are two great pressures on women in their thirties that make PMS intolerable. These two stresses are usually absent or minor in the lives of women in their forties. Even the anathema of approaching menopause has proved to be a saving grace. Slowly but surely the secretion of estrogen by the ovaries diminishes in the forties, accompanied by a diminishing of the symptoms associated with estrogen: abdominal bloating, headaches, migraine, epilepsy, fluid retention, and cyclic emotional disturbances.

For most women with premenstrual syndrome, even untreated, the forties is usually the beginning of the end. The worst is over in terms of severity and duration of symptoms, and for most women PMS will end with menopause.

Chapter 20

*"The process of maturing is an art to be
learned, an effort to be sustained. By
the age of fifty you have made yourself
what you are, and if it is good, it is
better than your youth."*

Marya Mannes, **More in Anger**

Menopause and
Post-Menopause

Reminders of mortality, like dunning notices from creditors, provoke
reactions as predictable as the plot of a Gothic romance: dread, fear,
avoidance, depression, or reluctant confrontation. For women, the start
of menopause signals a harsh reality: fertility is drawing to an end, the
autumn of life is at hand, what Anne Sexton called the "November of
the body." The shock is at least partly absorbed by the length of the
process; menopause spans three to seven years for many women. It's a
shock nonetheless. Doris Lessing's heroine of *The Summer Before the
Dark*, Kate Brown, a middle-aged wife and mother who reclaims her
independence and vitality one summer before her own autumn begins,
considered the situation thus: "Growing old is a matter of years. You
are young, and then you are middle-aged, but it is hard to tell the
moment of passage from one state to the next." She came to this
moment wearily, after some trying and irritating incidents with her
casually philandering husband and four college-age children. When she
reacted to the hostility and aloofness of her children by defiantly
adopting a stray cat and lavishing attention upon it, Lessing writes:
"Just the thing for the menopause,' she had heard Tim say to Eileen.
She had not started the menopause, but it would have been no use saying
so: it had been useful apparently, for the family's mythology, to have a
mother in the menopause."

The physical signs start in the forties, a time when some men that age are still dating twenty-year-olds. The menstrual cycles gradually decrease in length. At fifteen, the average cycle is thirty-five days; at twenty-five, it is thirty days; at thirty-five, twenty-eight days. Between forty and fifty, the cycle often shortens to twenty-one days. Then some cycles are missed, some are shorter, some are longer. The extreme irregularity of the cycles is confusing and frustrating to some women; usually the cycles have a clear-cut beginning but an uncertain end. Ovulation may still occur, but with diminishing frequency as estrogen levels ebb to a point where egg follicles are no longer stimulated. Slowly the transition from normal menstruation to permanent amenorrhea is completed: no longer is the month heralded with a flow of blood. Most women with PMS find their symptoms end at or after menopause, but despite the label "premenstrual syndrome," a small percentage of women who reach menopause or are post-menopausal do exhibit the cyclical and recurring symptoms. About ten percent of our patients have been through menopause but exhibit symptoms in a pattern that matches their earlier menstrual cycles. Our oldest patient was fifty-eight when she came to our office for treatment; she had been through menopause five or six years earlier but still had severe PMS. She was successfully treated with progesterone.

Delaying Menopause

Menopause used to occur around age forty, but women now are more likely to experience it at fifty or fifty-one. Women's longer reproductive life, with earlier puberty and menarche and delayed menopause, has evolved with improvements in nutrition and health care. In the 19th Century, menopause struck early. Elizabeth Barrett Browning, then a thirty-nine-year-old spinster, lamented her age and alluded to the rapid approach of menopause in the Sonnets from the Portuguese, in phrases like "colors fading," and an analogy to herself, a "casement broken in,/The bats and owlets builders in the roof!" Despite her gloomy outlook she conceived five times during her subsequent marriage to Robert Browning, producing a son amid four miscarriages.

Reproach does not emanate only from the women themselves. Throughout literature, women in the middle years are reviled or worse for their declining fertility. Autumn's approach is again a theme in

William Faulkner's *A Light in August,* where Joanna Burden is anxious over her waning reproductive years. When she thinks she is pregnant she happily tells her lover, Joe Christmas. But when it turns out to have been a false alarm, he strikes her, saying: "There is not anything the matter with you except being old. You just got old and it (menopause) happened to you and now you are not any good any more."

The obsession with fertility and making babies is primeval; two Biblical "miracles" are the reversals of the barrenness of Sarah, the wife of Abraham, and Elizabeth, the cousin of Mary and wife of Zacharias.

The depression, irritability, lowered self-esteem, crying spells, and flaring tempers that frequently accompany the onset of menopause have long been thought to be due to psychological factors — the primordial concern about fertility and the natural reaction to its end — rather than to endocrine changes. Women with PMS, though, may exhibit these symptoms cyclically because of their illness. Estrogen therapy may alleviate some of the psychological problems associated with menopause, but may exacerbate the symptoms of premenstrual syndrome.

Menopause is the grand finale of a gradual process of reproductive burn-out. By the age of fifty, most women have become too old to reproduce and sustain life. The body's store of follicles — which numbered two million at birth and about three hundred thousand at puberty — has simply been depleted. (Most of the follicles die; only about five hundred ever mature into eggs.) The irregular bleeding is the result of stimulation of the remaining follicles, which in turn secrete estrogen. As estrogen levels drop, the remaining follicles increasingly fail to muster the strength to reach ovulation. Without ovulation there's no corpus luteum, no secretion of estrogen and progesterone, no noticeable growth of the endometrium, and no bleeding. The decrease in estrogen takes a toll on the organs that had been nurtured by that hormone. The female reproductive organs wither. Without estrogen the vagina may begin to atrophy and excrete a brownish discharge as its capillaries break down and rupture. The secretion of mucus also dwindles. The uterus begins to shrink because the endometrium is no longer being stimulated by the follicles.

The immediate physiological signs of menopause are hot flashes, which are somehow linked to the loss of estrogen; hot flashes are alleviated by estrogen therapy. The flashes may last only a second or as long as ten minutes; they can be frequent, unsettling, manifested by a sudden sensation of heat or burning, followed by intense perspiration. Usually the flash begins with the sensation of a mild headache or cranial pressure. This quickly mounts to a burning, hot spell that spreads through the upper body with a resulting red flush. Often the flash will permeate the entire body in short, quick waves and the woman's temperature will rise for a moment until the sweating appears, restoring the temperature to normal. Hot flashes may also trigger fatigue, weakness, and dizziness. The mechanism causing the flashes is still unknown.

Estrogen Deficiency and Impact

The most serious health hazard of menopause is osteoporosis, a skeletal disorder where the bones begin to lose mass and strength, becoming brittle and easily broken. This is why the body shrinks with age. Osteoporosis is more common in women than in men; ovarian malfunction is one factor, but the cause of this degenerative disorder remains unknown. Everyone loses bone strength with age, partly due to loss of calcium. But an estrogen deficiency compounds the problem. Short-term estrogen therapy seems to halt the process of bone degeneration and calcium loss. Osteoporosis is a major reason that estrogen therapy is used in postmenopausal women. The risk of heart attacks also increases in women after they reach menopause apparently because estrogen is no longer secreted by the ovaries. But estrogen therapy also carries hazards. One is the increased risk of development of endometrial cancer; another is the elevation of blood pressure which can lead to hypertension. The side effects of estrogen are intolerable for some women: increased vaginal bleeding, breast swelling and tenderness, fluid retention, abdominal bleeding, migraine headaches. Decreasing the estrogen dosage or switching to an estrogen-progestogen program usually eliminates the side effects.

Normal menopausal symptoms — hot flashes, osteoporosis, vaginitis, and the like — are not cyclical. This is how menopausal symptoms can be distinguish from PMS. Some women suffer worse PMS symptoms in the pre-menopause years. We have also seen a few women whose PMS begins at menopause. It usually becomes clear that they had mild PMS prior to menopause, became worse with menopause and worsened afterward. But some really do suffer the onset at menopause. The symptoms tend to be irritability, vague muscle and joint aches, fatigue, lack of concentration, and sometimes excessive use of alcohol. Some doctors who diagnose PMS at this stage treat the menopause in a cycle of progesterone and estrogen (not just one or the other) and think this is the most effective treatment.

SECTION VI

The PMS
Prescription

Chapter 21

Do You Have PMS?

Premenstrual syndrome is a clinical diagnosis based upon a patient's history; there is no laboratory test that can be done to identify it conclusively. Critics often cite this lack of a biological marker for PMS in their attempts to discredit or downplay it. But these critics, many of them physicians, conveniently ignore the fact that a multitude of "recognized" medical and psychiatric disorders, including depression, are diagnosed from characteristic physical signs, symptoms, and history rather than from lab tests or x-rays. Eventually, with diligent and systematic research, a biological marker may be identified with PMS. So far, though, no research group has taken this issue seriously.

As we have previously explained, the predominance of women experience premenstrual syndrome to some degree. But not all women have it. And most women have only mild cases that do not require medical treatment. Ninety percent of all women who visit our office meet the criteria for a diagnosis of premenstrual syndrome. This is hardly surprising since the women who seek us out are self-selected. Most of them have extensive medical problems of many years' duration, and have been examined and treated by other physicians for their complaints. Only a handful have been accurately diagnosed as having premenstrual syndrome. Many are referred by physicians, either because they are unsure of the diagnosis or have diagnosed it but do not know how to adequately treat PMS. On occasion employers send their employees to us for screening. In the past two years, we have evaluated more than two thousand women from fifty states and half a dozen foreign countries.

About thirty percent of our patients have disorders in addition to PMS, including significant depression, that either have gone undiagnosed or have been misdiagnosed. That's why we carry out a complete physical examination and battery of laboratory and psychological tests on each patient. Some physicians think that these tests aren't necessary. But we think they're extremely telling. Our patients have severe symptoms. Their lives have been disrupted. Virtually all of them have been evaluated previously by other physicians, most by several physicians and several specialists; they usually have had several medications prescribed for them, which have proved ineffective. It is a group that is at high risk for other disorders. We have a responsibility to be cautious, to identify other disorders that may be mimicking PMS, or that should be treated in conjunction with the PMS. One of the caveats of the medical profession is"First, do no harm." This means the physician owes the patient an accurate diagnosis. Our evaluation is tailored to a precise evaluation, physically as well as emotionally. We try to make certain that the patient is treated, or referred for treatment, for all diagnosed disorders, not just PMS.

The most common secondary conditions we observe in our patients are endocrine disorders related to reproduction, including breast and mammary gland conditions, uterine and ovarian disorders, endometriosis, and pelvic inflammatory disease. We've also discovered cases of diabetes, thyroid disease, including thyroid nodules, and allergies. A number of our patients have extensive histories of allergies that haven't been appropriately evaluated or treated. The predominance of thyroid cases and allergies is unusual for the size of the population we've seen; research must be done to explore the possible connection between PMS and these maladies. Other common conditions accompanying PMS are significant clinical depressions, major affective disorders, and atypical depressions, requiring psychotherapy or medication.

Charting Your Symptoms

If you suspect that you may have premenstrual syndrome, the basic monitoring routine to follow requires tracking your physical, psychological, emotional, and behavioral symptoms daily over a two- to three-month period, and maintaining daily weight and temperature records.

For at least one complete menstrual cycle, we recommend that each morning upon arising you take your temperature with a basal (morning) rectal thermometer. A regular fever thermometer is not as accurate as the basal type and won't be as precise. Basal thermometers can be purchased at most pharmacies. The temperature record can be a useful tool in identifying the various stages of the menstrual cycle and can indicate whether ovulation has occurred. Many women tell us that keeping a temperature chart helps them understand their menstrual cycle and correlate their symptoms to it.

Next, you should empty your bladder and weigh yourself without clothes, recording your weight on the chart provided. This record will show whether you are retaining fluids. Symptoms such as abdominal bloating, breast swelling and tenderness, puffiness of the fingers, hands, ankles or around the eyes, backache, sinusitis, and headaches have been attributed to the retention of fluid. Our findings coincide with those of other researchers who report that only about thirty percent of the women who have these symptoms actually retain fluids. Research studies show that many women with PMS do not retain fluids; rather they undergo a redistribution of fluids already in their body during the premenstrual phase.

The symptom check list that follows should be filled out at approximately the same time each day. The list includes the most common complaints and symptoms of women with PMS. In addition we've included the signs of dysmenorrhea and other unrelated complaints, as part of our total monitoring program.

We ask our patients to have someone who lives with them or sees them every day independently to keep track of their observations of the patient's behavior and symptoms as a kind of double-check for accuracy.

We ask patients visiting our office for the first time to bring along the charts — of temperature, weight, and symptom check lists. By the time our patients arrive at the center, they have been keeping these records for one to six weeks. We will not make a diagnosis of PMS until two months of charts, or two complete menstrual cycles, have been maintained and reviewed by us.

During the first visit, which lasts four to six hours, we take extensive histories: a medical history to discern past illnesses, treatments, surgery, medications, and allergic reactions, a psychosocial history of the key events and stresses of the patient's life and her reactions to them, and a lifestyle history of diet and nutritional patterns, exercise, smoking, alcohol consumption, and drug use.

Then the patient is examined by a physician who reviews all this data, asks further questions, and reviews the body systems. Then a complete physical examination is carried out, including a pelvic examination and

DAILY WEIGHT CHART

DATES:

STARTING WT.
_____ LBS.

EACH BLOCK
REPRESENTS
ONE POUND

MENSTRUAL CYCLE SYMPTOM SCALE

	Absent	Barely Noticeable	Mild	Moderate	Strong	Severe	Incapacitating
1. Irritability	0	1	2	3	4	5	6
2. Leg Heaviness	0	1	2	3	4	5	6
3. Backache	0	1	2	3	4	5	6
4. Accidents	0	1	2	3	4	5	6
5. Diarrhea	0	1	2	3	4	5	6
6. Fatigue	0	1	2	3	4	5	6
7. Cramps (uterine or pelvic)	0	1	2	3	4	5	6
8. Affectionate	0	1	2	3	4	5	6
9. Abdominal Bloating or Swelling	0	1	2	3	4	5	6
10. Vaginal Discharge, watery	0	1	2	3	4	5	6
11. Vaginal Discharge, thick	0	1	2	3	4	5	6
12. Eye Pain	0	1	2	3	4	5	6
13. Difficulty Concentrating	Y	5	6	7	8	9	0
14. Increased Energy	0	1	2	3	4	5	6
15. Insomnia	0	1	2	3	4	5	6
16. Hives (rashes)	0	1	2	3	4	5	6
17. Clumsiness or Incoordination	0	1	2	3	4	5	6
18. Sore Throat	0	1	2	3	4	5	6
19. Tingling in Hands	0	1	2	3	4	5	6
20. Acne-like Eruptions	0	1	2	3	4	5	6
21. Poor Judgment	0	1	2	3	4	5	6
22. Orderliness	0	1	2	3	4	5	6
23. Panic Attack	0	1	2	3	4	5	6
24. Sharp One-Sided Ovarian Pain	0	1	2	3	4	5	6
25. Asthma Attack	0	1	2	3	4	5	6
26. Cravings for Sweet Foods	0	1	2	3	4	5	6
27. Headaches (Migraine)	0	1	2	3	4	5	6
28. Headaches (Tension)	0	1	2	3	4	5	6
29. Increased Arguments	0	1	2	3	4	5	6

	Absent	Barely Noticeable	Mild	Moderate	Strong	Severe	Incapacitating
30. Nausea and/or Vomiting	0	1	2	3	4	5	6
31. Breast Swelling	0	1	2	3	4	5	6
32. Vaginal Spotting	0	1	2	3	4	5	6
33. Menstrual Flow	0	1	2	3	4	5	6
34. Loneliness	0	1	2	3	4	5	6
35. Muscle Stiffness	0	1	2	3	4	5	6
36. Dull Abdominal Aching	0	1	2	3	4	5	6
37. Decreased Hearing Ability	0	1	2	3	4	5	6
38. Difficulty Using Contact Lens	0	1	2	3	4	5	6
39. Fear of Losing Control	0	1	2	3	4	5	6
40. Sinusitis	0	1	2	3	4	5	6
41. Craving for Salty Foods	0	1	2	3	4	5	6
42. Increased Sex Drive	0	1	2	3	4	5	6
43. Decreased Work/School Performance	0	1	2	3	4	5	6
44. Increased Need to Sleep	0	1	2	3	4	5	6
45. Feelings of Suffocation	0	1	2	3	4	5	6
46. Excitement	0	1	2	3	4	5	6
47. Conjunctivitis (itchy red eye)	0	1	2	3	4	5	6
48. Weight Gain	0	1	2	3	4	5	6
49. Forgetfulness	0	1	2	3	4	5	6
50. Leg Cramps or Tenderness	0	1	2	3	4	5	6
51. Decreased Sex Drive	0	1	2	3	4	5	6
52. Stay Home From Work/School	0	1	2	3	4	5	6
53. Painful or Tender Breasts	0	1	2	3	4	5	6
54. Cold Sweats							
55. Inefficiency	0	1	2	3	4	5	6

	Absent	Barely Noticeable	Mild	Moderate	Strong	Severe	Incapacitating
56. Depression (sad or blue)	0	1	2	3	4	5	6
57. Runny Nose (rhinorrhea)	0	1	2	3	4	5	6
58. Ankle Swelling	0	1	2	3	4	5	6
59. Sores in Mouth	0	1	2	3	4	5	6
60. Decreased Alcohol Tolerance	0	1	2	3	4	5	6
61. Constipation	0	1	2	3	4	5	6
62. Suspiciousness/Paranoid	0	1	2	3	4	5	6
63. Anger	0	1	2	3	4	5	6
64. Crying Spells	0	1	2	3	4	5	6
65. Heart Pounding	0	1	2	3	4	5	6
66. Finger Swelling	0	1	2	3	4	5	6
67. Mood Swings	0	1	2	3	4	5	6
68. Chest Pains	0	1	2	3	4	5	6
69. Hot Flashes	0	1	2	3	4	5	6
70. Numbness and Tingling in Feet	0	1	2	3	4	5	6
71. Confusion	0	1	2	3	4	5	6
72. Burst of Activity	0	1	2	3	4	5	6
73. Distractable	0	1	2	3	4	5	6
74. Increased Alcohol Consumption	0	1	2	3	4	5	6
75. Joint Pains	0	1	2	3	4	5	6
76. Seizures	0	1	2	3	4	5	6
77. Increased Need for Religion	0	1	2	3	4	5	6
78. Anxiety	0	1	2	3	4	5	6
79. Increased Thirst	0	1	2	3	4	5	6
80. Dizziness or Faintness	0	1	2	3	4	5	6
81. Avoid Social Activities	0	1	2	3	4	5	6
82. Restlessness	0	1	2	3	4	5	6
83. Ringing in Ears	0	1	2	3	4	5	6

	Absent	Barely Noticeable	Mild	Moderate	Strong	Severe	Incapacitating
84. General Aches & Pains	0	1	2	3	4	5	6
85. Tenseness	0	1	2	3	4	5	6
86. Vaginal Itching	0	1	2	3	4	5	6
87. Facial Swelling	0	1	2	3	4	5	6
88. Aggressiveness							
89. Hit Someone or Something	0	1	2	3	4	5	6
90. Indecision	0	1	2	3	4	5	6
91. Decreased Appetite	0	1	2	3	4	5	6
92. Blind Spots, Fuzzy Vision	0	1	2	3	4	5	6
93. Bladder Infection	0	1	2	3	4	5	6
94. Sensitivity to Light	0	1	2	3	4	5	6
95. Increased Sensitivity to Noise	0	1	2	3	4	5	6
96. Stye	0	1	2	3	4	5	6
97. Increased Frequency of Urination	0	1	2	3	4	5	6
98. Decreased Frequency of Urination	0	1	2	3	4	5	6
99. Bruising	0	1	2	3	4	5	6
100. Sense of Well Being	0	1	2	3	4	5	6
101. (Other) _____	0	1	2	3	4	5	6

Number of Suppositories Used Today _____

Morning Weight _____

Pap smear. Appropriate laboratory tests are then ordered, including a complete blood count, urinalysis, a chemical profile in which various biochemical factors in the body are screened, a fasting blood-sugar level, and a two-hour postprandial blood-sugar test for diabetes. We also measure thyroid function and production of various hormones, including prolactin, follicle-stimulating hormone, luteinizing hormone, progesterone, and estradiol, the major estrogen. Taking these measurements and considering the day of the patient's cycle and her basal temperature, we can make a fair assessment as to the efficiency of the hypothalamic-pituitary-ovarian axis.

The lab studies are not used to diagnose PMS, but to rule out other disorders.

Later we ask the patient to undergo a battery of psychological tests, including the Minnesota Multi-Phasic Personality Inventory, the Beck Depression Inventory, the Bender-Gestalt, Symptom Check List 90-R, or Cornell Medical Index, and an alcohol-use assessment inventory. A psychologist reviews the findings and prepares a profile of each patient, which adds another dimension to the evaluation. It's also a good screening method to rule out patients who have significant psychological problems, assess depth of depression, and identify organic factors that might affect emotional or mental functioning.

We also hold an informational and question-and-answer session of thirty minutes to an hour discussing the history and impact of PMS, lifestyle changes, alternative treatments, and progesterone therapy.

Family Support

At the initial visit, we bring together groups of six to twelve patients and encourage them to bring a relative or friend with them. Most do. This is important because it provides us with an additional source of information about the patient and confirms or expands what we can find out about the course of their illness and their lifestyle. For the relative, husband, or friend, it's an important means of including them in the evaluation and treatment of a condition that has probably intruded into their lives as well. They also find it reassuring to hear the experiences of other women and their families. Relatives frequently want to make certain that the "real story is told," that the extent of the problems for the woman as well as the family is made clear to us. This session is usually the first time these women have found others who understand exactly what they're talking about. Many friendships are made on the first visit that endure over many months and thousands of miles.

One husband from the Southwest told me that he had known in advance how much our evaluation would cost in terms of airfare, hotel, the clinical evaluation and laboratory studies, but he hadn't anticipated bills for long-distance telephone calls. His wife and many of the women she had met at our office, most of whom lived in different parts of the country, were operating an informal support network via telephone.

Following Up

Our patients are asked to maintain the daily records until they return for a second visit, which is scheduled anywhere from two to ten weeks later to ensure that charts for at least two complete menstrual cycles are completed. We insist on at least two complete cycles of charting before making the diagnosis of PMS. This is required to document any case of PMS; it is a belief that is shared by Dr. Katharina Dalton who has been evaluating and treating women with PMS for thirty years.

Usually the patient and our staff will be in contact with each other during this interval once or twice to assess how the patient is doing and answer questions about PMS or the charts. When the patient returns, she often again brings a relative or friend.

During the second visit, the patient meets briefly with a staff member to review the data she has brought, and to review their experiences during the interval since the first visit. Then she is seen by a physician. The physician integrates all the data, reviewing the history, the physical findings, lab data, psychological tests, chart material and such, discusses this with the patient and relative and then makes a diagnosis. We then recommend various ways that the patient may be treated for PMS, in light of individual needs and desires and the needs and desires of the family. Then a treatment program is mapped out, which may include lifestyle changes, nutritional supplementation, counseling, treatment with progesterone, or a combination of these.

Women with other medical disorders are referred for further specialty consultation or psychotherapy or counseling. Nutritional counseling, either in a group situation or individually, may also be required. Perhaps most importantly, we urge all our patients to join a PMS support group for reassurance and bolstering of their attitude and commitment to overcoming PMS.

For many women, maintaining a simple menstrual calendar is helpful, whether in addition to or instead of the detailed menstrual cycle symptom scale included earlier in this chapter. The menstrual calendar that appears here should be maintained daily for at least three months to determine if the pattern of your symptoms fits the diagnosis of premenstrual syndrome.

On each day of your menstrual flow, mark the letter M in the block corresponding to the date of the month. Each day that you experience mild symptoms, whether physical or psychological, pencil in a small x. On days that the symptoms are serious, pencil in a large X. If your symptoms recur in the same pattern, prior to the onset of menstruation, and followed by a symptom-free week, you may have premenstrual syndrome.

Making an accurate diagnosis of PMS is the first step toward eliminating the symptoms. The next step is the patient's. She must make a serious commitment to follow the course of treatment recommended by her physician. Chronic disorders, including premenstrual syndrome, can only be resolved when patients are committed to following a regular and diligent regimen. The commitment must be complete, but women with PMS must realize that they should approach their treatment program one day at a time. Slow but steady progress is the only way to deal with PMS.

MENSTRUAL CALENDAR

Name _____ Year _____

	Jan.	Feb.	Mar.	Apr.	May	Jun.	Jul.	Aug.	Sep.	Oct.	Nov.	Dec.
1												
2												
3												
4												
5												
6												
7												
8												
9												
10												
11												
12												
13												
14												
15												
16												
17												
18												
19												
20												
21												
22												
23												
24												
25												
26												
27												
28												
29												
30												
31												
Total												

Chapter 22

"Anything that might be cured with diet
should not be treated by any other means."

Moses Maimonides

The PMS Diet

"Let thy food be thy medicine," adjured Hippocrates more than 2500 years ago. That admonition is well applied to women with PMS, many of whom are overweight, some of whom face monthly cravings for sweet or salty foods. In the initial visit to our office, some of our patients are a little surprised that we are almost as interested in their eating habits as we are in their depressions and hormonal levels. If one applied "you are what you eat," to a premenstrual syndrome sufferer, the profile would be one of more refined carbohydrates, refined sugars, dairy products and sodium, and less zinc, B vitamins, magnesium, manganese, and iron than a woman without PMS. Many women with premenstrual syndrome have food disorders: binge eating is the most common problem, but we have also identified anorexics and bulimics at the center. Eating disorders, depression, and hormonal imbalances make comfortable bedfellows, as we have pointed out in preceding chapters.

Many of our patients on progesterone therapy find a welcome side effect: progesterone, which is known to have a sedative effect on the brain that may ease the panic or hunger sensations that fuel eating binges, helps them stick to a diet and lose weight effortlessly. As Jane Pownter said, "I'm symptom-free except for an occasional craving one day a week, usually the day before I menstruate. I've stuck pretty much to the diet and I've lost about ten pounds. I was dieting when I went there, because I am a big woman, and I'm continuing to lose weight." Greta Minter adds, "I know that I'm going to have to stick with this treatment. The diet I'm on is going to have to be a lifetime thing."

Hypoglycemia and Sugar

In a nation addicted to processed and fast foods and sugar in any form, it is hardly surprising that twenty million to forty million Americans suffer from a nutritional and endocrine imbalance stemming from overdoses of sugar. Hypoglycemia affects more women than men, especially women between thirty and forty years of age. Women in their thirties also constitute the high risk population for premenstrual syndrome. Many women with PMS have been misdiagnosed as suffering from hypoglycemia. We have also seen some women who suffer from hypoglycemia and do not have PMS. But a number of women with PMS do have altered glucose tolerance levels during the luteal phase of their menstrual cycle. That is why we will discuss hypoglycemia here.

The body takes all sugars introduced into its system and changes them into glucose, or blood sugar. Hypoglycemia — literally, low blood sugar — is a condition of faulty glucose metabolism in which an increased production of insulin drains the body of glucose. Because every cell of the body requires glucose to function, the resulting glucose starvation can play havoc with all systems.

Normally, following a meal, there is an immediate rise in the blood sugar level as carbohydrates, including refined sugar, are rapidly metabolized and absorbed into the bloodstream. This escalating level of glucose triggers the production of insulin, a hormone secreted by the pancreas. Insulin removes much of the glucose and stores it in the liver in the form of glycogen for later use as food for the body. In the hypoglycemic, however, the pancreas runs amok, producing too much insulin, which rapidly drains the blood of its glucose supply. Blood sugar levels plummet rapidly and the body becomes starved for food, despite the fact that it has recently been fed.

Most cells in the body can store some glucose. The brain cannot; it depends on a continual supply from the bloodstream. If the brain becomes starved for glucose, it will grow exhausted and misfunction. A healthy diet provides intermittent supplies of carbohydrates, protein, and fat throughout the day — that's why nutritionists usually recommend that people eat three balanced meals daily. The regulation of the body's glucose is controlled by the hypothalamus and involves hormonal secretions, the nervous system, and dietary intake. When the body's sensors indicate to the hypothalamus that a low blood sugar condition — hypoglycemia — exists, this complex system reacts to increase glucose levels in the blood and reduce the amount of glucose sent to the brain and peripheral cells, including muscles. It is this readjustment of the body's balance of glucose that triggers symptoms of hypoglycemia, including faintness, weakness, tremulousness, blurred vision, hunger, palpitations, fast pulse rate, sweating, tightness in the throat, restlessness, irritability, and even anxiety. If the brain is deprived of glucose for a sufficient length of time, other symptoms may occur, including depression, lassitude, headache, forgetfulness, confusion, lack of coordination, and eventually seizures and coma. The hypoglycemic episode ends when enough glucose is released from the liver or when the individual obtains enough glucose from food.

Hypoglycemia is a relative condition. Some individuals diagnosed as hypoglycemic may have low blood sugar levels that actually fall within the normal range. However, their bodies perceive the level to be abnormal and respond with a bombardment of insulin and epinephrine. This is a common occurrence in women with PMS. During the time of their symptoms, there is a change in glucose tolerance. The change may not be strictly interpreted as a hypoglycemic level when compared with normal glucose blood levels but these women's bodies respond as if they were hypoglycemic. The decline in blood sugar level is relative to what their bodies are used to and will increase insulin production.

Fewer than ten percent of our patients have hypoglycemia as well as PMS. However, some of our patients tell us that if they do not eat something every four to six hours during their symptom phase they develop symptoms very like those experienced during the mildest stage of hypoglycemia. Most of these women do not have hypoglycemia. The blood glucose levels of the vast majority of our patients remain in the normal range even during their symptom phase. It appears, though, that they have a lower individual threshold for glucose during their symptom phase, which signals to their body that a hypoglycemic condition exists. The body's reaction to this signal is what triggers the symptoms of hypoglycemia. These symptoms do not appear if these women eat several small meals throughout the day. And these symptoms do not occur during the non-symptom phase of these women's menstrual cycle, even when they fail to eat something every four to six hours.

Hypoglycemia is identified by a glucose tolerance test, which monitors the body's sugar metabolism over several hours, after fasting and after ingesting a large amount of carbohydrates and sugars. Many women with PMS have flattened glucose tolerance curves, indicating an increased tolerance for sugar. Obesity is a frequent complication because the hypoglycemic is often hungry. In recent years, some researchers have suggested a high rate of hypoglycemia among the obese, hyperkinetic children, schizophrenics, alcoholics, drug addicts, and juvenile delinquents.

Stress Worsens Condition

Caffeine, nicotine, and stress exacerbate the hypoglycemic response. Caffeine and nicotine are powerful stimulants that along with stressful situations provoke the generation of adrenalin, which in turn triggers the production of insulin. (One way the body reacts to stress is by lowering blood sugar levels.) As a result, the hypoglycemic may wind up feeling exhausted, hungry, depressed, anxious, and tense. If a lot of refined sugar is then consumed, the effects can be debilitating. The highly refined sugar you eat forces an amino acid into your brain cells where it is converted to serotonin. Too much serotonin may cause nervous tension, palpitation, and drowsiness. Combine stress with a high intake of refined sugar and you set in motion a self-perpetuating cycle.

Refined sugar triggers insulin release but in excess of what is needed. Refined sugar also increases the ability of insulin to act by three to eleven times. In the week before your period, your body is more responsive to insulin. All these factors tend to lower your blood sugar. In some women, the effect of sugar in the diet can be devastating. One of our patients says her preschool-aged children act as her anti-sugar sentries. "They know I can't eat sugar. I have fainted, become very, very irritable and weepy from eating sugar," she explained. "If my daughter sees me going to eat anything with sugar in it, she says 'that's a no-no.'"

Once hypoglycemia is detected, it can be treated with a proper diet. The aim of the diet is to stabilize the blood sugar level, which is why the hypoglycemic should eat several small meals or snacks several times a day rather than one or two or three large meals. Sugar is absorbed into the bloodstream the fastest of all foods. Complex carbohydrates, especially whole grains, nuts, and vegetables, are also converted to glucose after ingestion, but at a slower rate. Proteins and fats are metabolized more slowly as well; consequently the blood sugar rises much more slowly and consistently. The classic hypoglycemic diet substitutes proteins and fats for most of the sugar in a diet.

Some women with the premenstrual syndrome may also be hypoglycemic. But the classic hypoglycemic diet is not ideal for them because it usually contains too much calcium, too many fats, too much protein, and other substances that can exacerbate the symptoms of PMS. To correct the nutritional imbalances most of our patients suffer, we have developed a dietary program that restricts the amount of sugar, sodium, caffeine, dairy products, and red meat, and increases the intake of complex carbohydrates and foods high in the minerals and vitamins women with PMS need.

Our Diet Program

We recommend that women eat six times a day: three meals a day with a mid-morning snack, a mid-afternoon snack, and a snack before bedtime. This isn't a green light for gluttony, however. Women who are at their ideal weight should take in the same number of total calories as they would in three meals. Women who want to lose weight should cut their total daily caloric intake but divide it over six small meals or three meals and three snacks. We suggest that active women who do not need to lose weight restrict their daily intake to 1,500 calories and women who need to lose weight limit themselves to 1,000 calories a day. Consult your physician and/or nutritionist about the appropriateness of the program for your needs.

We recommend that women change their diet to:

1. Restrict themselves to less than three ounces of red meat a day, and limit total protein intake to four ounces of protein on a 1,000-calorie diet or seven ounces of protein on a 1,500-calorie diet. Protein should represent no more than 20 percent of total daily calories. The best sources of protein are fish, poultry, whole grains and legumes. Dairy products — eggs, cheese, milk, yogurt, butter — should be limited to two servings a day.

2. Increase intake of complex carbohydrates to account for 50 to 65 percent of total daily calories, the higher the better.

3. Reduce refined sugar intake to five teaspoonfuls a day. Eliminate candy, chocolate, cake, pie, pastries, and ice cream from your diet. If you must have something sweet, eat fresh fruit.

4. Limit intake of fats to polyunsaturated vegetable oil fats. These should account for less than 20 percent of calories a day.

5. Reduce salt intake to less than three grams a day. Soft drinks, club soda, and tonics — even diet sodas — have large amounts of salt in the form of sodium benzoate. Try drinking seltzer, mineral water, or plain tap water on ice instead.

6. Sharply reduce or eliminate caffeine (coffee, tea, cola drinks, chocolate). Use decaffeinated coffee or tea.

7. Sharply increase the intake of green, leafy vegetables, whole grains, cereals, and legumes.

8. Limit alcohol intake to one ounce of hard liquor a day, four ounces of wine or twelve ounces of beer.

9. Increase the intake of cis-linoleic acid which is contained in safflower oil and other foods. It is a precursor to prostaglandin E-1, which is thought to play a role in some of the symptoms of PMS.

10. Avoid most processed and fast foods, which contain large amounts of salt and sugar and chemicals.

Caffeine

We recommend that a woman reduce the amount of caffeine in her diet because it may increase the body's need for B vitamins. Caffeine is found in coffee, tea, most colas and soda drinks, and in chocolate. Caffeine makes breast symptoms worse — breast swelling, engorgement, and tenderness. It may increase irritability, hyperactivity, and headaches. Many women find that if they reduce or eliminate caffeine that one or another of their symptoms will improve, some to a very significant degree. Even those whose symptoms do not go away find some improvement.

Salt

Women who experience fluid retention — swelling of the face, hands, feet, breasts, weight gain in the days preceding their periods — as part of their premenstrual symptoms should try to eliminate salt from their diet, especially prior to menstruation.

Studies of women suffering from fluid retention have shown that they have elevated levels of hormones of the adrenal glands which control water and salt retention by the kidney. These salt-retaining hormones are stimulated when stress and high brain serotonin trigger the release of a brain hormone called ACTH. Excess refined carbohydrates increase brain serotonin. And insulin also plays a role. Excess refined carbohydrates trigger insulin release in excess. Insulin is known to prevent the kidneys from excreting salt. Salt and water retention is in part an insulin effect. For many women with PMS, the craving for sweets and subsequent ingestion of large amounts of refined carbohydrates or sugar precede the swelling and weight gain, which seems to confirm the roles of refined sugar-triggered insulin release. Poor nutrition decreases resistance to stress. Stress by itself causes the adrenal glands to release increased amounts of salt-retaining hormones into the blood, adding to the salt-retaining effect of insulin.

Foods To Avoid or Limit — High in Sodium

Processed and fast foods
Potato chips
Pretzels
Corn, taco and tortilla chips

Prepared, preserved or dried, smoked and canned meats and sausages

Frankfurters	Bacon	Ham
Sausage	Kidneys	Brains
Sweetbreads	Corned beef	Pastrami
Pate	Cold cuts	Herring
Anchovies	Sardines	Lox, or smoked salmon
Sturgeon	Caviar	

Preserved or pickled fish
Canned fish, except that packed in water and low in salt

Artichokes	Beets	Chard
Kale	Frozen peas	Sauerkraut
Frozen lima beans	White turnips	

Condiments:

Mustard	Catsup	Relish
Mayonnaise	Horseradish	Duck sauce
Barbecue sauces	Soy sauce	Pickles
Sweet and sour sauces		Olives
Worcestershire sauce		

Miscellaneous:

Bouillion cubes	Onion salt	Garlic salt
Molasses	Tomato juice	Celery salt and flakes
Instant cocoa	V-8 juice	Meat tenderizers

Magnesium and Calcium

Americans in general, but American women in particular, may have a deficiency of magnesium in their diet. Studies by Drs. Guy E. Abraham and Michael M. Lubran in Los Angeles of women with PMS indicate that they have even lower magnesium levels than women without PMS. This could explain some of the common symptoms of PMS such as mood swings, nervous tension, bloating and breast tenderness. Researchers have not yet discovered whether PMS causes this deficiency or if the deficiency causes PMS symptoms. In any event, an increase in magnesium in the diet may reduce PMS symptoms in some women. Magnesium helps calcium absorption and deposition in the bones where it belongs. But calcium interferes with magnesium absorption. Magnesium decreases the demand for calcium and calcium increases the demand for magnesium. It makes sense, then, to limit the amount of calcium in your diet — dairy products — because it interferes with magnesium absorption. Dairy products have ten times more calcium than magnesium. You should favor foods that have at least as much magnesium as calcium, with a daily allowance of 300 to 600 milligrams of magnesium.

Many women crave chocolate, which may be a sign of magnesium deficiency. Chocolate is relatively rich in magnesium and in phenylethylamine, a substance produced by the brain that is a cousin of amphetamine. Chocolate also contains caffeine, although in much lower amounts than coffee or tea. An ounce of bittersweet chocolate contains 5 to 10 milligrams of caffeine, compared with 100 to 150 milligrams of caffeine in a cup of brewed coffee.

There are much better sources of magnesium than chocolate: whole grains, green leafy vegetables, legumes, nuts, seeds, cereals, and shellfish.

We've provided the following list to help you make your choices of whole grains and vegetables from those with higher magnesium/calcium ratios. That doesn't mean that all foods with relatively low magnesium/calcium ratios are bad — lettuce, for example, has a ratio of 0.26 but it's a healthy, vitamin-filled, low-calorie food that is good to include in your daily menus.

Magnesium and Calcium Concentrations

	Magnesium (mg/100cal)	Calcium (mg/100cal)	Magnesium/Calcium Ratio
Spinach	315	365	0.86
Cabbage	76	200	0.38
Carrots	55	82	0.67
Tomato	64	61	1.0
Lettuce	63	238	0.26
Potato	45	9	5.0
Lentils	24	24	1.0
Cashew	48	7	7.0
Almond	45	39	1.2
Brazil nut	38	28	1.4
Hazel nut	36	33	1.1
Peanut	30	12	2.4
Chestnut	21	14	1.5
Walnut	20	15	1.34
Pecan	19	11	1.8
Sunflower seed	7	21	0.3
Rye	34	11½	3.0
Wheat	34	11	3.1
Oat	38	18	2.1
Corn	42	6	7.0
Brown rice	25	9	2.8
Barley	11	4.6	2.3
Millet	50	6.2	8.2
Buckwheat	69	34	2.0

Potassium

Potassium is a mineral critical to muscular contraction and nerve stimulation; it also regulates the body's water balance. Inadequate potassium may lead to muscle cramping. The body's concentration of potassium is regulated by the kidneys and requires a proper balance with sodium — salt. Muscle and nerve functioning suffer when there's an imbalance between sodium and potassium. An excess of one will cause the loss of the other in the urine. Diets high in salt lead to potassium deficiency. Women who take diuretics to prevent fluid retention, bloating, and weight gain before their periods may well be depleting their potassium reserves. Individuals with high blood pressure, diabetes, or liver disease also are high risks for potassium deficiency.

Bananas, oranges, orange juice, broccoli, lettuce, melons, wheat germ, unsalted peanuts, lentils, dates, potatoes, and squash are good sources of potassium. Hypoglycemia may result in a loss of potassium. It is important to add these foods to your diet. The recommended daily allowance of potassium is two to five grams.

Zinc

Of all the minerals in the body, zinc is one of the most important. It plays a major role in the synthesis of proteins and DNA and RNA; it is required for cell growth and the formation of connective tissues; it is a factor in forty or more enzyme reactions. Without zinc, for example, the carbon dioxide exchange in the cells could not be accomplished fast enough to keep a human alive. Zinc acts as the traffic cop of the cells and surrounding membranes, policing the metabolism of other minerals, including copper, magnesium, manganese, and selenium.

An excess of copper in the system can lead to zinc deficiency. In the United States, most drinking water passes through copper plumbing pipes, most over-the-counter vitamin supplements contain copper but not zinc, and freshly grown fruits and vegetables are harvested from soil severely deficient in zinc. Zinc deficiency is a common condition in women, especially those with copper IUDs. Some researchers report that the level of copper is high and that of zinc is low one week before the menstrual period when women are more liable to depressive disorders. Zinc levels can also be disturbed by estrogen, which is why women taking oral contraceptives may have zinc-related problems. A 1972 study found that estrogen raises the level of copper in the bloodstream and lowers that of zinc. Also, diuretics deplete zinc levels. If you take water pills for salt retention you may require zinc supplements.

The best sources of zinc are liver, mushrooms, milk, eggs, red meat, brewer's yeast, nuts, legumes, and seafood, especially oysters and herring. The recommended daily requirement is 15 milligrams for adults, 20 milligrams for pregnant women, and 25 milligrams for lactating women.

To help you plan your daily menus we've included the following calorie/portion guidelines.

Remember, if you're trying to lose weight, try to limit your daily caloric intake to 1,000 calories. If you want to maintain your weight, use 1,500 calories as your limit.

Protein

On a 1,500 calorie diet, you can include seven ounces of protein and a maximum of two dairy servings a day, with only three ounces of the protein represented by red meat. On a 1,000 calorie diet, you can include four ounces of protein, of which red meat can constitute only three ounces; again limit your dairy products servings to two.

Meat and meat substitutes contain 55 calories per ounce, seven grams of protein per ounce, three grams of fat per ounce.

The meat substitutes we are including are 1 egg, not fried; ¼ cup of Fleishman's Egg Beaters (low-cholesterol egg substitute), and ½ cup Nuform cottage cheese.

> 1 oz. low sodium cheese is equal to 1 oz. of meat and 1 serving of fat.
> ½ cup creamed cottage cheese is equal to 2 oz. of meat and 1 serving of fat.
> 2 tbsp. peanut butter without salt is equal to 1 oz meat and 2 servings of fat.
> If the meat you choose is marbled in fat, omit 1 serving of fat for each 1 oz. meat you eat.
> ¼ cup of canned tuna fish, packed in water and low in sodium equals one ounce of meat.
> ¼ cup of unsalted salmon equals one ounce of meat.
> Try to choose your protein servings from the above or from:

Poultry — chicken, turkey, cornish hen (remove skin)
Veal — especially the leg, loin and shoulder, cutlets (avoid patties; they usually include beef fat)
Fresh white fish (frozen is too salty)
Lamb — steak, leg, chop (trim all fat)
Beef — only lean cuts such as tenderloin, rump, round steak or roast, London broil, braciole, eye of round, 90 percent lean hamburger
Pork — sometimes the loin is lean enough

Dairy products (limit to two servings a day)
> See egg servings above
> 1 serving equals 4 ounces of skim milk,
> or low fat yoghurt without sugar or fruit,

or 2 ounces of evaporated skim milk
or 4 ounces of buttermilk.

Starch

1 serving equals 70 calories, 15 grams of carbohydrate and 2 grams of protein

One serving equals
1 slice white, rye, raisin or wheat bread
1 small roll (16 rolls to the pound)
1 ounce (saucer size) pita or Syrian bread

The following rolls weigh about 2 oz and are equal to 2 servings of starch and 140 calories:
Hamburger roll
Frankfurter roll
Bagel
English muffin

The following breads only weigh ½ ounce a slice. Two slices are equal to one serving of starch:
Hollywood
Weight Watcher's
Melba Thin (Arnold or Pepperidge Farm)
All of the following equal 1 serving of starch:
1 tortilla
1 matzoh (six-inch round)
5 Melba toast rectangles
8 Melba toast rounds (half dollar size)
25 unsalted pretzel sticks
4 Uneeda Biscuits
3 Zwieback Toast
2 bread sticks (unsalted, 8 inches long)
3 cups unsalted popcorn (no added fat)
6 salt-free Venus Wafers
4 Arrowroot cookies
3 Ginger snaps
5 Vanilla wafers
3 Lorna Doone shortbread cookies
1½ inch square of angel or sponge cake
2 Graham crackers

½ cup Jello (with sugar)
2 tbsp cornstarch
2 tbsp flour
3 tbsp cornflake crumbs
1½ tbsp uncooked barley
¼ cup Graham cracker crumbs
¾ cup unfrosted cereals
¼ cup wheat germ
½ cup cooked cereal (unsalted)
½ cup dried beans or dried peas (cooked and unsalted)
⅓ cup whole kernel frozen corn (unsalted or canned without salt or sugar)
1 6-inch ear of corn, no salt in the water
½ cup frozen lima beans (unsalted)
⅔ cup fresh parsnips (unsalted)
½ cup frozen peas (unsalted, frozen or canned without salt or sugar)
1 small unsalted potato (about size of tennis ball)
½ cup mashed potato (not instant, unsalted)
¾ cup fresh pumpkin (unsalted)
½ cup fresh or frozen winter squash (unsalted)
½ cup pasta (noodles, spaghetti, macaroni; unsalted)
½ cup rice, cooked (unsalted)

The following foods contain more fat than other starches and more calories (about 115 calories per serving). They equal 1 starch and 1 fatty food per serving.

1 waffle or pancake (about size of saucer)
8 unsalted French fried potatoes
1 small muffin (without salt or sugar)
1 small biscuit (without salt or sugar)

Fatty Foods
Our nutritional program limits fats to about 20 percent or less of total calories.

1 serving contains 5 grams fat and 45 calories. (All nuts and seeds should be salt free):

1 tsp butter
1 tsp margarine

⅛ avocado
1 tsp oil (any; but corn oil and safflower oil are better)
2 tsp Miracle Whip
1 tsp mayonnaise
1 tbsp almonds
2 Brazil nuts
5 Filbert nuts
1 tsp pecans
1½ tbsp pine nuts or pignolis
15 pistachio nuts
1 tbsp walnuts
1 tbsp pumpkin seeds
2 tsp sesame seeds
2 tbsp coffee cream (light)
2 tbsp sour cream
1 tbsp heavy cream (whipping cream)
1 tbsp cream cheese

Our nutritional program requires patients to make complex carbohydrates account for 50 to 65 percent of total calories — the higher the better. The following fruits and vegetables are complex carbohydrates.

Vegetables
One serving equals one-half cup of fresh or frozen vegetables, no salt added. Dietetic canned or no salt vegetables may also be used. Avoid sauerkraut. Do not add salt in cooking.

Asparagus	Greens (chard, kale, spinach, collards, mustard, beet, dandelion)	
Bean sprouts	Lettuce (all kinds, no limit on servings)	
Beets	Mushrooms	
Broccoli	Okra	
Brussel sprouts	Rhubarb	
Cabbage	Rutabaga	Cauliflower
Carrots	String beans	Summer squash
Celery	Tomatoes	Eggplant
Green pepper	Zucchini	Turnips

Fruits
One serving equals 40 calories of fresh, frozen or canned without sugar.

If packed in concentrated fruit juice, omit the juice. Frozen juices usually do not contain sugar, but read label to check.

Apples 1 small   Oranges 1 small
Apple juice ⅓ cup   Orange juice ½cup
Applesauce (unsweetened) ½ cup
Apricots, fresh 2 med   Papayas ¾ cup
Apricots, dried 4 halves   Peaches 1 med
Bananas ½ small   Pear 1 small
Berries   Persimmon 1 med
    ½ cup of blackberries, blueberries, raspberries
    ¾ cup of strawberries
Cherries 10 large   Pineapples ½ cup
Cider ⅓ cup   Pineapple juice ⅓ cup
Dates 2   Plums 2 med
Figs, fresh 1   Prunes 2 med
Figs, dried 1   Prune juice ¼ cup
Grapefruit ½   Raisins 2 tbsp
Grapefruit juice ½ cup   Tangerines 1 med
Grapes 12   Nectarines 1 small
Grape juice ½ cup   Cranberries — no limit if no
Mangoes ½ small   sugar added.
Melons
    Cantaloupe ¼ small
    Honeydew ⅛ med
    Watermelon 1 cup

Complex Carbohydrates

Whole grain breads and cereals
Pita bread
Pastas (avoid those made from white flour;
try whole-wheat or spinach noodles)
Brown rice
Barley Bulgur
Legumes: lentils, beans, peas
Millet
Oats
Wheat germ

Dairy products (limit to two servings a day)
Eggs
Fleishman's Egg Beaters (low-cholesterol egg substitute)
Skim milk
Buttermilk
Low-fat yoghurt
Skim-milk cheeses
Farmer's cheese
Cottage cheese

Fish

Almost all fresh and frozen fish are acceptable; avoid salted and pickled fish and those packed in brine or oil. Choose instead canned tuna and salmon packed in water with reduced salt. Shellfish are high in sodium but low in fat; women with problems with fluid retention may want to limit these items.

Blue fish	Clams
Flounder	Lobster
Halibut	Oysters
Monk fish	Scallops
Salmon	Shrimp
Sea bass	
Snapper	
Sole	
Trout	
Tuna	
Whiting	

Lean Meats

Remove skin from poultry; trim fat from meats. Broil, bake or boil; do not fry. Do not use fats in cooking.
Turkey
Chicken
Cornish game hen
Veal
Limit intake of beef, lamb and pork

Vegetables (Starchy, eat in moderation)
Corn

Lima beans
Parsnips
Frozen peas
Potatoes
Pumpkin
Winter squash

Good snack foods are:
Apple, orange and grapefruit juice
Bananas or any fruit on above list
Melba toast
Matzoh
Unsalted pretzels
Unsalted, unbuttered popcorn
Zwieback toast
Unsalted whole wheat crackers
Arrowroot cookies
Ginger snaps
Vanilla wafers
Lorna Doones
Angel food cake, without icing
Graham crackers

Chapter 23

"Our studies at Harvard suggest that the average physician knows a little more about nutrition than the average secretary unless the secretary has a weight problem. Then she probably knows more than the average physician."

Jean Mayer, M.D.

Vitamin Therapy

Women with premenstrual syndrome, like runners preparing for the Boston marathon, need to take all the preventive measures they can to fight the stress and physical effects of their symptoms. They can ill afford the luxury of imbalanced diets or vitamin deficiencies. We recommend that our patients adopt a daily vitamin and mineral supplement as part of the overall lifestyle program. It's especially important for women with poor nutritional habits because dietary changes can't be accomplished overnight. For women with mild to moderate PMS, improved diet, regular exercise, and vitamin supplements may be sufficient to control the illness.

Our own assessments confirm those of other researchers that many women with PMS have faulty eating habits and nutritional deficiencies. If you are able to balance your food intake and achieve the recommended dietary allowances (RDA) recommended by the National Academy of Sciences, you may not need vitamin supplementation. Or you may need only a few months of additional vitamin intake to compensate for your past dietary deficits. We urge you to consult your own physician or a trained nutritionist concerning your specific dietary needs.

At our centers we recommend that women with PMS consume a mid-range of all the important vitamins and minerals over a period of four to eight weeks in order to assess each patient's individual needs and response to these nutrients. Age, weight, height, lifestyle, and health status are contributing factors in determining an individual's nutritional requirements. We use the following range of daily allowances for our patients:

Fat Soluble:

Vitamin A	5,000-12,000 I.U.
D	400-600 I.U.
E	100-300 I.U.Water Soluble (essential):

Water Soluble (essential):

Vitamin C	1,000-3,000 milligrams
Folic acid	500-1,000 mg
Thiamine (B_1)	50-150 mg
Riboflavin (B_2)	50-150 mg
Niacin (B_3)	100-300 mg
Pyridoxine (B_6)	100-300 mg
Cobalamin (B_{12})	50-150 mg
Pantothenic Acid	100-200 mg
Biotin	50-150 mg

Water Soluble (not established):

Inositol	100-200 mg
PABA	50-150 mg
Pangamate	25-75 mg
Bioflavonoids	50-100 mg

All of the essential B vitamins must be taken together in balanced quantities to be most effective and to avoid aggravating various forms of anemia. The greatest flexibility can be achieved by choosing three separate supplement products — one containing Vitamin C alone, another with the water-soluble vitamins, and a third with the fat-soluble vitamins. Or you may choose a product such as Optivite, which was developed by Dr. Guy Abraham after he undertook research into the nutritional imbalances of women with PMS.

We also emphasize the importance of the B-complex vitamins, particularly B_6.

The B-Complex

The B-complex vitamins — B_1, B_2, B_3, B_6, and B_{12} — are in the starting line-up of the body's essential nutrients. As a team, they play an important role in producing energy, in central nervous system function, in the metabolism of carbohydrates and proteins, and stimulation of the immune response. B_{12}, which contains cobalt, is essential to the formation of the nucleic acids RNA and DNA in the rapid regeneration of bone marrow and the production of red blood cells.

The B-complex vitamins' involvement in premenstrual syndrome was identified more than forty years ago, when some symptoms — nervous tension, anxiety, irritability, and mood swings — were observed in women with B-vitamin deficiencies. But the physician who reported this link noticed marked improvement in his patients after treatment with rice bran extracts and brewer's yeast. Further research revealed that the liver could not deactivate estrogens when a B-vitamin deficiency existed; one theory suggests that an excess of estrogens in some women with PMS is caused by the inability of the liver to deactivate them due to B-vitamin deficiency. This theory meshes with recent findings that elevated blood estrogens in some premenstrual syndrome patients are active estrogens. The liver normally inactivates estrogens and the inactivated estrogens are cleared by the kidney in the urine.

Foods containing the B vitamins include:

B_1, or thiamine, and B_2, or riboflavin — liver and organ meats, pork, brewer's yeast, lean meat, eggs, green leafy vegetables, whole grain breads and cereals, nuts and legumes.

B_3, or niacin — liver and organ meats, fish, tuna, dried peas and beans, whole grains, nuts, eggs.

B_{12} — organ and muscle meats, milk, eggs, brewer's yeast, seafood (especially clams, oysters and shrimp).

Vitamin B_6

Pyridoxine, or Vitamin B_6, eases the symptoms of severe PMS, but it usually does not eradicate them. It takes the edge off irritability and reduces fatigue and depression. It may reduce or eliminate breast swelling and headaches. It's not clear how or why B_6 has these effects. We know that it acts on the central nervous system, which might affect the neurotransmitters dopamine and serotonin in the chain of actions that regulate the production of progesterone and other hormones. It may also aid in the liver's metabolism of estrogen. Some women seem unable to tolerate B_6; they may become nauseated or dizzy with vitamin supplements. This is usually because they've been given too high a dosage. Decreasing the dosage will usually resolve the problem. B_6 and the B-complex supplement should be taken with a meal to increase their absorption. We usually start our patients with 50 milligrams of B_6 and slowly build up to 200 to 500 mg.

B_6 might be viewed as the most valuable player of the B-complex, a critical component in growth, repair of cells, and the production of energy. It aids in the breakdown of the body's building blocks, amino acids, from ingested proteins, their synthesis from compounds within the body, their subsequent absorption into the cells, and their eventual formation into proteins. It also acts as a co-enzyme in the formation of hemoglobin, the protein that carries oxygen from the lungs to each of the cells. (Hemoglobin circulates in the bloodstream). Pyridoxine also is active in the metabolism of fats and carbohydrates. Without B_6 the body's cells could not produce energy.

A deficiency of B_6 first affects the nervous system, especially in children; in adults, especially women, it may be manifested as depression. This is because the brain needs proteins to function and with a B_6 deficiency the protein supply to the brain is greatly reduced. Since B_6 is involved in the metabolism of amino acids, as well as in the formation of the substance that holds them together — collagen — a deficiency not only interferes with repairs and growth but can result in serious structural damage to the gums, teeth, bones, and liver, and lowered immune response.

B_6 deficiency is not common, in part because the vitamin is stable to heat and acid; it's more resistant to food processing and storage than other vitamins and minerals. Adequate amounts of B_6 are usually obtained in a normal diet. Women taking oral contraceptives, however, commonly have B_6 deficiencies, marked by depression. Not all women become depressed when using oral contraceptives. And of those who do, not all depression is necessarily due to pyridoxine deficiency. But among women on the pill who also have a B_6 deficiency, B_6 supplements can usually eliminate the depression. Some researchers have concluded that women with a history of depression, premenstrual depression, or depression during pregnancy — and who become worse after starting the pill — are most likely to respond to pyridoxine. In one study, two hundred twenty out of two hundred fifty women responded to pyridoxine therapy for their depression. Oral contraceptives also interfere with the body's ability to metabolize carbohydrates and remove them from the bloodstream for storage in the liver. In some women, this side effect can reach a state similar to that of diabetes. Supplements of B_6 help restore the glucose metabolism to a more normal range.

B_6 has also been found to alleviate nausea and discomfort in pregnant women, and it plays a role in fertility. Large doses of B_6 suppress the secretion of prolactin, a hormone which stimulates lactation and inhibits conception, thus preventing pregnancy. This is one of the body's protective devices to prevent pregnancy in a woman who's already pregnant or breast-feeding. Dr. Guy Abraham has shown that when a group of fourteen infertile women with premenstrual tension were given supplements of pyridoxine, ranging from 100 to 800 mg, for at least six months, twelve of them suddenly became fertile and conceived.

Nutritional sources of pyridoxine are liver and organ meats, whole grain cereals and bread, wheat germ, soybeans, brewer's yeast, nuts, red meat, fish, spinach, avocados, bananas, green beans, green leafy vegetables, potatoes, molasses, cabbage, and green peppers. Vegetables should be eaten raw because cooking destroys the vitamin.

Pyridoxine is available in supplements ranging from 5 to 500 milligrams; most over-the-counter vitamin supplements include 2 mg of B_6, the recommended daily allowance. There is no known toxicity of large doses of B_6; although it has been suggested by researchers that doses exceeding two grams per day may cause peripheral nerve damage. Overdoses from the normal diet are all but impossible.

Optivite, the supplement developed by Dr. Abraham, is available from Optimox Inc., P.O. Box 7000-280, Rolling Hills Estates, CA. 90274.

Chapter 24

"The wise, for cure, on exercise depend."

John Dryden, *Epistle*
to John Driden of Chesterton

Getting Physical

Regular exercise is another important weapon in the anti-PMS arsenal. It ameliorates the symptoms of depression, anxiety, fatigue, irritability, nervous energy, premenstrual headaches, and cramps. Depression is especially helped by regular exercise; studies have shown that the improvement in the efficiency of the cardiovascular and respiratory systems by aerobic exercise speeds recovery from depression. The patients we see who begin a regular exercise program do report a lessening of the severity of their PMS symptoms. Women with mild to moderate cases may find that exercise and nutritional changes may be sufficient therapy, either to eliminate the symptoms completely, or to reduce them to a minor inconvenience. Many women find that exercise alone is not enough; some must also adhere to a dietary program to gain relief. We put all of our patients at the center on an exercise program because we believe that PMS treatment requires a combination of therapy: diet, exercise, and stress management are essential. In many cases, vitamin supplements are called for; severe cases of PMS, of course, will also require progesterone therapy.

Why does exercise help? It speeds up weight loss on any type of diet. It improves circulatory and oxygenating capacity. It may also increase the secretion of progesterone and beta-endorphins, the hormones that are released by the brain and produce a sensation of mild euphoria.

We strongly advise women, whether or not they have PMS, to begin and continue an exercise routine. By regular, we mean three times a week for a minimum of fifteen to thirty minutes each time. Fifteen minutes of vigorous exercise are required to boost your heart rate and increase its efficiency. No more than two days should elapse between workouts or the gains made on Monday will be lost by Wednesday night.

Before undertaking any exercise program, however, make sure to:

1. *Consult a physician.* Make sure you are in good health and can undertake a program without potential problems. A physician can identify any medical problems you might have, point out your limitations and suggest suitable forms of exercise that will not jeopardize your health.

2. *Choose appropriate clothing.* Wear warm, comfortable, and loose-fitting clothing. It is better to be overdressed than underdressed. On cooler days muscles take longer to warm up and relax. To avoid tears and strains of muscles you need extra protection. Proper footwear protects the sensitive bones and muscle in the feet and legs. A structured bra gives extra support to the breasts.

3. *Begin a regimen slowly and carefully.* Always warm up slowly before beginning calisthenics or any athletic activity. Don't push yourself beyond your limits initially. Your body will tell you when to stop. Exercise should stretch and flex your muscles, not cause pain. If you feel pain, stop. Aches and stiffness, however, are the natural byproducts of a new exercise regime. A long soak in a hot tub, sauna, or jacuzzi will turn that stiffness into a memory.

One way to determine if you're in good condition is the pinch test for body fat. Extend your arm away from your body so that the upper arm is level with your shoulder and bend your elbow slightly to make a muscle. With the thumb and forefinger of the other hand, pinch the skin on the back of the raised arm over your triceps muscle in the middle of your under-upper-arm. The pinch should be made lengthwise. Estimate the amount of skin and fat you could pinch, or have a friend measure it with a ruler. The average amount of skin and fat a physically fit person has is one-half to three-quarter inches. If you have less than one-quarter of inch of skin and fat, you have a very low body fat level and are probably in better-than-average shape. If you have more than three-quarters of an inch, you've got a lot of work to do to get in shape.

If you're already an active woman of normal weight who follows some kind of exercise program, you should be able to complete the following calisthenics regime quickly and advance to more intensive aerobic exercises, like aerobic dancing, swimming, running, bicycling, or other sports. If, however, you are out of shape, overweight, or haven't been exercising regularly, you'll have to take it slow at first. Here's how to start:

Warm Ups: Relaxation and Breathing Exercises

1. Reach both hands over your head, stand on tiptoe and stretch, breathing in very slowly and deeply. While breathing out, gently fold at the waist and try to touch your toes with your fingertips. Do not strain yourself doing this. Repeat this exercise six times with a stretch and inhale up, and relax and exhale down.

2. While standing with your feet apart, extend one arm loosely above your head with the other at your side. Bend slowly six times to the side opposite your extended arm. Then reverse the position of your arms and bend six times to the other side. Be certain to come up fully to the upright position after each repetition.

3. Sit down comfortably on the floor with your legs extended straight in front of you and slightly apart. Stretch as far as you can toward your toes without pain, come back up to the upright position and stretch your arms over your head and down to your toes again. Remember, inhale up, exhale down. Six repetitions.

4. Lie flat on the floor, legs stretched out straight in front of you. Raise one leg. Using your hands, pull your knee toward your chest. Return to the original prone position. Repeat six times with each leg.

5. Remain in the prone position, arms extended flat on the floor at the shoulder level. Slowly bend your legs and bring your knees up to your chest. Keeping your knees together, roll slowly to one side until the outside knee touches the floor. Then roll to the other side and touch the other knee to the floor. Six repetitions.

Walking

After completing the warm-up exercises, it's time to go outside for a brisk walk. Remember to breath deeply and slowly as you walk. Start out slowly with a walk around the block the first day. Over a two-week period, increase the distance of your walk to a mile. Increase your walking distance and speed as you desire and feel comfortable. Try to walk at least one mile briskly each day five days a week.

Those who choose walking as their primary exercise should slowly but surely increase the distance of the walk, but decrease the amount of time it takes to cover.

A good progression, to be covered five times a week, is:

WEEK 1	1 mile in 15 minutes.
WEEK 2	1 mile in 14 minutes.
WEEK 3	1 mile in 13 minutes and 45 seconds.
WEEK 4	1½ in 21 minutes and 30 seconds.
WEEK 5	1½ in 21 minutes.
WEEK 6	1½ in 20 minutes and 30 seconds.
WEEK 7	2 miles in 28 minutes.
WEEK 8	2 miles in 27 minutes and 45 seconds.
WEEK 9	2 miles in 27 minutes and 30 seconds.

The routine is varied from this point on:

WEEK 10 2 miles in 27 minutes and 30 seconds three times a week and 2½ miles in 35 minutes and 30 seconds twice a week.

WEEK 11 2 miles in 27 minutes and 30 seconds three times a week and 2½ miles in 35 minutes twice a week.

WEEK 12 2½ miles in 34 minutes and 30 seconds four times a week and 3 miles in 41 minutes and 30 seconds once.

WEEK 13 2½ miles in 33 minutes and 15 seconds three times a week and 3 miles in 42 minutes twice a week.

WEEK 14 2½ miles in 33 minutes three times a week and 3 miles in 41 minutes and 30 seconds twice a week.

WEEK 15 3 miles in 42 minutes five times a week.

WEEK 16 4 miles in 56 minutes four times a week.

Calisthenics

For those who prefer calisthenics as their primary form of exercise, we recommend following the first two weeks of the walking program to ease yourself into a routine. Walking is an excellent base for any exercise program. We encourage our patients to walk a mile a day briskly before undertaking any other exercise. Once you've reached that one mile walking goal, you're ready to try calisthenics.

From the following exercises, choose two to three exercises from each category and do them at least three times a week. And remember: Relax, breath deeply and slowly, and enjoy yourself.

For the Waist

Moderate.
Stand upright, feet planted widely, arms extended straight overhead and hands clasped. Bend your knees slightly and fold forward at the waist, keeping your head between your arms. Circle at the waist four times clockwise and four times counterclockwise, raising your head and arms slowly as you progress, until you are upright with head and hands extending toward the ceiling. Repeat six times. Remember to breath deeply as you exercise.

Moderate.
This exercise requires an object that weighs about two pounds, a household item, like an iron or can of fruits or vegetables. Stand with feet wide apart, arms at side. Hold the weight in one hand at the side of your body. Bend side to side, dropping your head with your body as you bend. Repeat ten times.

Moderate.
Sit comfortably on the floor with feet wide apart, arms extended at shoulder level, straight out to the sides. Bend your body slightly forward and twist it gently at the waist to touch your right hand to your left foot. Repeat with left hand to right foot. Return to upright position. Repeat ten times.

Moderate.
Kneel on the floor. Extend one leg straight out to the side, with arms straight out overhead, hands clasped. Bend sideways over the out-stretched leg. Keep looking forward. Take ten bends to one side. Then switch and extend the opposite leg and complete ten repetitions to the other side.

Advanced.
Lie on the floor, legs wide apart. Extend arms straight overhead with hands clasped. Do a full situp. With arms still straight overhead, stretch twice toward your left foot, stretching as far as comfortably as possible. Return to upright position. Repeat twice toward right foot, and then twice toward the space between your feet. Lie back down in prone position. Repeat this eight times.

For the Arms

Moderate.
Hold your two-pound weight in one hand with an underhand grip. Keeping your elbow at your side, flex your elbow and raise the weight to chest level. Then lower it. Repeat with each arm ten times.

Moderate.
Stand with legs apart, knees slightly bent, bending forward at the waist, arms at your sides. Swing one arm forward and the other backward. Repeat ten times. Then hold arms straight out at sides for a slow count of twenty.

Moderate.
Lie down on your back on the floor. Take your two-pound weight in your right hand and rest it on the floor beside you. Supporting your upper right arm with your left hand, extend your elbow and lift the weight with a straight right arm toward the ceiling slowly. Return to original position. Repeat with each arm ten times.

Advanced.
Stand facing a wall, hands in front of you braced against the wall, extended at shoulder level. Lean into the wall, bending your elbows toward the floor. Straighten your arms and push yourself away from the wall. Be sure to keep your back straight and breathe deeply. To increase the difficulty of the exercise, increase your distance from the wall. Eight repetitions.

Advanced.
Stand with legs apart, knees slightly bent, bending forward at the waist, arms at your side. Take two two-pound weights in each hand. Swing one arm forward and the other backward. Repeat ten times. Then hold arms straight out at sides for a slow count of twenty.

For the Abdomen
Moderate.
Lie flat on your back on the floor, arms extended straight overhead. With one knee bent, one leg out straight, bring outstretched leg straight

up halfway. Then bring top half of body up to meet the leg in the middle. Hold for a count of five. Relax and repeat eight times for each leg.

Moderate.

Lie on your back on the floor with hands clasped behind your head. Legs should extend straight out. Lift your head and upper body as you tuck your right knee to your chest. Touch your left elbow to the right knee and return to beginning position. Repeat with right elbow and left knee. Eight repetitions.

Moderate.

Lie on your back with your hands under your buttocks to flatten the arch in your back. Tuck your knees into your chest. Extend legs straight in the air. Tuck them back to your chest. Extend legs straight out on floor. Eight times.

Advanced.

Sit on the floor with your feet tucked under the edge of a heavy chair or courch. Lie flat on the floor with knees bent and arms extended straight overhead. Move your buttocks as close to your feet as is comfortably possible. Try to keep your biceps at ear level and chin tucked into your chest as you crawl up and touch your knees. Inhale as you lower your body and exhale as you sit up. Eight repetitions.

Advanced.

Lie on the floor on your back, resting your weight on your elbows with legs extended straight. Push up elbows and tuck knees into chest simultaneously. Move as far as possible with feet off floor. Return to original position. Eight times.

Bust

Moderate

Clasp right wrist with left hand, left wrist with right hand directly in front of your chest. Grip securely and push one arm against the other. Hold for a count of five and release. Eight times.

Moderate

Sit comfortably and clasp your hands behind your head. Pull your elbows back so your shoulder blades come together. Hold for a count of five. Repeat five times.

Moderate

Lie face down, elbows to the side, hands clasped, palms on the floor. Rest your forehead on your hands. Lift head, hands and elbows two inches from the floor. Hold for count of five. Eight times.

Hips, Buttocks

Moderate

Lie on the floor on your side. Support your head with your hand. Lift your upper leg, straight up, with toe pointing. Eight times.Roll over and repeat eight times with other leg.

Moderate

On your hands and knees, extend one leg out to the side, raise leg and lower. Repeat ten times with each leg.

Moderate

Lie face down on the floor, hands clasped in front of you with chin resting on the back of your hands. Slowly lift one leg straight up and hold for a count of five. Relax. Repeat six times with each leg.

Moderate

Stand up straight. With arm extended to your side at shoulder level, grasp the back of a chair. Lift outside leg and make ten large, slow circles. Repeat with other leg.

Moderate

Still holding on to the chair, lift outside leg forward, to the side, and back ten times. Repeat with other leg.

Moderate

Sitting on the floor, one leg out straight and the other leg with knee bent and foot against the inside of the opposite knee. Keep your hands resting on the floor. Bring your bent knee to touch the floor on both sides, going back and forth. Ten times.

Moderate

Lie on your back with your hands under your buttocks to support your back. Lift your legs and pedal as if you were riding a bicycle. Count to thirty slowly. Rest and repeat.

Moderate
Stand up straight, feet widely planted. Hold a pole or broom handle, palms down. Lift the pole straight overhead, inhale deeply. Exhale as you bend your elbows and lower the pole behind your back. Inhale as you extend the pole over your head and exhale as you return it to the original position. Six times.

Moderate
Stand straight up with feet widely planted, hold the pole or broom overhead with arms fully extended. Bend your knees slightly and lean from side to side at the waist slowly in a continuous motion. Eight times.

Advanced
Lie on your side with your body straight and your head resting on your hand. Lift both legs lightly off the floor with top leg slightly off bottom leg. Kick in a scissor fashion for thirty seconds. Roll over and repeat on the other side.

Advanced
On your hands and knees, tuck one knee into chest and tuck head down as close to knee as possible. Lift your head and extend leg straight out behind you. Repeat ten times with each leg.

Advanced
On hands and knees, extend one leg straight out to your side. Lift it as high as is comfortable to the side. Swing it directly in back of you and lift. Repeat six times with each leg.

After completing the basic beginner's calisthenics program, you may want to advance to a more strenuous exercise regimen. We recommend aerobic exercise as a supplement to any good fitness program because it increases cardiovascular respiratory efficiency and strength and flexibility of the large muscles of the body. The best aerobic exercises are aerobic dancing, bicycle riding, swimming, jogging, and running. Remember that to bring any health benefits, a program must be undertaken at least three times a week for a minimum of twenty minutes of strenuous activity.

How can you tell if an exercise is aerobic? The exercise should increase cardiopulmonary fitness, and condition muscles but not strain them. The program should help you reach a "target zone" of sixty to eighty percent of your maximum attainable pulse rate. Generally this maximum attainable rate is determined by subtracting your age from the number 220. Sixty to eighty percent of that figure is your target zone. (If you're thirty years old, your target zone is 114 to 152 beats a minute, or sixty to eighty percent of 190.)

To test yourself, pause at intervals during your workout and take your pulse. In taking your pulse at your wrist, never use the thumb because it has a pulse of its own. Instead, use the second and third fingers, placing them along the inside or thumb side of your wrist. Press in gently until you feel the beat of the artery. Looking at the second hand of a clock or watch, count the beats in a ten-second time period and multiply by six to determine the rate per minute. An alternative method is to take the pulse of the artery in your neck. Again using the second and third fingers, gently probe down from the jaw bone and push in lightly until you feel the pulse beat. Again, count the beat in a ten-second period and multiple by six.

If you're just beginning an aerobics program, keep your pulse rate down toward the lower limit of the target zone so you won't overtax your heart. As your body condition improves and the cardiorespiratory system strengthens, you should try to approach the upper limit. Remember, keep all your exercise routines at a comfortable and slow pace initially.

Any aerobic regimen should include:

● *A five to ten minute* warmup and moderate aerobic exercises to stimulate the circulatory system and warm up the muscles.

● *A ten to twenty minute* peak period in which you reach and maintain your target zone pulse rate.

● *A five to ten minute* cool down routine of moderate aerobic exercises that permits the blood to return to all parts of the body and not remain trapped in the hands or feet.

An important aspect of any aerobic program is enjoyment. Whatever method of exercise you choose should be something that you can look forward to at least three times a week, week in and week out over a lifetime.

Chapter 25/*Managing Stress*

Stress is a damaging factor in most of our lives and is an element implicated in all diseases. Like the oily extortionist in a turn-of-the-century melodrama who ties the stubborn heroine onto railroad tracks as a speeding train approaches, stress is the villain pressuring us, threatening our health and emotional stability. In an illness as complex and chronic as premenstrual syndrome, stress adds a dangerous and volatile variable to the scene; it compounds the problems and exacerbates the symptoms of PMS, which itself is a major source of stress. Women with PMS cannot be successfully treated for their illness unless they reduce the stress in their daily routine and learn to manage the stress they can't avoid.

In his book, *The Stress of Life*, the late Dr. Hans Selye explained that stress could be caused by such disparate factors as infection, noise, overcrowding, tumultuous but generally positive events such as vacation, Christmas and other holidays, marriage, or a sudden rise in financial status. The body adapts to these diverse stressors in the same way no matter what the source of the stress or what organ is involved. Selye, who won the Nobel Prize for his identification of what he termed the General Adaptation Syndrome or GAS, identified three stages in the stress syndrome: alarm, resistance, and exhaustion. Each of the stages is associated with specific bodily changes in the same organs.

Stress encompasses any event, whether positive or negative, that forces the body to make an adjustment. To illustrate, if you suffer a minor cut, a localized mechanism called the Local Adaptation Syndrome, or LAS, is activated. LAS is linked, in the case of the cut, to the process of local repair of injured tissues. The GAS and the LAS are closely linked, like the command and operating units of fire and police departments. The GAS is the command unit, answering the body's stress symptoms as if they were a call to 911. LAS is the on-the-scene emergency crew, the engine crew or police squad sent off to report on and repair the damage. Both set off identical physical defenses in the body. Both involve the release of a pituitary hormone that stimulates the adrenal gland to secrete the hormones necessary for the defense or repair of the body. The physical changes that result from stress are the body's attempt to somehow adapt to the cause of stress, be it noise, grief, or extreme cold. Our bodies pay as high a toll for emotional stress as they do for physical stress, especially if it's chronic, because the changes brought on by either are identical.

The three stages of stress are actual physiological events, but psychological factors play an important part in the way the body copes with stress. As Dr. Jay M. Weiss of the Rockefeller University, a leader in stress disease research, says the more helpless one feels in a situation, the more likely one is to develop a stress-related disease. The secret of remaining calm is a great one to master, but it isn't simply a matter of repressing feelings of anger or fear triggered by stress.

How the Body Deals With Stress

The hypothalamus and the pituitary, both of which orchestrate the production of sex hormones, also orchestrate the body's response to stress. When the alarm stage of stress is triggered, the hypothalamus sends frantic hormonal messages to the pituitary gland. That signal means the body needs energy to cope with a physical emergency. This is most commonly known as the fight or flight response. The pituitary, as soon as it receives the hypothalamus's message, sends out a hormone called ACTH. ACTH goes to a part of the adrenal gland known as the adrenal cortex. It acts exclusively on the adrenal cortex, which finds its home wrapped around the adrenal gland above each kidney. The triggering of the fight-or-flight hormone increases the blood sugar level, while pupils dilate, muscles contract, and blood pressure rises temporarily. The body prepares to make a stand. As a kind of contingency action, it also releases certain substances which aid the cells in repairing themselves. These substances released by the adrenal gland include one most closely linked with feelings of anger and tension: norepinephrine, which is secreted by the inner portion of the adrenal, the medulla. This stimulates the central nervous system, an experience we undergo when we are angry. An injection of norepinephrine into the brain will cause anyone to feel anger, no matter how peaceful they were the moment preceding the injection. Individuals who secrete this substance in excess will feel tense and angry a lot of the time. Norepinephrine constricts the blood vessels; it also acts in conjunction with another hormone from the adrenal cortex, aldosterone, to raise one's blood pressure. The activation of the response in a person with a high sodium intake can turn anxiety into a very real and deadly physical malady. In today's world, most people have little opportunity to vent their emotions or act out the fight/flight response. As a result, the hormones keep the body in a state of constant preparation for battles that are never fought. The resultant tension without release changes the body's response to excess sodium, making it more easily retained.

With aldosterone acting to retain salt and fluids and norepinephrine constricting the blood vessels, the result is high blood pressure. The increase in blood pressure, when triggered by stress, lasts as long as the stress lasts. In major stress, the body reaches the stage of exhaustion.

Stress leaves scars on the internal organs, especially on the adrenal glands. Dr. Selye was fond of noting that no one dies of old age, they just lose their ability to adapt to stress. Instead of bending, they break. To prevent the breaks and teach individuals how to bend, several stress evaluation systems and a score of stress management techniques have been developed over the past two decades, including biofeedback and the relaxation response program of Dr. Herbert Benson of the Harvard Medical School and Beth Israel Hospital in Boston. A classic stress measurement test was developed in 1967 by Thomas Holmes and Richard Rahe, psychiatrists at the University of Washington School of Medicine. Their barometer, which they call the Social Readjustment Scale, rates the stressfulness of various life events from little stress (1) to most stressful (100). Review the items and check off those that you have experienced within the previous twelve months. If your score reaches or exceeds 300, you're over-stressed and have a 90 percent chance of becoming ill or having a major accident because of stress.

Social Readjustment Scale

Death of spouse	100
Divorce	73
Marital separation	65
Incarceration (prison term)	63
Death of immediate family member	63
Personal injury or illness	53
Marriage	50
Discharged from job	47

Marital reconciliation	45
Retirement	45
Change in health of family member	44
Pregnancy	40
Sexual problems	39
Gain of new family member	39
Business readjustment	39
Change in financial status	38
Death of a close friend	37
Change of careers	36
Change in number of arguments with mate	35
Mortgage over $10,000	31
Foreclosure of debt	30
Change in job responsibilities	29
Child leaving home	29
Trouble with in-laws	29
Outstanding personal achievement	28
Begin or end of school	26
Spouse begins or stops work	26
Change in living conditions	25
Change in personal habits	24
Conflicts with employer or supervisor	23
Change in work hours or conditions	20
Change of residence	20
Change of schools	20
Change in recreation	19
Change in church activities	19
Change in social activities	18
Mortgage or loan less than $10,000	17
Change in sleeping habits	16
Change in eating habits	15
Vacation	13
Christmas	12
Minor violations of law	11

Adapting this social stress measure to women with premenstrual syndrome, we ask our patients to indicate what stress indicators they may have experienced in the past two years and within the past twelve months to determine how stressful their lives are, what role stress may be playing in adding to or exacerbating the PMS symptoms, and to identify and help them reduce specific stressors. The questionnaire we use follows. Look it over. How many of these stressors are present or

Life Events

The following checklist consists of events which are sometimes important experiences. Please read down the list until you find events that have happened to you personally. Then indicate two things:

When did the event occur? Check "Time Period"

Do you still think about the event? Often, At Times, No?

Life Event	Time Period			Still Think About It		
	Within past 2 years	More than 2 years		Often	At Times	No
Death of Spouse						
Divorce						
Marital separation						
Jail term						
Death of a close family member						
Personal injury or illness						
Marriage						
Fired at work						
Marital reconciliation or serious problem						
Retirement						
Change in health of family member ...						
Pregnancy						
Sex difficulties						
Gain of a new family member						
Business readjustment						
Change in financial state						
Death of a close friend						
Change to different line of work						
Change in number of arguments with spouse						
Mortgage over $50,000						
Foreclosure of mortgage or loan						
Change in responsibilities at work						
Son or daughter leaving home						
Trouble with in-laws						
Outstanding personal achievement						
Spouse begins or stops work						

Life Event	Time Period		Still Think About It		
	Within past 2 years	More than 2 years	Often	At Times	No
Begin or end school					
Change in living conditions					
Revision of personal habits					
Trouble with boss					
Change in work hours or conditions ..					
Change in residence					
Change in schools					
Change in recreation					
Change in church activities					
Change in social activities					
Mortgage or loan less than $50,000					
Change in sleeping habits					
Change in number of family get-togethers					
Change in eating habits					
Vacation					
Christmas					
Minor violation of the law					

have been present recently in your life? To accommodate the inflationary spiral of housing costs, you'll note that we have pegged our mortgage and loan levels to $50,000, instead of the $10,000 used by Holmes and Rahe in 1967.

Relaxation Techniques

Any number of methods of relaxation can be used to slow the heart rate and lower blood pressure: relaxation response, meditation, deep breathing exercises, yoga, biofeedback, cognitive training. If you have tried any of these techniques and found they work for you, continue to use them. Two basic methods to divert your mind from stress that can be used twice a day, or whenever you're in a stressful situation, involve breathing and muscle exercises. Both of them can be done at your desk, at home, in connection with other exercises, or even in bed if you have trouble falling asleep.

Breathing Exercise

Sit back in a comfortable chair, feet flat on the floor, arms loose. Close your eyes, relax all your muscles, starting from the feet up, calves, thighs, abdomen, arms. Loosen up your shoulders, head, and neck. Sit quietly, breathe very slowly and naturally. Try to clear your mind. Choose a word or number that you will focus on repeatedly during the exercise. Those who meditate or use yoga may already have a mantra, or single syllable upon which they concentrate as they try to empty their mind of diversionary thoughts. If you have a mantra, use it during this exercise. As you breath slowly and quietly, say the word or number to yourself as you exhale. At each exhalation, repeat the word to yourself. Other thoughts may intrude, but let them pass. Don't get annoyed at that or focus on it. Just keep breathing slowly, and as you exhale, repeat your chosen word to yourself. Let's say your word is love. Breath slowly and deeply, and as you exhale repeat the word love to yourself. Inhale, exhale while thinking of the word love. Inhale, exhale, repeating love. Do this for several minutes. Keep your eyes closed, but slowly begin to let your mind focus on normal thoughts. Then very slowly open your eyes.

This is a good exercise to do twice a day for 10 to 20 minutes, to clear your mind and force yourself to slow down. You might find it easy to adopt this method into your daily routine immediately, but most people find that it takes several days for them to be able to handle a 10- to 20-minute session.

Muscle Relaxation

Sit in a comfortable chair, in a comfortable position, both feet on the floor, arms loose.

Focus on your toes. Think about them. Then tighten up your toes, hold that position for a count of three, and release.

Next focus on your calves. Tighten the calf muscles, hold the pose for a count of three, and release.

Then the thighs. Tighten the top muscles of the thighs, hold it for three seconds, and release.

Continue this progressive concentration on the major muscle groups of the body: buttocks and abdomen, small of back and waist, upper body, chest and back.

Now make your hands into fists. Clench them tightly, count to three and release.

Then try to tense your lower arms, the upper arms and biceps, shoulders and neck muscles, and finally, the face. Grimace as tightly as you can to contract the face muscles, hold it for a count of three, and release.

If after finishing this routine you feel that a part of your body is still gripped in tension, repeat the routine for that muscle group. This is a good exercise to adopt two or three times a day.

Chapter 26

> *"Science is a first-rate piece*
> *of furniture for a man's upper*
> *chamber, if he has common sense*
> *on the ground floor."*
>
> Oliver Wendell Holmes, **The Poet**
> at the Breakfast Table

The Progesterone Story

For women with chronic cases of premenstrual syndrome the search for treatment has most likely resembled an odyssey with many more than twelve obstacles blocking the way. The frustration and anger that mounts each time a promised "cure" fails feeds a relentless need. By the time they come to us for treatment many women are looking for a miracle. Progesterone is not a miracle cure, not a magic bullet. It is simply the most effective treatment known for premenstrual syndrome. For most of the women we have treated, it has eliminated or sharply reduced the symptoms. But progesterone cannot work miracles; and it does not produce the best results unless it is used in conjunction with the lifestyle changes discussed in earlier chapters.

The results of progesterone therapy are impressive. In examining the treatment results of a small sample of our patients — one hundred women treated at our clinic for six to fourteen months — seventy-seven of the women were symptom-free at the time of the survey. Twenty-three patients were significantly improved: most of their symptoms had abated, but one symptom remained (usually headaches). But it, too, was less frequent and/or less intense. Five patients no longer required progesterone because their symptoms had remitted. Each patient had a severe case of PMS with multiple symptoms that had been present for more than five years; each woman had made at least three prior attempts at treatment for PMS without success. None of these patients had ever had a term pregnancy, i.e. actually delivered a child.

We don't know yet precisely how or why progesterone alleviates the wide-ranging symptoms of premenstrual syndrome. Medical science must first identify the scope of the role of progesterone and estrogen in the body, and research must be done to pinpoint the cause or causes of premenstrual syndrome. Progesterone does have analgesic and sedative properties; it makes you feel good. Some physicians say that the analgesic effect is what eases the complaints of many women. The complexity of PMS and its range of symptoms indicate, however, that the disorder is too complicated to be put to rest by a sedative and that progesterone plays a critical role in an intricate hormonal balance that is somehow disturbed, producing PMS.

Before we go any further, you need to master the vocabulary we'll be using:

Progestational agents — substances, either produced by the body or compounded synthetically, that act to stimulate uterine changes essential to pregnancy. Progestational means favoring pregnancy, conducive to gestation.

Progestin — a generic term for any substance, natural or synthetic, that has some of the properties of progesterone. The word is used interchangeably with progestogen.

Progestogen — any substance that acts to stimulate uterine changes essential to pregnancy. Progesterone is a progestogen. Only two progestogens occur naturally in the human body: progesterone and 17- alpha-hydroxyprogesterone. All other progestogens are synthetically produced. There are structural molecular differences between these various progestogens, which are reflected in their function within the multiple biological systems in the body and the effects they produce.

Progesterone — the female sex hormone produced primarily by the ovaries during the reproductive years to prepare a woman's body for pregnancy. A molecularly identical compound to naturally occuring progesterone produced by pharmacists is available in injectable or suppository form and is used in the treatment of women with severe cases of premenstrual syndrome. It is this molecularly identical compound we refer to when we use the word "progesterone." Progesterone is both a progestogen and a progestin, but many substances that are progestogens and progestins are not progesterone.

Provera — a prescription drug brand name for a compound of medroxyprogesterone, a synthetic progestogen. It is a compound related to, but distinguishable from, progesterone, and its properties are very different. Physicians all too often confuse Provera with progesterone.

Steroid hormone — substances derived from cholesterol involving a distinctive ring-like chemical structure. The sex hormones — progesterone, estrogen, testosterone, and the corticosteroids — are steroid hormones.

Confusion Over Substances

Many physicians confuse progesterone with other progestational substances, natural or synthetic; they speak of these substances as if they had the same properties and they prescribe them for their patients as if they had the same properties. Progesterone and only progesterone as it naturally occurs in the body is the appropriate therapy for premenstrual syndrome. Many progestogens have properties that antagonize and worsen premenstrual syndrome. Sometimes, to make the distinction between progesterone and progestogens more clear, we emphasize to our patients that progesterone is a naturally occuring substance and that the other progestogens are not. Hence, some women refer to "natural progesterone" vs. "synthetic." This is not precisely accurate, of course. Any substance manufactured in a laboratory is synthetic, including the progesterone suppositories or liquid injectable forms used in this country. But these progesterone compounds are molecular twins of progesterone as it is produced by the ovaries. Progestogens, like Provera and those contained in birth control pills, are made of compounds similar to progesterone, except for subtle differences in molecular structure. It is that subtle difference that can mean pain or relief to a woman with premenstrual syndrome. And it is that subtle difference that many physicians refuse to recognize or do not have the sophistication and training in steroid chemistry to understand.

Progesterone was first used successfully for the treatment of premenstrual syndrome in 1934, the year it was first isolated by Dr. Willard Allen, among others. Since then, a number of researchers have reported its successful use. The rationale for its use was first published by Leon Israel in 1938 who suggested that an uncontrolled estrogen effect resulting from a deficiency of progesterone was the cause of the symptoms. A relative progesterone deficiency in relationship to a possible estrogen excess was subsequently documented in studies of luteal phase steroid levels in women suffering from PMS.

Another documented consequence of deficient luteal phase progesterone levels is the defect which results in an apparent under-development of the lining of the uterus, the endometrium. The endometrium does not develop sufficiently to sustain the implantation of a fertilized egg. Often this is attributed to insufficient progesterone production by the corpus luteum. Miscarriages will result and, in some women, infertility. Luteal phase deficiency occurs in about three percent of the female population, but it has been found in thirty-five to fifty percent of women who suffer from repeated spontaneous abortions and miscarriages. Infertility and miscarriages due to luteal phase defects have been successfully treated with progesterone suppositories. Unless there is an underlying disorder, such as hypothyroidism, the deficiency can be treated with progesterone, usually 25 milligrams twice a day beginning three to four days before the onset of the luteal phase and continuing until the onset of menstruation.

There are no reported significant side effects of progesterone, no adverse interaction between progesterone and other drugs has been documented, and it would be almost impossible to overdose on it. The female body produces ten to thirty times more progesterone in the second and third trimesters of pregnancy than in the peak level of the luteal phase. As Dr. Charles Lloyd, a prominent endocrinologist and former director of the Worcester Foundation for Experimental Biology, where oral contraceptives were first developed, says: "If I were looking for an innocuous substance to take, it would be progesterone. There are no side effects, except in some, a cutting down of the sex drive."

In our clinical experience, peak blood levels of women being treated with progesterone have not approached the blood levels observed in the late second and third trimesters of pregnancy. Probably the only means by which a woman could overdose on progesterone is by intravenous administration. Occasionally, in women who have never carried a child to term and thus have not been exposed to the large amounts of progesterone usually present during pregnancy, progesterone doses by suppository exceeding 400 milligrams may produce mild euphoria, restless energy, faintness, and some uterine cramping.

Studies of the side effects of the long-term use of progesterone have not been completed. Dr. Katharina Dalton has followed many women who have been on continuous progesterone therapy for over ten years and has reported no adverse effects. She has also begun reviewing the medical records of her patients of the last thirty-five years; her results are eagerly awaited. However, these earliest patients of Dr. Dalton who took progesterone for many years need to be assessed in a well-designed epidemiological study to determine if there are possible adverse, or perhaps protective, side effects from the long-term use of progesterone.

No Side-Effects Reported

Progesterone has been administered intravenously over many days continuously in doses of 100 to 150 mg per day without apparent adverse effect and with minimal toxic symptoms. In some published studies, progesterone administered in 500-mg doses intravenously and in several thousand-milligram doses over several days by injection produced no apparent adverse effects and minimal toxic symptoms. Progesterone administered intravenously or by injection reaches the bloodstream directly, so the dosages are lower than those in suppository form. By the suppository method, progesterone is absorbed through the mucus membranes of the vagina or rectum and taken into the system; not all of the progesterone may be absorbed from the suppository and some of its strength and effectiveness is lost in the absorption process. And women metabolize progesterone at varying rates. As a result, suppositories are made with 200 milligrams and 400 milligrams of progesterone.

The minimal doses of progesterone we prescribe for our patients are 200 milligram suppositories for the last eight to sixteen days of the menstrual cycle. Patients with severe cases of PMS who absorb progesterone poorly and metabolize it rapidly may require a 400-milligram suppository four to six times a day for the last ten to eighteen days of the cycle. A patient may need to take the progesterone for six to eight months or for many years. Eventually, for most women, the total dose can be reduced to a minimal amount each day and used only the last four to eight days of the cycle.

Progesterone can be administered orally, intravenously, by injection, in suppositories, or in rectal solution. At some point, it may also be made available in transdermal "patches," nasal spray or drops, or vaginally through slow-release "rings" and artificial membranes, or subcutaneous pellets and microcapsules. At present, the best available means of administering progesterone is the suppository form. Progesterone must be absorbed into the system, raise the blood level of the hormone significantly, and keep it raised to a level sufficient to counteract the symptoms. The suppositories generally do this best. The half-life of progesterone in blood is several minutes, with only a small amount of progesterone stored in body fat. When taken orally, in a pill or liquid, progesterone is rapidly absorbed into the bloodstream and just as rapidly metabolized by the liver to an inactive substance. Consequently, large doses of progesterone would be required for the hormone to be effective by oral administration. But future research may produce an effective oral administration of progesterone.

Intramuscular injectable progesterone reaches a peak blood level within eight hours with the return to base line occuring within eighteen to forty-eight hours. Many women cannot tolerate progesterone injections. When the hormone is suspended in a water base, the injections are extremely painful; when it is suspended in an oil base allergic reactions and sterile abscesses may develop. Nonetheless, progesterone in oil injections should be considered for patients who are hospitalized, where close supervision is required, especially with patients who are suicide risks, or are likely to become involved in child abuse or alcohol abuse, or who show no response to suppositories. If injectable progesterone is required, the starting dose in women who have not had a term pregnancy is 50 mg once or twice daily and in women who have had children, 100 mg once or twice daily. Injections may be supplemented by suppositories or on occasion alternated with suppositories.

Progesterone administered by suppository via the rectum or vagina reaches peak blood level within four to eight hours with the return to base line occurring within twelve to twenty-four hours. Even when the suppositories are absorbed well, a woman may require several administrations per day to maintain adequate blood levels. Some women absorb progesterone poorly via the rectal or vaginal mucosa; a number of factors can affect the absorption rate including the type of base used in the suppository. Women who do not absorb progesterone well may require a suppository that contains more than 200 mg of progesterone, up to a maximum dose of 400 mg per suppository.

A study by Dr. Robert Reid, a Canadian endocrinologist, compared progesterone absorption from three different suppository bases — polyethylene glycol, glycolgelatin, and cocoa butter — demonstrating that peak circulating levels achieved with polyethylene glycol suppositories were significantly higher than either of the other two bases. A polyethylene glycol base or fatty acid base progesterone suppository is available upon prescription by a physician and compounded by pharmacists. Many American pharmacists experienced at compounding are Fellows of the American College of Apothecaries, which is located at 874 Union Avenue, Memphis, Tennessee 38163. The progesterone suppository used safely in England for the past fifteen years has a fatty acid base. No adverse effects have been reported with any of these types of suppositories, although they may cause minor irritation due to mechanical effects. The suppository produced in England may interfere with the effectiveness of vaginal diaphragms used for contraception, according to some reports.

For women who have never been pregnant the starting dosage is 200 to 400 milligrams per suppository daily; for women who have born a child it is 200 to 400 mg twice a day. If after starting progesterone, a woman notices a recurrence of symptoms, she should immediately increase the number of suppositories used each day. Once she increases the number, however, she should not decrease that amount during that particular cycle. If the woman gains no relief after her first course of progesterone, beginning with the next cycle of treatment she should increase the dose of progesterone to 200 mg two or three times a day if she's never had a term pregnancy and up to 400 mg four times a day if she's carried a fetus to term. Higher doses seem to be required by women who have had more pregnancies, and particularly those with a history of toxemia, hypertension in pregnancy, or postpartum depression. A woman who requires more than six 400 mg suppositories per day probably is not absorbing progesterone well and may require the use of a suppository with a different base.

Progesterone is usually administered from the time of ovulation to the onset of menstruation. But timing may need to be adjusted for the following reasons:

1. *Symptoms at ovulation.* Start progesterone two days before expected onset of symptoms.

2. *Irregular and prolonged cycles.* Stop progesterone at time of expected onset of menstruation.

3. *Length of cycle.* Ovulation usually occurs about fourteen days before onset of menstruation except in a short cycle of twenty to twenty-two days when ovulation tends to occur ten to twelve days before the onset of menstruation.

4. *Short episode of symptoms* (lasting only one to five days). Start progesterone three to five days before the expected onset of symptoms.

5. *Symptoms continuing into menstruation.* During the first two to four treatment cycles, discontinue progesterone at the expected onset of menstruation. Often symptoms continuing into menstruation will then cease. If they persist, however, reduce progesterone dosage to one-half the usual dose during the first few days of menstruation, then discontinue.

Once dosage, timing and absorption have been sufficiently achieved and the relief of symptoms has been gained, continue the same dose of progesterone for three symptom-free cycles. Then gradually reduce the dose by starting the course of treatment two days later each month. If the symptoms return, the next month's course should be started at the shortest course producing complete symptom relief and continued for a further two or three symptom-free months before attempting to reduce the dose again. Women in their thirties, especially those who have not had a term pregnancy, often require progesterone therapy for six to twelve months. Women over forty usually need progesterone until menopause. Women between thirty and forty are more difficult to predict in terms of length of treatment. An increasing length of treatment usually is required for women with a number of pregnancies and for those with a history of toxemia or postpartum depression.

Adjustments of Timing

When problems do develop with progesterone therapy, it is usually because the timing of the progesterone treatment needs to be adjusted. Some of the problems with timing and the appropriate adjustments include:

1. *Shortening of cycle.* During the next cycle, start the progesterone one to two days later.

2. *Lengthening of cycle.* Stop progesterone at the time of the expected onset of menstruation, and bleeding will usually occur within 48 hours.

3. *Spotting at mid-cycle* will occur if progesterone is used too early in the follicular phase.

4. *Spotting in the premenstruum.* Stop progesterone, then start the next course of treatment one to two days later.

5. *Erratic cycles.* Usually this is an indication that the patient has forgotten to use her progesterone for one to two days.

6. *Hives or rash.* This may occur as a reaction to the vegetable oil used in injectable progesterone. Discontinue the injections and continue further treatment with suppositories.

The Controversies: The FDA and Cancer

Injectable progesterone in oil is commonly produced in the United States, but progesterone suppositories are not. The suppository form is tolerated best by most women, which is why it is important to make progesterone suppositories readily available throughout the country. Pharmacists are permitted to compound suppositories for individuals upon a physician's prescription. But the research trials necessary to meet Food and Drug Administration regulations must be completed and approved before suppositories can be made by a pharmaceutical manufacturer here.

Obtaining FDA approval for the commercial production and distribution of progesterone depends on the outcome of investigative studies proposed to be carried out at Duke University in cooperation with L.D. Collins Ltd., the British manufacturer of progesterone suppositories, which would like to produce them in this country. Other studies are being carried out by Gail Keith, a nurse practitioner working under the supervision of Dr. W.N. Spellacy at the University of Illnois, at Vanderbilt University Hospital, at the National Institutes of Mental Health, and at our own centers. With the assistance of Dr. Charles Lloyd of Bowman Gray School of Medicine and Dr. Phillip Stubblefield of Massachusetts General Hospital, in 1981 we filed with the F.D.A. the first double-blind, placebo-controlled crossover study sponsored by L.D. Collins Ltd. Unfortunately, the F.D.A. chose to limit that study to a maximum 200 milligram progesterone suppository once a day for the last fourteen days of the cycle. From our clinical experience and that of Dr. Dalton's, we know that this limited dose would be effective in fewew than ten percent of the women with significant PMS. Such a restricted study, we felt, would have been unfair to our patients and a poor use of the limited resources of time, energy, and money. Other academic researchers agreed with us. Subsequently, we withdrew from the study and assisted L.D. Collins in arranging to carry out their studies with the Department of Obstetrics and Gynecology at Duke University, where Dr. Charles Hammond, a prominent gynecologic endocrinologist, is the department chairman. The move to Duke was made with the hope that they could persuade the F.D.A. to allow studies to proceed using higher dosages of progesterone. In early 1983, an advisory committee to the F.D.A. decided after a hearing on the subject that pharmacologic kinetic studies could go ahead. If those studies did not cause greatly elevated blood levels of progesterone, the advisory group said it would approve higher dose clinical studies of progesterone in the treatment of PMS. The results of the pharmacologic kinetic studies were not available as this book was written.

Has progesterone been implicated as a carcinogen? The answer is a resounding no. In fact, progesterone very likely has a cancer preventive quality. A recent study of women evaluated for infertility suggested that a deficiency of progesterone increased the risk of premenopausal breast cancer by 5.4 times and increased the risk of death by all cancer by ten times. That suggests that progesterone is a factor in reducing the incidence of cancer. There's other evidence of progesterone's protective characteristics.

Studies of progesterone's effect on mice, rats, rabbits, and dogs have been similar to research of the progestogens that are used in oral contraceptives.

The progestogens commonly used in oral contraceptives produce tumors in animals. Norethynodrel alone will increase the incidence of pituitary tumors in mice of both sexes and in combination with the estrogen, mestranol, it will increase the incidence of pituitary, vaginal and cervical tumors in female mice and of malignant mammary tumors in rats of both sexes. Ethynodiol diacetate, another progestogen in the Pill, also caused an increased incidence of malignant mammary tumors in female rats. However, we know now that the birth control pill protects women from the risk of some types of cancer. Recent research studies of women who have taken the birth control pill for a significant period of time have demonstrated that oral contraceptives reduce the risk of endometrial cancer by fifty percent and significantly reduce the risk of various disorders, including benign breast disease, ovarian cysts and cancer, pelvic inflammatory disease, iron deficiency anemia, tubal pregnancies, and rheumatoid arthritis.

The research and results of these studies are similar to those for progesterone.

The research studies of progesterone in animals have involved subcutaneous or intramuscular injection of the hormone in mice, rats, rabbits, and dogs, and subcutaneous implantation in mice and rats. Progesterone alone was tested in mice and dogs; in rats it was tested in combination with other chemicals; in mice it was also given in combination with known carcinogens. Given alone it increased the incidence of ovarian, uterine, and mammary tumors in mice. In dogs, long-term, continuous progesterone exposure in high dosages resulted in increases in the incidence of mammary nodules similar to that seen with medroxyprogesterone, a compound related to progesterone. This is viewed as a special circumstance; the results are limited only to experiments with beagles. There is no clinical evidence for a relationship between progesterone use and breast cancer in women. From the experience of the animal research studies with progestogens used in oral contraceptives — which increase the incidence of some tumors in animals but are protective against some tumors in humans — research may well confirm that progesterone is also protective against cancer in humans. In England, where Dr. Katharina Dalton has treated women with premenstrual syndrome for thirty years with progesterone, no in-depth epidemiological study has been undertaken into the long-term effects of progesterone; however, no links between progesterone and incidence of cancer have been reported either. Again, the overall protective effect of progesterone may be illustrated by the sharply reduced cancer risk in women with progesterone deficiencies.

Need for Research

Research studies need to be conducted into progesterone and hormone levels in women with PMS and women without the syndrome. No double-blind control study of progesterone treatment has been done yet, despite the hundreds of clinical papers published on related topics. We are preparing just such a study in Massachusetts that will assess the presence of estrogen, progesterone, testosterone, cortex steroid-binding protein, and sex steroid-binding protein in non-PMS and PMS women throughout the cycle. We will see if we can define normal and abnormal estrogen and progesterone hormone ratios, and if it's possible to determine a cut-off point, a point up to which behavior and physical state are normal, and beyond which women experience PMS. These and other investigations will ultimately lead us to discover what causes PMS and why progesterone diminishes the symptoms.

SECTION VII / *The Broader View*

Chapter 27

Fame Is No Protection

The impact of premenstrual syndrome on the behavior of women may explain the erratic, contradictory, or volatile behavior on the part of those who lived before the PMS diagnosis was part of the medical vocabulary. The rich and famous have no immunity to the disorder. We have already seen what appears to have been PMS-like episodes in Lizzie Borden and Joan Crawford. While it is difficult to make precise psycho-historical evaluations without knowledge of a woman's medical history and menstrual cycle, the legacy of biographical material about a number of notable women indicates that premenstrual syndrome may have influenced the behavior of Pauline Bonaparte, Maria Callas, Sylvia Plath, Mary Todd Lincoln, Alice James, and Judy Garland, among others.

Letters, diaries, chronicles and biographies of some members of the British royal family indicate that PMS may have been woven into the fabric of the daily life of Mary Tudor, Katherine of Aragon, Queen Victoria, and perhaps Elizabeth I.

Mary Tudor, the daughter of Henry VIII and Katherine of Aragon, "had not been entirely well since about the age of fourteen, when with the onset of puberty she began to experience symptoms of a disorder known to Renaissance doctors as 'strangulation of the womb' or 'suffocation of the mother,' " writes Carolly Erickson in her book *Bloody Mary*. These terms encompassed various disorders related to the female reproductive system, including amenorrhea, abdominal swelling and bloating, and depression. The range of symptoms that led 16th Century physicians to the diagnosis of strangulation of the womb included headache, nausea, vomiting, lack of appetite, melancholy, and "longing, an ill habit of body, difficulty of breathing, trembling of the heart, swooning, fearful dreams, and watching, with sadness and heaviness." The medical profession then believed that the condition was caused by sexual abstinence. "Every woman, whatever her age, rank or degree of virtue, was at the mercy of her voracious uterus — what for centuries had been called the 'raging womb,' " Erickson writes. Widows, or

257

wives suddenly deprived of the "company of a man," fell into an aggrieved state of melancholy and were troubled with amenorrhea. Even young girls who were strictly kept away from men suffered pain, mental anguish and irregular menstruation, and the only satisfactory cure was marriage. Widows were urged to marry again; wives were advised to engage in "wanton copulation" with their husbands. Physicians told the parents of young girls to arrange matches for them without delay, and in the meantime to send them out horseback riding for several hours a day. No record of the treatments Mary Tudor was given survives, but it is certain that she followed the recommended therapy of daily horseback rides.

Elizabeth Tudor, Queen Elizabeth I, was thought to be healthy, but was known for her periodic, recurring outbursts of virulent temper, Alison Plowden relates in *Elizabeth Regina*. "When stirred to passion, her Highness was quite capable of filling the air with good round oaths and was subject on occasion 'to be vehemently transported with anger.'" Elizabeth in a rage could be heard several rooms away and she was not above throwing things, or boxing the ears of the nearest maid of honor. "When she smiled," wrote her godson, John Harington, "it was a pure sunshine that every one did choose to bask in; but anon came a storm from a sudden gathering of clouds, and the thunder fell, in wondrous manner, on all alike.'"

Victoria's Outbursts

Temper, outbursts, uncontrolled behavior, and the throwing of objects was a pattern laid to Queen Victoria, documented in letters between Prince Albert to the Queen, and in virtually all biographies of her reign. Albert dreaded the outbursts of his wife, primarily because he understood reason better than emotion. Louis Auchincloss in his book *Persons of Consequence, Queen Victoria and Her Circle* writes about these recurring incidents, noting that they may have affected the couple's sex life. "I find it easy to imagine that she may have wanted to make love more frequently than he did, but there is nothing to suggest that he was not usually ready and willing to comply. The Queen was probably fairly easily satisfied; she had no one to compare him with, nobody even to discuss such matters with. Sex must have been an easy price for the peace and quiet that he craved. It may, too, have warded off the temper tantrums that he so dreaded... Outside the bedroom Albert showed, at first, little ability in handling her. When the Queen exploded during arguments and even threw things at him, he would retire to his study to make out a long list of all the reasons that he was right and she was wrong.'' These lists were the famous ''Dear Child'' letters from Albert to Victoria that reveal the cyclical nature of her temper, leading us to conclude that a disorder like premenstrual syndrome may have been the triggering mechanism.

David Duff, in *Albert and Victoria,* writes that the Prince Consort ''knew nothing of the imponderable in women. He was completely inexperienced. He did not appreciate the unreasoned emotions which surged like a maelstrom in Victoria's brain. Albert's answer to all the problems of life was to exercise reason... When Victoria began throwing things and screaming her accusations into his face, he would retire to write a paper on the cause of the outburst... Albert soon learned that any action that he took at such times was wrong. Answering back led to faster, louder vituperation. Remaining quiet was classified as insulting. Retiring behind a locked door eventually led to an attack upon its panels by royal fists. If Albert had taken a stiff whisky, armed himself with a stick and chased Her Majesty along the corridor and up the stairs, he would have discovered that tantrums would have been less frequent and accompanied by less bravado... Even Melbourne, a past master at dealing with women, had on one occasion quavered and feared to sit down as the fire blazed in the eyes of the eighteen-year-old Queen. A cabinet minister was known to fly from her presence, too frightened to follow the rule of withdrawal. (The rule requires those in the Queen's presence to ''back'' out of a room rather than turning about and showing their back to the Queen.) Thus Albert looked forward to the period of pregnancy — it gave emotion a reason... When she was pregnant he was always kind, thoughtful, attentive of her every wish. Here was a problem that he could understand, a train of events to which he could attend.''

Victoria, however, dreaded pregnancy and was disgusted by all things related to menstruation and reproduction. She had difficult pregnancies followed by severe postpartum depression and other complications, again possible evidence of PMS. In *Victoria and the Victorians,* Herbert Tingsten tells us that Victoria ''felt tired and depressed during and after her numerous pregnancies." She also wrote with frankness about marriage. Nuptial night was a shock to her, ignorant as she was in matters of sex. She equated sexual intercourse with the unpleasantness of pregnancy. Looking back on the eve of the wedding of her seventeen-year-old daughter Vicky, Victoria wrote to her: "Yes dearest, it is an awful moment to have to give up one's innocent child to a man, be he ever so kind and good — and to think of all she must go through! I can't say what I suffered, what I felt, what struggles I had to go through — (indeed I have not quite got over it yet) and that last night when we took you to your room, and you cried so much, I said to Papa as we came back 'after all it is like taking a poor lamb to be sacrificed.' You know now — what I meant, dear. I know God has willed it so and that these are the trials which we poor women must go through; no father, no man can feel this! Papa never would enter into it at all! As in fact he seldom can in my very violent feelings."

David Duff also documents these feelings. "Victoria hated being pregnant... She was wearied by the 'constant aches and sufferings, miseries and plagues.' She was bitter at being robbed of her enjoyments, particularly dancing and riding. She felt pinned down, her wings clipped, and only half her real self. She referred to pregnancy as the shadow side of marriage and thought it unfair that men did not take a share of that shadow. A woman, she considered, was morally and physically the man's slave and that, she commented, 'always sticks in my throat... If these selfish men, the cause of all one's misery, only knew what their poor slaves go through.' She thought of herself more in the role of cow than a blessed vehicle giving birth to an immortal soul. The general attitude was not conducive to good temper."

On one occasion, Duff writes, "Queen Victoria and Prince Albert were having tea. Those in attendance upon them noted that Her Majesty had the storm flags flying. There were red patches on her cheeks and her eyes were hard as glass. She raised her cup toward her lips. Then, quick as a flash, she hurled the contents into her husband's face... Before her daughter, the Princess Royal, had been christened, the Queen had become pregnant again. The realization flooded her with depression and anger and she made her feelings very clear to her husband. He, understating as was his habit, informed his brother: 'Victoria is not very happy about it.'"

After the birth of her son, the Prince of Wales, she suffered from severe postnatal depression. She reportedly told King Leopold: "I am very strong as to fatigue and exertion, but not quite right otherwise; I am growing thinner and there is a want of tone... I have likewise been suffering so from lowness that it made me quite miserable, and I know how difficult it is to fight against it."

With our knowledge that a genetic predisposition to PMS exists, it may well be that the syndrome has been a source of medical and psychological problems to current royalty as well.

A Corsican Princess

Another royal princess, Pauline Bonaparte, the sister of Napoleon, may also have suffered from PMS. Pauline is described as a volatile Corsican beauty who shocked European society with her sexual excesses. In *Imperial Venus* by Len Ortzen, we learn that Pauline's first and only pregnancy was a difficult one, whose "effects were to trouble her for many years." She was moody, difficult, had outbursts of temper, and was plagued with medical complaints that made it difficult for her to endure travels by coach and required long hours of rest and the taking of the baths at spas throughout Europe.

"Pauline left the heat of Florence in early July and went at last to Bagni di Lucca," Ortzen writes. "The exact nature of the disorder for which she was seeking a cure is not known; it was not the custom in her day to reveal such details, especially of female ailments, always supposing that they were within the scope of the medical knowledge of the time. Her ailment probably had its origins in the complications following the birth of (her son) Dermide. Her habit of reposing on a chaiselongue, for much longer periods than the prevailing fashion required, and the distress she suffered on long coach journeys, suggest that she was subject to some kind of internal disorder. One of the foremost gynecologists of the day later diagnosed her condition as a chronic inflammation of the womb, accompanied by general prostration and exhaustion."

A letter written by Doctor Jean-Noel Halle, a prominent gynecologist, to her personal physician, Doctor Peyre, discussed this condition. "My dear colleague, I have thought very carefully about the condition of Her Highness and the state of hysteria we found her in yesterday. The womb was still sensitive, though a little less so. The ligaments still exhibited signs of the painful inflammation for which we prescribed baths last Thursday. The spasms in her arms were due to hysteria, as were the pains in her head. Her general state is one of prostration and exhaustion. The inflammation is by no means usual. The present condition of the uterus is caused by a constant and habitual excitation of that organ, and if this does not cease a most grievous condition may result.'' Later, Napoleon's favorite medical adviser Jean-Nicolas Corvisart was summoned from Paris to consult about her health. ''A series of rare complications,'' he wrote, ''has resulted in a condition that is a malady *sui generis,* of which I do not think the exact nature and limits are known. A thousand times unhappy is the Princess who suffers from it, and equally unfortunate are the physicians called in to attend so ambiguous a case.''

Another PMS symptom, increased libido, was experienced by Pauline Bonaparte, who had many love affairs during her marriage to Prince Borghese. One story related by Ortzen is that Pauline ''created a sensation when she commissioned Antonio Canova to carve a statue of her 'almost naked.' He proposed to represent Pauline as Diana the Huntress. But when she learned the legend attached to this goddess, she refused. 'Diana asked her father, Jupiter, to endow her with eternal virginity,' said Pauline. 'If I were represented as that goddess, everyone would have fits of laughter.' It was decided to represent her more appropriately as Venus.''

Mary Todd Lincoln

Abraham Lincoln's wife, Mary Todd Lincoln, has also been portrayed as a woman plagued by recurring, periodic medical and mental disorders that seem to add up to a diagnosis of premenstrual syndrome. Her emotionalism, outbursts, and other complaints, especially migraine headaches and depression, began after the birth of her children — she had four sons. She also had numerous panic attacks and incidents of bizarre behavior. In *Mrs. Abraham Lincoln,* W.A. Evans writes: ''Pregnancy, childbirth, household drudgery, and sick headaches were beginning to tell on this abnormally intense little woman. She was easily frightened into a panic... Mary, finding her child missing, would become hysterical, and, rushing out onto the terrace in front of the house, would scream: 'Bobbie's lost! Bobbie's lost!'... The husband knew, as no one else did, what Mary had to contend with. He had seen her in prostrating, nauseating headaches when her head could not be raised from the pillow and a jarring step on the floor was torture. Lincoln was the only one who knew whether those hysterical outbursts of fear or anger had a time relation to her headaches or to periodic and other ills." Abraham Lincoln repeatedly wrote and told friends that "Mrs. Lincoln is not well."

After the birth of her fourth child Tad in 1853 she wrote to a friend: "I have been seriously sick. (My disease is of a womanly nature, which you will understand has been) greatly accelerated by the last three years of mental suffering. Since the birth of my youngest son, for about twelve years, I have been more or less a sufferer." Around 1865 an observer noted that "Mrs. Lincoln's personality included its list of liabilities. In impulsiveness and imprudence, in emotional immaturity, in that tendency to view things personally which shuts out broader wisdom, in susceptibility to flattery, in nervousness aggravated by migraine headaches and the mental tensions of the menopuase, in growing irrationality as to money, she had hidden weaknesses that were to pull her down in one of the most taxing situations a woman ever faced. These defects were not apparent like blindness or a crippled limb. She was like a foot soldier with secret lameness who must march long instances day after day through four years of war. Lincoln at this time was probably finding Mary's moods unpredictable, as has happened to other husbands when their wives reached the forties." Another writer noted her periodic, sharp mood swings. "It was not easy to understand why a lady who could be one day so kindly, so considerate, so generous, so thoughtful and so hopeful, could, upon another day, appear so unreasonable, so irritable, so despondent, so even niggardly, and so prone to see the dark, the wrong side of men and women and events."

Mary Lincoln's problems grew worse with age, exacerbated by the assassination of her husband and the deaths of three of her sons, and eventually developed into severe depression and other psychiatric disorders that led her at one point to attempt suicide. Eddie Foy, the vaudevillian whose mother was a nurse and companion to Mrs. Lincoln, wrote that she "had always been a woman of rather unusual disposition.

After her husband's assassination she fell into deep melancholy and after her son Tad died, she suffered from periods of mild insanity. She had many strange delusions.''

Alice James

Alice James, the younger sister of William and Henry James, was another woman whose life was shadowed by periodic recurring illness, anxiety, and psychiatric problems. In her biography of *Alice James,* Jean Strouse paints a picture of a woman so constricted by her health that her life was in many ways very narrow, while intellectually very full. Alice never married, did not bear a child, and produced no great works. From the age of nineteen she was variously described as delicate, fragile, high-strung, nervous, hysterical, and given to prostrations and nervous breakdowns. In many ways, of course, she fulfilled the Victorian ideal of beauty in women, marked, as Strouse notes, by a graceful languor, pallor, and vulnerability. "Illness made a woman ethereal and interesting," observes Strouse. Susan Sontag makes that point in her work, *Illness as Metaphor,* in which she notes that tuberculosis was seen to spiritualize life, a disease almost to be proud of because it was "the sign of a superior nature... a becoming frailty." For Alice James, illness was a part of her life; she was constantly visiting physicians, spas, or sanitariums for the treatment of both physical and mental complaints, although she had periods of good health and enthusiastic, positive mental states as well. But periodically, she suffered episodes of hysteria and paralysis of limbs, suicidal and murderous thoughts. Alice once described wanting to "knock off the head of the benignant pater as he sat with his silver locks, writing at his table," of sitting in the library, reading, when "violent inclinations" made her want to throw herself out the window or harm her father. She wrote of not being able to control her thoughts at school, of "impossible sensations of upheaval" that made it impossible for her to focus and concentrate on her studies. The cycle of good health-ill health is documented by Strouse. At one point she notes, "Since Alice's return from Europe in 1872, her health had gone through its usual (by this time) range of improvements and reversals." In 1878 she had a serious breakdown and became increasingly obsessed with death and suicide. She ultimately developed a tumor, but when she learned of her terminal illness, Strouse says: "Death now seemed to Alice to promise not eternal life but simply peace. It would annihilate all the questions of control, distinction, and selfhood that had plagued her life; it would obliterate the ceaseless conflicts between body and will, male and female, love and hate, good and evil, struggle and acceptance, success and failure. In the face of death, her life took on a new clarity. Death was consummation of struggle and pain, the apotheosis and the cessation of suffering. Alice went out to meet it like a lover keeping a long-awaited assignation, yearning to surrender to its large, dark, overwhelming force."

More Traces of PMS

Premenstrual syndrome may also have been part of the lives of such 20th Century women as Sylvia Plath, Maria Callas, and Judy Garland among others. Judy Garland's volatility, emotionalism, mood swings, depression, insomnia, and many medical problems all worsened after the birth of her three children, notes Christopher Finch in his book, *Rainbow.* She had insomnia in adolescence and mood swings. Her compulsive eating and subsequent weight problem (that had been fairly well controlled during her teens) became a major recurring problem after her pregnancies, which led to her dependence on amphetamines, first used as an appetite suppressant and later, together with alcohol, as a mood-altering substance. Whether her periodic, recurring problems were connected with her menstrual cycle is unclear, but they may well have been.

It is easier to see the cyclical nature of the outbursts, volatility, depression and health problems of opera singer Maria Callas. In her biography *Maria Callas,* Arianna Stassinopoulos details the endless emotionalism and lack of self-esteem of the diva. By examining the dates provided in the biography to many of the incidents, though, we can see a pattern. Almost all of the negative feelings and behavior, health problems, sinus attacks, and binge eating occurred throughout her life from the end of the month through the first ten days — usually from about the 20th to the 10th day. Many happy times and details of Callas' triumphs occurred in the middle of the month. It's a cycle that perhaps could be explained on some other basis, but it fits the pattern of premenstrual syndrome. Callas, according to a friend Francois Valery, had "talked about not feeling good when she had her periods." She suffered from recurring headaches and sinus attacks, as well as violent mood swings. "She became intensely irritable, annoyed by trifles, exaggerating their importance and unable to shake off her excessive concern with them. When she was not irritable she would sulk," Stassinopoulos writes. "Sulks were for Maria a rarely used weapon, but they were a weapon that occasionally took complete control of her... Standing near the pinnacle of worldwide fame, Maria was ambivalent about it, one moment radiant in the attention and admiration and the next moment snappish and resentful in the fear that it would all come to an abrupt end." The episodes are numerous: irritability, rage, grief, losing her voice, problems with her sinuses, emotional quarrels with spouse and manager, fear, shattered nerves, low blood pressure, deep anguish — all of these are variously dated on July 9, December 2, May 31, August 18, January 21, May 29, June 29-30, October 31 by Stassinopoulos. And occasions when the singer was described as in an expansive mood, in peak form, radiant, and feeling fine were dated December 18, August 10, August 15, and so on.

Callas' lack of self-esteem, a natural outgrowth of these cyclical bouts of depression and ill health, was notorious. As Stassinopoulos writes: "Because Maria's store of self-approval remained, most of the time, very low, she came to rely almost entirely on the approval of others. So the woman who had cast her spell on so many was in even greater need of them than they were of her. The greater the adulation the tighter the trap, especially since as she said herself, she was plagued with endless doubt and feelings of unworthiness. 'Even when people look at me with obvious affection, that makes me twice as angry. You think these people are looking at you in admiration — why should they? I don't deserve it.' The less she felt that she deserved admiration, the more she was determined to present to the world a version of herself that was deserving." The frustration and anger that she felt as a result in turn fueled her outbursts and temper tantrums. Depression cloaked the diva for as much as two to three weeks of each month, even when she had much to be happy about. "The end of her year of triumph found Maria in a desperate state. Her dark view of life and the world was once again confirmed, only this time, coming so soon after so much success and so much glory, it was more deeply painful than ever before."

During her prime singing years, we learn she suffered from nervous tension and fueled her performance schedule with food binges, "she was beginning to be increasingly bothered by headaches, fainting spells and attacks of car sickness which she attributed more to the excess weight she carried than to anything else."

Sylvia Plath

Sylvia Plath, whose depression and obsession with suicide were themes woven throughout her poetry and prose, was a woman who clearly had enormous psychiatric problems and suffered with a major clinical depression most of her life. But she may also have had premenstrual syndrome, which could have worsened during a two-year period in which she had two children and a miscarriage and a number of other health problems. Again, by examining the dates of many of her journal entries and examining the material written about her works and the circumstances under which her poetry was written, a pattern seems to emerge. Plath had recurring sinusitis and cyclical mood swings which seem to come and go monthly. The dates of her bad days and good days are very similar to those of Maria Callas — the end and beginning of months seem marked by the worst depressions, suicidal thoughts, and violent feelings while the middle of the months are days of brighter thoughts.

On November 3, 1952, she wrote: "God, if ever I have come close to wanting to commit suicide, it is now, with the groggy sleepless blood dragging through my veins..." On February 18, 1953: "Oh, I would like to get in a car and be driven off into the mountains to a cabin on a wind-howling hill and be raped in a huge lust like a cave woman, fighting, screaming, bitching in a ferocious ecstasy of orgasm... I wonder at my morbid obsession with daydreams." On August 9: "I have never in my life, except that deadly summer of 1953, and fall, gone through such a black lethal two weeks..." On March 28: "Occasionally I lifted my head, ached, felt exhausted. Saturday I groaned, took pellets of Bufferin, stitched in the worst cramps and faintness for months which no pills dulled..." Jan. 22: "Absolutely blind fuming sick. Anger, envy and humiliation. A green seethe of malice through the veins. "But on December 12 she wrote: "Ever since Wednesday, I have been feeling like a 'new person.' Like a shot of brandy went home, a sniff of cocaine, hit me where I live and I am alive and so there." On September 18: "Much happier today — why? Life begins, minutely, to take care of itself — an odd impulse brings a flood of joy, life..." On December 16: "I have been happier this week than for six months." February 10: "How clear and cleansed and happy I feel. Why?"

Clearly, it is impossible to impose explanations on behavior without detailed knowledge of all the influences on feelings, attitudes, and health. But our knowledge of the pervasiveness of premenstrual syndrome in the general female population makes it likely that some of these women whose lives we have studied were influenced to some degree by PMS.

Chapter 28

*"Premenstrual tension is a settled scientific
fact, which the law is bound to accept and
deal with, just as it must deal with the
phenomena of insanity. . ."*

Howard Oleck, "The Legal Aspects of PMS," 1953.

The Defense Pleads PMS

Between 1970 and 1979 Sandie Craddock, a thirty-year-old English-woman, was convicted of criminal offenses, mostly minor, at least thirty times. She received repeated psychiatric counseling, and her doctors concluded that she suffered a severe personality disorder which led her to seek constant attention. One night in May 1979, she was working in a pub when a dispute broke out, and she stabbed a fellow barmaid to death. While in prison awaiting trial, the monthly pattern of her outbursts was identified as premenstrual syndrome; she was treated with progesterone, and it worked almost immediately. Based largely on the diagnosis of Dr. Katharina Dalton, rather than an independent examination by court-appointed doctors, Craddock was convicted on a lesser charge of manslaughter. The court concluded that her case fit the category of "diminished responsibility," meaning that her medical condition lessened her ability to take responsibility for her actions. The charge was reduced to manslaughter from murder and she was released on three years' probation, with the stipulation that she continue to receive progesterone treatment.

But in the fall of 1980, for reasons that are not made clear in the court record, Craddock went for several days without receiving her usual progesterone treatments. Then, during a trip to a town west of London she tossed a brick through a window. She immediately turned herself in, and was released as soon as her condition and therapy were explained to the local magistrate. In April, 1981, soon after her daily doses were substantially reduced from their initial high levels, Craddock lost control once again. She attempted suicide. In late May she threatened a local police sergeant (whom she accused of being rude to her). Using letters crudely scissored out of newspapers and magazines, she had pasted up the message "I Gona Kill You." Several days later she telephoned the police department and stated that she would kill the sergeant. "I hate him. I'm going to kill him. I'll get him." When she was discovered the next morning outside the police station with an open knife in her jacket pocket, she again threatened the sergeant and was arrested. Sandie Craddock is not the world's most sophisticated criminal, but her case posed some very sophisticated issues for the British legal system. Those questions remain unanswered today and anticipate similar issues that will undoubtedly, in time, confront the American courts.

Historically, defendants have been held responsible for their actions unless they can prove that a disability prevented them from conforming to society's accepted standards of behavior. A central issue is whether the courts should include PMS in that category of diseases which so impair the rational faculties of its victims that they are relieved of responsibility for their actions. Defining those "disabilities" continues to be a point of debate. Insanity is the most accepted of these defenses, but in recent years it has come under sharp attack. Critics contend that it is often abused, and that many criminals who pose a continuing danger to society are freed on the basis of questionable expert testimony. Even defenders of the insanity defense, and of its related defenses, concede that it is sometimes misapplied. But they still argue that it would be unjust to hold individuals to a standard of conduct that they are simply unable to meet. So the question for the judicial system becomes: at what point do the courts draw the line between a true disability and lesser conditions that many people must bear as part of everyday life?

Historically, menstrually-related problems were accepted as legal defenses for a range of criminal acts. Three notable cases: Martha Brixey, a servant who without any motive murdered an employer's child in 1845 and made no attempt to avoid detection, was acquitted on the grounds of insanity caused by "obstructed menstruation." Six years later Amelia Snoswell was acquitted of the murder of her infant niece, again on the grounds of insanity, this time due to "disordered" menstruation. A woman accused of stealing a fur boa was acquitted in 1845 at Carlisle Quarter Sessions on the grounds of temporary insanity "from suppression of the menses."

Need for Establishment Recognition

Despite the colorful history of the 19th Century, PMS is not widely recognized by the medical or the legal establishment today. Until the medical profession reaches broad agreement that PMS can profoundly influence criminal and violent action, judges are likely to view it with extreme skepticism. "I don't see why it is any different than any other illness," says Alan A. Stone, a professor of law and psychiatry at Harvard Law School and Harvard Medical School, expressing a still common view of the legal profession. "The question is whether such a condition would lead to an inability to substantially conform" to the law, he says. "And I think that is patently absurd." The law will likely not come to grips with PMS until medicine does, and even then it will be an uphill battle.

Even among those who agree that there is overwhelming evidence that PMS causes criminal outbreaks, there remains sharp disagreement about whether it should be permitted as a defense. At one extreme are those who argue that proof of PMS at the time of a criminal action should be sufficient to relieve the woman of all responsibility for her acts. They contend that just as juries are permitted to return a verdict of "not guilty by reason of insanity" because the accused had no control over his actions, women who truly suffer from the disease should be declared not guilty by reason of PMS. Premenstrual syndrome does share some legal characteristics with insanity, but it differs in many key respects.

At the other extreme are those who don't believe that PMS, even if proven to be the motivating factor in a crime, should be permitted as a defense at all. Two distinct groups take this hardline position, but they reach the same conclusion for radically different reasons. One group contends that biology is no excuse for criminal behavior. Males, too, have hormonal imbalances, they point out, but it is impossible to say with certainty how great or little a role those imbalances play in providing a "proximate cause" for criminal behavior.

"Women have long been subject to sexist slurs about hormonal behavior, but modern knowledge is more equanimous," wrote Michael Newman, director of the Warm Spring Harbor Laboratory for Qualitative Biology, in a letter published in The New York Times in 1982. "Male sex offenders, too, have hormonal problems, often high levels of testosterone. And Type A coronary personalities have been found to have very high levels of steroid hormones. It may be that every criminal is chemically deranged. Soon we all may be. The ones who don't hurt people have to be protected from the ones who do.'' What Newman was arguing, in essence, is what lawyers refer to as the "slippery slope" problem: allow one type of hormonal imbalance, no matter how severe, to serve as an absolute defense, and soon everyone who claims a similar disorder, no matter how inconsequential, will make a case for special treatment. "Let the law tamper with small medical knowledge, and what order is left in society will perish with the notion of common sense," Newman concluded.

Ardent feminists comprise the second group holding that PMS is no excuse for criminal action. They fear that any legal precedent that establishes women as inferior to men, or brands them with a disability that distorts their ability to think and act logically, may serve as a basis for discrimination. "It could become a tremendous sword," said Elizabeth Holtzman, a former congresswoman who is now District Attorney of Brooklyn, N.Y. "It could become a basis for refusing to hire women. It could become an excuse to go back to all kinds of discrimination that we have been trying to get away from."

Others fear that legal recognition of PMS would prompt some to question if a woman with even the slightest symptoms of PMS could be trusted with national security secrets, or could be given the power to launch a nuclear war? Concludes Holtzman: "I think that we ought to be able to say that women can be held accountable for their acts just as men" are.

The Middle Course

In between these two extreme views lies a compromise position. That is essentially the stand taken by the British courts in the Craddock case and one other. By declaring that Sandie Craddock suffered from diminished capacity to control her acts, the court was able to enter a verdict of guilty, but reduce her sentence and order proper medical treatment. Logical as the approach seems, diminished capacity is not a formal defense in the United States. Nonetheless, the theory exists, for all practical purposes, in the power of judges to take extraordinary circumstances into consideration when passing sentence. And, with certain safeguards to ensure that the PMS defense is not abused, that is how we believe the American criminal justice system should handle cases involving *bona fide* PMS victims.

In some respects, PMS differs from any diseases, both of the mind and the body, that have previously confronted the judicial system. The cyclical nature of PMS episodes defies most legal categories. Temporary insanity and other mental disorders occur in fits and starts, not in cycles. A PMS victim, however, may be perfectly normal for all but a few days, sometimes a week or two, each month. Because her violent actions are likely to recur regularly, they cannot be dismissed by a judge as a singular event unlikely to repeat itself. At the same time, her acts cannot be regarded as symptomatic of a permanent condition that requires institutionalization for the protection of society and the patient.

The premise of Western law is that citizens are held responsible for their actions when they are in control of their rational faculties. When they are not, judges and juries have an added responsibility to ensure that the criminal receives treatment, not punishment. At the same time, they still have a responsibility to ensure that the community is protected against violent acts, whether rationally motivated or not. For 150 years, lawyers and lawmakers have argued over how to define the law so that both responsibilities are met. They are still arguing. As we have seen, the complications of a PMS case have not yet reached a United States court. But they have been anticipated in a number of scholarly journals and law review articles, the most articulate and thorough of which is a comprehensive study published in 1971 in the *Law Review of the University of California, Los Angeles*. The authors, Aleta Wallach and Larry Rubin, concluded that PMS victims must be ''assured the same medical and legal rights purportedly accorded to those who suffer from similar defects and diseases.'' But they admitted, and later writings have confirmed, that nothing is similar enough to resolve the thorny legal questions.

What has become clear is that PMS falls into a legal no-man's land between insanity and ''automatism,'' the condition in which an individual acts automatically and without conscious knowledge of his acts. As a result, when faced with PMS cases, judges are likely to rely heavily on insanity, automatism, and other instances in which organic or biological events play a decisive role in patterns of behavior. Insanity, the best known and most controversial of the defenses, is a good starting point. Both the American and British definitions of insanity harken back to the case of Daniel M'Naughton, who was accused of killing a member of Parliament in 1843. In M'Naughton's case, it was established that one can use insanity as a defense if "the party accused was laboring under such a defect of reason, from disease of the mind, as not to know the nature and quality of the act he was doing; or, if he did it, that he did not know he was doing what was wrong."

PMS, like some other diseases that have brought the M'Naughton rule under criticism, does not quite fit the bill. First, it is not at all clear that PMS is a "disease of the mind," as we have illustrated throughout this book. Secondly, there is no evidence that PMS victims, even while in the most violent fits, are unaware of their actions, or do not know that the actions are wrong. In that regard, the disease resembles kleptomania, pyromania, and other conditions in which the criminal action is the result of an "irresistible impulse." Some states have broadened the M'Naughton rule, making the insanity defense available to those who are unable to control their actions even if they fully understood their implications. Under this definition, PMS and insanity, or at least temporary insanity, bear a close resemblance.

The problem with allowing an "irresistible impulse" as a defense, however, is that some illnesses seem to involve not only "impulses" but careful planning and premeditation. (Sandie Craddock, it should be remembered, talked about her attempted murder of the sergeant over a period of several days.) In 1954, in *Durham v. United States*, the U.S. Court of Appeals tried to avoid this distinction with the simpler, if broader statement that "an accused is not criminally responsible if his unlawful act was the product of mental disease or mental defect." Predictably, the effort at simplification only added more complications. First, it treated the mind as a separate entity, divorced from the body's biological activities. Secondly, the Durham rule made it necessary to prove that the act was the "product" of the defect, a nearly impossible standard to meet with one hundred percent certainty.

Still a third test, devised by the American Law Institute, says that there should be no responsibility for criminal conduct if the accused "lacks substantial capacity either to appreciate the criminality of his conduct or to conform his conduct to the requirements of the law." That eliminates some of the ambiguity of the Durham rule, but it is of little help in figuring out how to treat PMS victims. Except when they endure periodic episodes, they know as well as any citizen the difference between right and wrong. And even when controlled by strong impulses, they usually know if they are doing something they should not be doing.

In short, insanity differs too much from PMS to be of any real help in fashioning legal guidelines. Broadly speaking, under almost any insanity test, a defendant must show that her mental state prevented her from premeditating, deliberating, entertaining malice toward her victim, or holding the intent to kill. At various times, a PMS victim might demonstrate all of these characteristics.

In some ways, PMS should pose fewer difficulties for the courts than insanity. The cyclical behavior of PMS victims make it easier to determine who has the disease and who is faking it. The symptoms, while varying from individual to individual, are not as variable as those of insanity. More importantly, even if PMS victims could be treated like the the insane in the eyes of the law, it would not likely be in their best interest to be so. A successful insanity plea means that the court is free to institutionalize the defendant for an indefinite time period. With an illness like PMS, in which effective therapy with progesterone can control the symptoms, there is no evidence that incarceration would do anything but isolate the victim from society. It would have no "reforming" effect. Moreover, it would equate women who suffer from PMS with those who our society has said must be wards of the state because they cannot function on their own.

The law has not only relieved the insane from responsibility for their actions; it has, in some cases, found that the non-insane may also be subject to "irresistible impulse." The case law in this area has been inconsistent, and it has embraced a wide range of abnormalities. But most common among the "non-insane" defenses is automatism, an altered state of consciousness during which one's personality changes suddenly, but usually in a limited way. Usually automatism is accompanied by amnesia, or selective amnesia. Often it is triggered by a traumatic event, such as rejection by a lover. The defense has been used to explain murders, assaults, and attempts to evade the police, among other events.

The first problem raised by such claims is proof. In most countries, the courts have ruled that it is not enough simply to claim automatism; some evidence must sustain the contention. Thus, there is almost no way to sustain the automatism defense of someone who committed an unwitnessed crime. But a man named Gottschalk, accused of theft and assault in Canada in 1975, was acquitted primarily because witnesses who saw him immediately after the crimes said that he appeared to be in a state of shock. That testimony corresponded with the findings of a psychiatrist who examined the defendant. The Gottschalk decision and others like it have been criticized because the acquittal set the defendant free without any requirement that he obtain treatment — an unlikely result had he been found not guilty by reason of insanity. There is no assurance that his "non-insane" condition will not return. Indeed, the line between automatism and temporary insanity is a thin one, and it is unclear where one condition begins and the other ends.

Similar defenses have been offered by those who suffer from "post traumatic stress disorder," which has also been called "Vietnam syndrome," because it is commonly found among veterans who have survived heavy combat. They suffer a delayed reaction to the immense stress of the front lines. The symptoms resemble those of automatism: often a recurring sound or sight, like helicopter noise, brings on a dissociative state. It is a temporary condition. The syndrome was used successfully as a defense in the case of a Vietnam veteran who held a guard captive at a congressman's district office in California. Another received a suspended sentence after pleading that the stress disorder led him to take a church congregation hostage one Sunday afternoon.

Both automatism and post-traumatic stress disorder have been much criticized as legal defenses because they rely so heavily on expert psychiatric testimony. Usually the defendants seek to prove that the disorder was a one-time occurrence, explained by some unusual aspect of their personal history or medical background. Both differ from insanity in that they are singular events, usually prompted by an external stimulus. In many cases, though, the line between these afflictions and temporary insanity is a blurry one. It is extraordinarily difficult to make the distinction, and that explains the inconsistency of the verdicts. But in many cases juries have been convinced that a cause-and-effect relationship exists between the disorder and the criminal action.

Documentation Possible

Critics of the insanity defense, whose ranks have grown since the acquittal of John Hinkley, the attempted assassin of President Reagan, say that such defenses open a Pandora's box. They may be right. More often than not, at least one medical expert can be found to back every contention, however frivolous. Could the same criticism be made of the PMS defense? Yes, especially if it is diagnosed by "experts" who are simply hired hands aiding the execution of legal legerdemain. But extensive psychiatric testimony is not necessary to prove the existence of PMS, as it is for insanity, automatism, and post-traumatic stress disorder. The cyclical nature of PMS lends itself to careful documentation that should establish beyond any doubt whether the defendant truly suffers from the disease, or whether she is simply using it.

Dr. Estelle Ramey, a professor of physiology and biophysics at the Georgetown University Medical School, is also a researcher into the effects of sex hormones. She says that PMS has a place in the courtroom "if you can establish that a woman in her past history belongs to the group of women who are really disabled, emotionally and physically, during this period." Dr. Dalton suggests that the plea of PMS requires a woman to "produce positive evidence of similar episodes of loss of control, confusion, amnesia or violence" in the three previous menstrual cycles. Such evidence, she says, might be supplied by the woman's employer, friends or family, or by searching through diaries, medical files, police records, or prison documents. Moreover, the characteristics of the crime should very nearly match the typical profile of the PMS sufferer: she should have been acting alone, the event should not have been premeditated (usually; there are exceptions), the action should have occurred without a clear motive, there should be almost no attempt to escape detection. Imposing such a stiff standard is the only way to ensure that the PMS defense is not diluted by constant use and abuse. Dalton applauds the rejection of the PMS plea made by a travel agent's clerk accused of absconding with travelers' checks. The defendant said she suffered from PMS, but could only narrow the date of the crime to a nine-month period.

A highly publicized case in Brooklyn, N.Y. in 1982 that promised to be the first litigated case of the PMS defense in the United States was similarly ill-starred. A Legal Aid attorney representing Shirley Santos, a twenty-five-year-old mother of six accused of child abuse, announced her intention to use PMS as the defense because the defendant had said the incident occurred on the first day of her period. The District Attorney of Brooklyn is Elizabeth Holtzman, a former congresswoman who is a feminist and champion of women's rights; she has also adopted a conservative view of her role as prosecutor and keeps herself and her cases very much in the public eye. Legal Aid vs. Holtzman drew enormous pre-hearing publicity and promised to be a precedent-setter for the PMS defense in this country. Holtzman clearly was not going to move from her position, repeated in interview after interview, on *The Phil Donahue Show,* with *The New York Times* and in half a dozen press conferences. "I have long argued that there is no basis for the use of this defense," she told *The New York Times.* "There is no scientific evidence that there is any such thing as a syndrome which causes women to become insane or violent in connection with the menstrual cycle."

Behind the publicity and press conferences, the case itself was springing leaks. The harm to the child was minor, which made the case ripe for plea-bargaining. No information indicating that Shirley Santos had premenstrual syndrome, or had ever experienced PMS-type episodes in previous menstrual cycles, or had ever been treated for recurring cyclical health problems apparently existed. It was a bad case at the wrong time to start with, but it was torpedoed by the defendant herself. Shirley Santos, interviewed on local television at the courthouse when a scheduled hearing was postponed, looked right into the camera and said that PMS: "isn't my defense, it's my lawyer's... My nerves are not that bad that I am just going to beat up on my kid because my period comes down." Compounding the problems was a sudden strike by Legal Aid attorneys, which caused one postponement of the Santos hearing, and, legal observers in the Brooklyn court district said, contributed to the mutual decision to settle the case out of court. Appearing before Judge Donald Jacobi on November 3, 1982, Santos said she struck her daughter, Quadina, when she refused to be quiet. Pleading guilty to a lesser charge of harassment, which is a violation not a crime, she was given a conditional discharge with the stipulation that she would continue for a year in a counseling program. At a news conference afterward, Holtzman said, "The withdrawal of this defense is a signal that PMS is a defense without merit." The District Attorney conceded that many women experience "irritability, depression, and pain accompanying the menstrual cycle," but nothing constituting a condition that would justify a legal defense. In any event, she added, Santos had undermined any claim to such a defense when she disavowed the syndrome in the memorable television interview.

In a letter to *The New York Times* published November 15, Stephanie Benson, the Legal Aid attorney for Santos, "respectfully" disagreed. "I wholeheartedly believe that without the PMS arguments Miss Santos would still be facing criminal charges. The fact that they were all dropped is, instead, a testament to its validity... My hope is that in the future women with such difficulties will be able to recognize and receive appropriate treatment for them — free of social stigma or ill-conceived fear of economic reprisals."

Given the predominance of premenstrual syndrome in the population at large, it is only a matter of time before a woman, somewhere, sometime, finds herself swept up in an incident that she didn't plan, didn't intend, wouldn't have conceived of doing, outside of a premenstrual episode. When that happens, the American judicial system will be confronted with the PMS defense. Until an actual courtroom drama unfolds, we can only speculate about the issues and responses.

Our courts would do well to borrow from the British concept of diminished responsibility, which in the words of one legal scholar would allow the jury "to mitigate the punishment of a mentally disabled but sane offender in any case where the jury believes that the defendant is less culpable than his normal counterpart who commits the same criminal act." The criminal act is judged by the standards of the community — standards that a PMS sufferer, during much of the month, can appreciate, understand, and obey. At the same time, the sentence would reflect the extenuating circumstances under which the crime was committed. This approach does not preclude a jail term, especially for repeat offenders. But it makes proper medical treatment a likelihood. It is a practical approach. The issue of guilt or innocence can be decided without reference to the disease, an approach that should be more satisfactory both to feminists and those concerned that every hormonal imbalance may soon be offered as a defense. And until the existence of PMS is widely recognized, judges will likely be more amenable to adopting a system over which they have more personal control.

An exemplary case in this regard occurred in England only a few months after the Craddock case. In December 1980, thirty-seven-year-old Christine English, a woman with a long history of treatment for depression and premenstrual syndrome, had a series of raging, no-holds-barred battles with the man whom she was seeing regularly; he was married, an alcoholic, and an inveterate philanderer. On the night in question he planned to meet another woman. Christine English picked him up at a pub, where he had gotten drunk, and apparently agreed to drive him around in search of the woman he was supposed to meet. During the drive, they resumed their fight; he got out of the car. She drove away. But suddenly she made a U-turn, accelerated and drove the car directly at him, pinning him to a streetlamp. He died days later. Under the Homicide Act of 1957, English's history of PMS enabled her to plead guilty to a reduced charge of manslaughter. The judge heard testimony indicating that at the time of the murder she was in a state of great hormonal imbalance. Instead of sentencing her to prison, the judge put her on probation, ordered her to receive treatment — and forbade her to drive a car.

Both the Craddock and English decisions drew headlines and news reports in Britain and around the world. Fleet Street journalists made much of the implications of murder without punishment. But serious journals repeated the basic questions posed by PMS: "Despite legal cases which seem to have established the premenstrual syndrome as a mitigating condition in women who commit serious crimes, the disease status of the syndrome is seriously questioned," opined *The Lancet*. An article in *New Society*, *"Do Women Go Mad Every Month?"* concluded that accepting PMS as a mitigating factor in murder cases was not likely to serve the interests of women. What these and other critics neglect to consider is that a small number of women have been observed to have a severe and extreme disorder that occasionally causes them to do things in an uncontrollable state that they would not consider doing when they are symptom-free. Few of them are criminals, with intention and motive; little purpose would be served by incarcerating women whose only crime is a physiological defect beyond their control. What they do need is treatment. That was the basis of the sentences in the Craddock and English cases, which balanced the demands of society to protect itself from and punish criminals, with the more fundamental need to rehabilitate and make whole a transgressor. When progesterone therapy can "rehabilitate" a woman with PMS, why should she be imprisoned at great cost to the taxpayer in an environment that can breed crime rather than eradicate it? The aim of the law, after all, is to protect society and to aid and reform the individual. The magistrates in the English and Craddock cases bore the aim in mind, and recognized and ordered treatment for the disease.

Chapter 29

"We should all be concerned about the future because we will have to spend the rest of our lives there."

Charles Franklin Kettering, **Seed for Thought**

Making Progress

"To me, PMS is a woman's issue," one of our patients says. "It's equal health. Equal pay and equal jobs aren't going to do women any good if they're not well enough to take them." We agree, but not everyone does. The outcry over premenstrual syndrome that was triggered by the attempted use of the disorder as a legal defense is likely to expand by geometric progressions as information about PMS travels. Some feminists have already staked out the battlefield, charging that an acceptance of PMS is a tacit assumption that women are biologically disadvantaged, incapable of rational decision-making because of their vulnerability to monthly hormonal surges. They fear its recognition will lead to a regression, taking us backward to a pre-liberation world in which women are denied responsible jobs, promotions, political victories, and academic appointments because of their hormonal fluctuations.

The Feminist Debate

The feminist tendency to batten down the hatches, foreclosing attacks on women's abilities, is more understandable in light of the notoriety of certain sexist arguments. It was Dr. Edgar Berman who exploited the term "raging hormones" in a 1970 debate with Dr. Estelle Ramey, the Georgetown University Medical School professor. "Men and women are programmed more than we ever thought we would be," he says. "It's all evolutionary and genetic... Just as the rowdy kiddies of the 60s went back to home economics and dental school at the birth of the 70s, so shall this feminist uprising recede into history in the 80s." His view: "I just don't think you can make a Doberman pinscher out of a French poodle, or a Nelson Bunker Hunt out of a Bo Derek." Last year Berman renewed the furor over the biological differences between men and women in a polemic *The Compleat Male Chauvinist*.

Even the feminists aren't denying the biological differences between men and women but they are concerned about how these differences are perceived by society as a whole and used by women themselves. Susan Brownmiller, author of *Against Our Will,* takes a more measured view of PMS than some, but is extremely critical of its role as a legal defense. Brownmiller told us in an interview, "There are tremendous biological differences. But biological differences are not an excuse for violent crime." She calls a PMS legal defense "special case pleading" by women. "It's falling on the mercy of the court because you are a woman. Are men going to plead that it is an excess of testosterone that drives them to crime? I don't believe that PMS could drive a woman to a criminal act, unless she had crime on her mind... We are rational people who know what a violent crime is." Brownmiller continues, "I do not support it as a legal defense. As a legal defense it is very dangerous. It's not an excuse for a crime." She does not accept a defense that "relieves you of the responsibility of your actions... unless you're totally crazy," she says, which indicates she has some acceptance of the insanity defense.

Yet Brownmiller concedes that premenstrual syndrome exists as a disorder affecting many women. "I *know* it exists... As far as irritability or bursting into tears, I can see it for that." She told us in an interview that she feels that PMS "is neither positive or negative" in terms of a woman's issue. "It's something that should be dealt with."

Liz Creighton, who owns an engineering company in California, was among the women reluctant to recognize the existence of premenstrual syndrome. "I didn't really want to think I was subject to raging hormones." But since progesterone therapy has worked so effectively for her, she says it's better to accept the problem "and bring it out of the closet." What changed her attitude, she says flatly, "was being treated. Realizing that it was a problem that could be treated. I was ready to try anything. It was a question of my life." A major part of her problem in dealing with PMS, she recalls, was her deep-felt insistence on not being burdened by "women's problems... My generation was not going to be burdened with 'the curse,' As soon as I started menstruating I decided that it wasn't going to stop me; I was going to swim, wear Tampax, live a life. This denial started very early on." She says her mother in a way

contributed to the denial: ''She saw to it [by telling her about menstrua-
tion] that I wasn't going to go through the trauma she went through.''
She takes issue with Brownmiller's rigid denial that the PMS disorder
can lead to a loss a control. ''When I wasn't suffering from PMS, I
could control myself. My anger was uncontrollable [during PMS]. It
was hurting my work. I was getting more and more ineffective. I was reluctant to take on new projects because I was no longer sure if I would be
able to handle them. It brought on a crisis of confidence.''

Eliminating the Stigma

There should be no stigma attached to a woman who has a physiological disorder. And that is precisely what PMS is. We feel that the real
feminist issue is the abysmal disregard of women by the male-dominated medical community, the years of misdiagnosis and improper or lack
of treatment for the condition. By acknowledging the existence of PMS
and moving quickly to treat it properly, discrimination against women
with PMS will end. To do this, we first must go public with the facts
about the condition and stop attaching labels like ''raging hormones'' to
women with PMS. As Creighton says, ''This was never an easy trauma
for me to talk about. Of course, it's easier now, because I'd like to see
other women get help. If we hide it, and don't bring it out and get help,
we really are limiting ourselves.'' I think the women who are seeking
treatment now ''are women like me. They are aggressive and intelligent
enough to feel that they deserve control over their own bodies.'' While
some of her women friends and physicians have not been supportive of
her PMS-related problems, Creighton says, ''Men I know and work
with know other women who have PMS. They try to get them to get
help. The men see the problem recurring cyclically and are more apt to
make the first diagnosis.''

The balancing act surrounding PMS — the need to protect women
from external attacks from those who would label them as hormonally
inferior and the necessity of responding to their internal physical
disorder — will ultimately serve to resolve the controversy about the
syndrome. For once the physiological condition is properly treated and
the symptoms are eliminated, there will be no phases of ''raging
hormones'' or periods of erratic behavior for anyone to cite as evidence
of women's biological weakness.

Need for Education

No current medical school textbook — on obstetrics-gynecology, psychiatry, or general medicine — provides more than a paragraph of information on premenstrual syndrome. While some university medical schools have begun to offer an occasional special lecture on the subject, PMS is not part of the curriculum and physicians-to-be are not held responsible for learning about its symptoms and treatment. Before a doctor can diagnose a condition he has to be taught that it exists, what its symptoms are and what the best therapy is. Not only must medical schools integrate material about PMS into their curricula but continuing education seminars and publications must be made available to practicing physicians, not only in America but around the world. The incidence of premenstrual syndrome surpasses that of lung cancer, diabetes, and arthritis in women; that's a reality to which the medical profession must respond.

As we have explained in the course of this book, many women with premenstrual syndrome are chronically ill. Their symptoms recur cyclically over long periods of time and lead them to seek advice and treatment from many different specialists at different times. Premenstrual syndrome alone probably accounts for a very hefty percentage of the health-care visits of women between the ages of eighteen and forty-four, the group that accounts for the largest number of female visits to physicians. Not only are women with PMS among the most aggressive and vocal consumers of health care in this country but they are also the most disenchanted. As a patient of ours who suffered with PMS for fifteen years before receiving appropriate treatment said: ''When you go to the best endocrinologist in town and she or he can't do anything for you, and you traipse from doctor to doctor for years, you lose total faith in the medical profession.

As information and education about PMS is circulated and more physicians begin to treat the disorder, women will benefit as well as society. This should also ease demands on the health-care delivery system and improve its efficiency, by eliminating hundreds of thousands of physician and hospital visits each year that had been made by women who were repeatedly misdiagnosed or mistreated for symptoms that were actually manifestations of PMS. And it should also lower health-care costs for many women, who will be able to obtain evaluation and treatment quickly instead of spending months and years in repeated visits to various specialists for PMS symptoms.

Filling the Emotional Needs

Providing emotional and psychological support for the women and their families is another important kind of treatment. Two national nonprofit organizations founded by women with PMS — the National PMS Society and PMS Action — have taken giant steps toward filling this need by organizing local support groups in communities around the country where women can meet and share with other PMS sufferers their experiences. The National PMS Society, founded in 1981 by Lindsey Leckie and Patty Cannon, has set up affiliated support groups in many communities around the country. PMS Action, founded in 1980 by Virginia Cassara with the assistance of Julie Egger, provides information and counseling about PMS; with the help of Beth Jones, PMS Action also presents seminars about the disorder. Both groups help women find physicians in their area who treat PMS. Cassara herself has PMS; after a futile four-year search for medical treatment in this country, she finally traveled to London for evaluation and treatment by Dr. Katharina Dalton in the late 1970s. Upon her return, she began to disseminate information about PMS and progesterone therapy.

More and better research into PMS is also critical. So far the diagnosis and treatment of premenstrual syndrome has been based on the limited investigations of a few dedicated pioneers, notably Dr. Katharina Dalton. But no one has invested the time, money, and effort to undertake directed research — the double-blind controlled studies — that must be done to uncover the cause of the disorder and to answer a score of questions: whether PMS is one or several disorders, what are its causes, what role sex hormones play in the illness, how progesterone acts to alleviate the symptoms, what the long-term effects of progesterone therapy are, whether other therapies might be effective or more effective as a treatment, whether PMS is hereditary, whether progesterone is protective against cancer. To this end, we are undertaking a number of research studies that should begin to provide the answers to these questions. Other researchers at universities in this country, in Canada and Europe have also begun sex hormone research that is likely to broaden our understanding of premenstrual syndrome.

Now that PMS has come out of the closet and attention has begun to be focused upon it, women can look forward to the day when premenstrual syndrome can be treated readily and effectively.

For information about support groups in your area, contact:

The National PMS Society
P.O. Box 11467
Durham, N.C. 27703

PMS Action
P.O. Box 9326
Madison, Wisconsin 53715
(608) 274-6688

For more information about premenstrual syndrome, its evaluation and treatment, contact:

PMS Program Inc.
800 Eastowne Drive
Chapel Hill, N.C. 27514
or
PMS Program Inc.
40 Salem Street
Lynnfield, Mass. 01940

For information about the non-profit, tax-exempt foundation to support research into premenstrual syndrome and develop educational programs for health-care professionals, or to make a tax-exempt contribution, write:

National PMS Foundation Inc.
P.O. Box 3798
Portland, Oregon 97208-3798

Chapter Notes

Chapter 1 PMS: What It Is and What It Isn't

Robert T. Frank. "Hormonal Causes of Premenstrual Tension." *Archives of Neurology and Psychiatry,* 26: 1053, 1931.

Paula Weideger. *Menstruation and Menopause.* New York: Alfred A. Knopf, 1976, pp.135-137.

Helene Deutsch. *The Psychology of Women.* New York: Grune and Stratton, 1944, vol. I, pp.166-167.

K. Jean and R. John Lennane. "Alleged Psychogenic Disorders in Women — A Possible Manifestation." *New England Journal of Medicine,* 288, February, 1973.

Sheila MacLeod. *The Art of Starvation.* New York: Schocken Books, 1982, p.4.

Lawrence Sanders. *The Third Deadly Sin.* New York: Berkley Books, 1982.

Brian Moore. *I Am Mary Dunne.* New York: The Viking Press, 1966.

Estelle Ramey. "Men's Cycles (They Have Them Too, You Know)." *Ms.,* 8-14, Spring, 1972.

Telephone interview, Dr. William Keye, assistant professor of obstetrics and gynecology, University of Utah Medical Center, Salt Lake City.

Telephone interview, Brian Moore, Toronto, Canada.

Chapter 2 Eve's Curse

Pliny the Elder. *Natural History,* Book 7, translated by H. Rackham. Cambridge, Mass.: Harvard University Press, 1961.

Soranus. *Gynecology,* translated by Owsei Temkin. Baltimore: Johns Hopkins University Press, 1956.

Margaret Mead. *Male and Female,* New York: Dell Publishing Company, 1970.

Ruth Benedict. *Patterns of Culture.* Boston: Houghton Mifflin, 1934.

Mary Chadwick. *Psychology of Menstruation,* New York and Washington: Nervous and Mental Disease Publishing Company, 1932.

O.W. Smith and G. van S. Smith. "Menstrual Toxin," in Menstruation and Its Disorders, E.T. Engle ed. Springfield, Ill.: Charles C Thomas Publisher, 1950.

Alison Kane and Eric T. Carlson. "A Different Drummer: Robert B. Carter and Nineteenth Century Hysteria." *Bulletin of the New York Academy of Medicine,* 58,6: 519-529, September 1982.

Sigmund Freud. *Totem and Taboo,* Harmondsworth, Middlesex: Penguin Books, 1938.

Raymond Crawfurd. "Superstitions of Menstruation." *The Lancet,* December 18, 1915.

Sheila MacLeod. *The Art of Starvation,* op. cit., pp. 38-40.

Erik Erikson. *Identity Youth and Crisis.* New York and London: W.W. Norton and Company, 1968.

Vern Bullough and Martha Voght. "Women, Menstruation, and Nineteenth-Century Medicine." *Bulletin of Historical Medicine,* 47: 66-82, 1973.

British Medical Journal, Letters, 1878

Maudsley. *Sex in Mind and in Education.* New York: James Miller, 1884.

S. Icard. *La Femme Pendant la Periode Menstruelle.* Paris: Felix Alcan, 1890, p.136.

Mary Jacobi. *The Question of Rest for Women During Menstruation,* 1876.

Leta Hollingworth. *Functional Periodicity: An Experimental Study of the Mental and Motor Abilities of Women During Menstruation.* New York: Teachers College, 1914.

For an overview of the cultural and social attitudes toward menstruating women and the taboos surrounding menstruation, the following provide basic references:

Sir James Frazer. *The New Golden Bough,* London: S.G. Phillips Inc., 1959.

Bruno Bettelheim. *Symbolic Wounds.* New York: Collier Books, 1962.

Janice Delaney, Mary Jane Lupton and Emily Toth. *The Curse, A Cultural History of Menstruation,* New York: E.P. Dutton & Co., 1976.

Simone deBeauvoir. *The Second Sex.* New York: Alfred A. Knopf, 1952.

Mary Douglas. *Purity and Danger: An Analysis of Concepts of Pollution and Taboo.* Baltimore: Penguin Books, 1970.

Barbara Ehrenreich and Deirdre English. *Complaints and Disorders, The Sexual Politics of Sickness.* Old Westbury, N.Y.: The Feminist Press, 1973.

The following medical papers are cited in order of their appearance in the text:

Robert T. Frank. *The Female Sex Hormone.* Springfield, Illinois and Baltimore: C.T. Thomas, 1929.

Robert T. Frank. "The Hormonal Causes of Premenstrual Tension," *Archives of Neurology and Psychiatry,* New York, 1931.

Alexandre Jacques Francois Brierre de Boismont. "De la menstruation, consideree dans ses rapports physiologiques et pathologiques." Paris: Germer-Bailliere, 1842.

Senator New York: W. Wood and Company, 1878.

Icard. op. cit.

J.D. Morgan. "Menstrual Arthritis." *American Journal of Obstetrics,* New York, 1907, lvi: 207-210, pp. 235-238.

M.E. Binet. "Crises Gastriques Premenstruelles et Lithiase Biliare." *Tribune Medicale,* Paris, 1909, XLI, 133-136.

Ruth Okey and Elda I. Robb. "Studies of the Metabolism of Women. Variations in the fasting Blood Sugar Level and in SUgar Tolerance in Relation to the Menstrual Cycle." *Journal of Biological Chemistry,* 65: 165-189, 1925.

Robert T. Frank. "Clinical Data Obtained with the Female Sex Hormone Blood Test," *Journal of the American Medical Association,* January 14, 1928.

W.A. Thomas. "Generalized Edema Occurring Only at Menstrual Period." *Journal of the American Medical Association,* 101: 1126-1127, October 7, 1933.

J.S. Sweeney. "Menstrual Edema; preliminary report." *Journal of the American Medical Association,* 103: 234-236, July 28, 1934.

A.J. Ziserman. "Ulcerative Vulvitis and Stomatitis of Endocrine Origin." *Journal of the American Medical Association,* 104: 826, March 9, 1935.

S. L. Israel. "Premenstrual Tension." *Journal of the American Medical Association,* 110: 1721-1723, May 21, 1938.

E.C. Hamblen. *Endocrine Gynecology.* Springfield, Illinois: C.C. Thomas, 1939.

J. Geber. "Desensitization in the Treatment of Menstrual Intoxication and Other Allergic Symptoms", *British Journal of Dermatology,* 51: 265-268, June 1939.

J.P. Greenhill and S.C. Freed. "Mechanism and Treatment of Premenstrual Distress with Ammonium Chloride." *Endocrinology,* 26: 529-531, March 1940.

L. A. Gray. "The Use of Progesterone in Nervous Tension States." *Southern Medical Journal,* 1004-1010, September 1941.

Morton S. Biskind. "Nutritional Deficiency in the Etiology of Menorrhagia, Metrrohagia, Cystic Mastilis and Premenstrual Tension, Treatment with Vitamin B Complex." *Journal of Clinical Endocrinology and Metabolism,* 3: 227-234, 1943.

Benjamin N. Tager and Shelton Kost. "Personality Changes in Endocrine Disorders." *Journal of Clinical Endocrinology and Metabolism*, 239-242, 1943.

Harvey E. Billig Jr. and S. Charles Spaulding Jr. "Hyperinsulinism of Menses." *Industrial Medicine*, 16: 336-339, July 1947.

Stieglitz and Kimble. "Premenstrual Intoxication," *American Journal of Medical Sciences*, 1949.

E.Y. Williams and L.R. Weekes. "Premenstrual Tension Associated with Psychotic Episodes," *Journal of Nervous and Mental Diseases*, 116: 321-329, 1952.

W. Bickers. "Premenstrual Tension and its Relationship to Water Metabolism." *American Journal of Obstetrics and Gynecology*, 64: 587-590, September 1952.

Joseph H. Morton. "Premenstrual Tension," *American Journal of Obstetrics and Gynecology*, 60: 343-352, 1950.

R.E. Hemphill. "Incidence and Nature of Puerperal Psychiatric Illness." *British Medical Journal*, 2: 1232-1235, December 6, 1952.

Katharina Dalton and Raymond Green. "The Premenstrual Syndrome," *British Medical Journal*, May, 1953.

British Medical Journal, Editorial, 1953.

Linford Rees. "Psychosomatic Aspects of the Premenstrual Tension Syndrome," *Journal of Mental Sciences*, 62-73, January 1953.

Harvey E. Billig Jr. "The Role of the Premenstrual Tension in Industry," *Symposium on Premenstrual Tension, International Record of Medicine*, November 1953.

S. Charles Freed. "History and Causation of Premenstrual Tension," in *Symposium on Premenstrual Tension, International Record of Medicine*, November 1953.

J.P. Greenhill. "Treatment of Premenstrual Tension by Electrolytes," *Symposium on Premenstrual Tension, International Record of Medicine*, November 1953.

Leon Israel. "The Clinical Pattern and Etiology of Premenstrual Tension," in *Symposium on Premenstrual Tension, International Record of Medicine,* November 1953.

Lamb et al. "Premenstrual Tension: E.E.G., Hormonal, and Psychiatric Evaluation." *American Journal of Psychiatry,* 109: 840-848, May 1953.

Joseph H. Morton, ed. *Symposium on Premenstrual Tension, International Record of Medicine,* November 1953.

Joseph H. Morton. "Treatment of Premenstrual Tension," *Symposium on Premenstrual Tension, International Record of Medicine,* November 1953.

Edward L. Suarez-Murais. "The Psychophysiologic Syndrome of Premenstrual Tension," *Symposium on Premenstrual Tension, in International Record of Medicine ,* November 1953.

Mukherjee. "Premenstrual Tension: A Critical Study of the Syndrome," *Journal of the Indian Medical Association,* 1954.

Katharina Dalton. "The Similarity of Symptomatology of PMS and Toxaemia," *British Medical Journal,* 1954.

A.B. Hegarty. "Post-Puerperal Recurrent Depression." *British Medical Journal,* 1955.

G.W. Thorne. "Cyclical Edema." *American Journal of Medicine,* 23: 507, 1957.

Erle Henriksen. "The Melancholies of Menstruation or Premenstrual Tension," *Clinical Obstetrics and Gynecology,* 252-259, 1965.

P.W. Adams et al. "Effects of Pyridoxine Hydrochloride (Vitamin B-6) upon Depression Associated with Oral Contraception." *Lancet,* 1: 899-904, April 28, 1973.

International Congress of Psychosomatic Obstetrics and Gynecology, Sixth Annual Session, Berlin, September 1980.

Guy Abraham. "Premenstrual Tension." *Current Problems in Obstetrics and Gynecology.,* III, 12:5-39, April 1981.

Robert Reid and S.S.C. Yen. "Premenstrual Syndrome." *American Journal of Obstetrics and Gynecology*, 139: 85-104, 1981.

Chapter 3 Migraine

Joan Didion. "In Bed" in *The White Album*. New York: Pocket Books, 1978.

Katharina Dalton. "Progesterone Suppositories and Pessaries in the Treatment of Menstrual Migraine." *Headache*, 12,4: 151-159, January 1973.

Katharina Dalton. "Do It Yourself." *Migraine News Letter of British Migraine Association*, April 1975.

Katharina Dalton. "Food Intake Prior to a Migraine Attack." *Headache*, 15, 3: 188-193, October 1975.

M.T. Epstein et al. "Migraine and Reproductive Hormones Throughout the Menstrual Cycle." *The Lancet*, 543-549, March 8, 1975.

Chapter 4 Epilepsy

Fyodor Dostoevsky. *The Idiot*. New York: Signet Classics, 1969.

Alfred Gordon. "Epilepsy in its Relation to Menstrual Periods." *New York Medical Journal*, XC, 16: 733-736, October 16, 1909.

John Logothetis et al. "The Role of Estrogens in Catmenial Exacerbation of Epilepsy." *Neurology*, 352-360, date TK.

R.H. Mattson et al. "Psychophysiological Precipitants of Seizures in Epileptics." *Neurology*, 20: 407, 1970.

R.H. Mattson et al. "Precipitating and Inhibiting Factors in Epilepsy: A Statistical Study." *Epilepsia*, 15: 271-272, 1974.

Susan Hall. "Treatment of Menstrual Epilepsy with Progesterone Only Contraceptives." *Epilepsia*, 18,2: 235-236, 1977.

Trevor R.P. Price. "Temporal Lobe Epilepsy as a Premenstrual Behavioral Syndrome." *Biological Psychiatry*, 15,6: 957-963, 1980.

Interview with Dr. Allen Hauser, assistant professor of neurology and public health, Columbia University and assistant director of Columbia's Sergievsky Center for the study of epilepsy and cerebral palsy.

Chapter 5 Mood Swings and Depression

Hans Christian Andersen. "The Snow Queen," in *Fairy Tales*. New York: Grosset and Dunlap, 1981.

Dr. Myrna Weissman, quoted in Maggie Scarf's *Unfinished Business,* New York: Ballantine Books, 1981, pp. 594-601.

Constance Berry and Frederick L. McGuire. "Menstrual Distress and Acceptance of Sexual Role," *American Journal of Obstetrics and Gynecology,* 114:1, September 1, 1972, p. 84.

Paula Weideger. *Menstruation and Menopause,* op.cit.

Karl Menninger, quoted in Weideger.

George S. Glass et al. "Psychiatric Emergency Related to the Menstrual Cycle." *American Journal of Psychiatry,* 128,6: 61, December 1971.

Natalie Shainess. "Psychiatric Evaluation of Premenstrual Tension." *New York State Journal of Medicine,* 3573-3579, November 15, 1962.

Katharina Dalton. "Menstruation and Accidents." *British Medical Journal,* 1425-1426, November 12, 1960.

Walter R. Gove. "Sex Differences in Mental Illness Among Adult Men and Women." *Social Science and Medicine,* 12B: 187-198, 1978.

Meir Steiner and Bernard J. Carroll. "The Psychobiology of Premenstrual Dysphoria: Review of Theories and Treatments." *Psychoneuroendocrinology,* 2: 321-335, 1977.

Phyllis Chesler. *Women and Madness.* New York: Avon Books, 1975.

Brian Moore. *I Am Mary Dunne,* op.cit. pp. 211, 215 and 217.

Chapter 6 Eating Disorders

Mary Gordon. *Final Payments.* New York: Ballantine Books, 1979.

Hilde Bruch. *Eating Disorders.* New York: Basic Books Inc., 1973.

Stuart Smith and Cynthia Sauder. "Food Cravings, Depression, and Premenstrual Problems." *Psychosomatic Medicine,* XXXI, 4: 281-286, 1969.

H. Sutherland and I. Stewart. "A Critical Analysis of the Premenstrual Syndrome." *The Lancet.*

J.N. Fortin et al. "Psychosomatic Approach to Premenstrual Tension Syndrome." *CMAJ,* 79: 978, 1958.

J.H. Morton et al. "A Clinical Study of Premenstrual Tension." *American Journal of Obstetrics and Gynecology,* 65: 1182, 1953.

Mara Selvini Palazzoli. *Self-Starvation.* New York: Aronson, 1978.

Sheila MacLeod. op. cit., pp.56-57.

Chapter 7 Problems with Alcohol and Drugs

Joyce Rebeta-Burditt. *The Cracker Factory.* New York: Bantam Books, 1978.

Marian Sandmaier. *The Invisible Alcoholics.* New York: McGraw-Hill Inc., 1981.

Edith S. Gomberg. "Problems with Alcohol and Other Drugs." *Gender and Disordered Behavior.* New York: Brunner/Mazel, 1979.

Myron L. Belfer et al. "Alcoholism in Women." *Archives of General Psychiatry,* 25: 540-544, December 1971.

Jean Kinney and Gwen Leaton. *Understanding Alcohol.* St. Louis: The Mosely Press, 1982.

Interview with Dr. Michael Murphy, president of the Bay Area Comprehensive Alcoholic Program, Boston, Mass.

Chapter 8 It Runs in Families

References drawn from our practice and interviews with patients.

Martha K. McClintock. "Menstrual Synchrony and Suppression." *Nature,* 229,244: 5282, 1971.

Section III Living With PMS
Chapter 9 Strains on Relationships

References drawn from our practice and interviews with patients.

Chapter 10 On the Job

Studs Terkel. *Working*. New York: Avon Books, 1975.

References from our practice and interviews with patients.

Chapter 11 Striking Out

Victoria Lincoln. A Private Disgrace, Lizzie Borden by *Daylight*. New York: G.P. Putnam's Sons, 1967.

Ann Jones. *Women Who Kill*. New York: Fawcett Columbine, 1981.

Katharina Dalton. "Cyclical Criminal Acts in Premenstrual Syndrome." *The Lancet*, 1070-1071, November 15, 1980.

D.P. Ellis and P. Austin. "Menstruation and Aggressive Behavior in a Correctional Center for Women." *Journal of Criminal Law, Criminology and Police Science*, 62: 388-395, 1971.

P. Epps. "Women Shoplifters in Holloway Prison," in *Shoplifting*, ed. by T.C.N. Gibbens and J. Prince. London: Institute for the Study and Treatment of Delinquency, 1962, pp.132-145.

Katharina Dalton. "Children's Hospital Admissions and Mother's Menstruation." *British Medical Journal*, 27-28, April 4, 1970.

P.T. d'Orban and J. Dalton. "Violent Crime and the Menstrual Cycle." *Psychological Medicine*, 10: 353-359, 1980.

Christine Crawford. *Mommie Dearest*. New York: Berkley Books, 1981.

C. Henry Kempre and Ray E. Helfer. *Helping the Battered Child and His Family*. Philadelphia and Toronto: J.B. Lippincott Company, 1982.

Chapter 12 Suicide Attempts

Leslie Farber. *The Ways of the Will*. New York: Basic Books, 1966.

Boris Pasternak. *An Essay in Autobiography*. TKTK.

Cesare Pavese. *This Business of Living,* translated by A. E. Murch. London and Toronto: 1961.

Rollo May. *Power and Innocence.* New York: Delta Books, 1981.

Sylvia Plath. *The Collected Poems.* New York: Harper and Row, 1982.

Sylvia Plath. *The Bell Jar.* New York: Bantam Books, 1972.

Sylvia Plath. *The Journals of Sylvia Plath.* New York: Dial Press, 1982.

A. Alvarez. *The Savage God — A Study of Suicide.* New York: Random House, 1970.

Richard D. Wetzel et al. "Premenstrual Symptoms in Self-Referrals to a Suicide Prevention Service." *British Journal of Psychiatry,* 119: 525-526, 1971.

Richard D. Wetzel and J.N. McClure Jr. "Suicide and the Menstrual Cycle." *Comprehensive Psychiatry,* 13,4: 369, 1972.

Dorothy Parker. "You Might As Well Live" in *The Portable Dorothy Parker.* New York: The Viking Press, 1973.

Walter R. Gove. "Sex, Marital Status and Suicide." *Journal of Health and Social Behavior,* 13: 204-213, June 1972.

Section IV Female Complaints

Chapter 13 The Pill

Richard I. Shader and Jane I. Ohly. "Premenstrual Tension, Femininity and Sexual Drive." *Medical Aspects of Human Sexuality,* April 1970.

J.R. Udry and N. Morris. "Distribution of Coitus in the Menstrual Cycle." *Nature,* 220:593, November 1968.

Chapter 14 Pregnancy

Sandra McPherson. "Pregnancy," in *A Book of Women Poets,* edited by Aliki Barnstone and Willis Barnstone. New York: Schocken Books, 1980, p. 556.

Katharina Dalton. "Progesterone in Toxaemia of Pregnancy." *Medical World,* December 1955.

Katharina Dalton. "Ante-natal Progesterone and Intelligence." *British Journal of Psychiatry*, 144: 1377-1382, 1968.

Katharina Dalton. "Controlled Trials in the Prophylactic Value of Progesterone in the Treatment of Pre-Eclamptic Toxaemia." *Journal of Obstetrics and Gynaecology* (U.K.), 69: 463-468, June 1962.

Mohamed B. Sammour et al. "Progesterone Therapy in Pre-Eclamptic Toxaemia." *Acta Obstetrica Gynecologica Scandinavica*, 54: 195-202, 1975.

Pentti K. Siiteri. "Progesterone and Maintenance of Pregnancy: Is Progesterone Nature's Immunosuppressant?" *Annals of the New York Academy of Science*, 286:434-445, March 1979.

Chapter 15 Post-Partum Depression

Doris Lessing. *A Proper Marriage*. New York: Plume Books, 1970.

Katharina Dalton. "Prospective Study into Puerperal Depression." *British Journal of Psychiatry*, 118: 689-692, 1971.

A.B. Hegarty. "Post-Puerperal Recurrent Depression." *British Medical Journal*, 637-640, March 12, 1955.

Brice Pitt. "Maternity Blues." *British Journal of Psychiatry*, 122: 431-433, 1973.

C. Dean and R.E. Kendell. "The Symptomatology of Puerperal Illnesses." *British Journal of Psychiatry*, 139: 128, 1981.

Brice Pitt. "Psychiatric Illness Following Childbirth." 409-415.

Amos Weiner. "Childbirth-Related Psychiatric Illness." *Comprehensive Psychiatry*, 23,2: 143-154, March/April 1982.

Willis H. Bower and Mark D. Altschule. "Use of Progesterone in the Treatment of Post-Partum Psychosis." *The New England Journal of Medicine*, 254,4: 157-160, January 26, 1956.

Chapter 16 Sterilization

Montagu G. Barker. "Psychiatric Illness After Hysterectomy." *British Medical Journal*, 91-95, April 13, 1968.

C.T. Backstrom et al. "Persistence of Symptoms of Premenstrual Tension in Hysterectomized Women." *British Journal of Obstetrics and Gynaecology*, 88: 530-536, 1981.

Section V Life Phases

Chapter 17 Adolescence

Carson McCullers. *The Member of the Wedding*. New York: Bantam Books, 1950.

Erik Erikson. *Identity Youth and Crisis*. New York and London: W.W. Norton and Company, 1968.

Janet W. McArthur. "Common Menstrual Disorders in the Adolescent Girl." *Clinical Pediatrics*, 3,11: 663, 1964.

Mark D. Altschule and Jacob Brem. "Periodic Psychosis of Puberty." *American Journal of Psychiatry*, 119: 1176-1177, 1963.

Fred S. Berlin et al. "Periodic Psychosis of Puberty: A Case Report." *American Journal of Psychiatry*, 139,1: 119-120, January 1982.

Jagdish S. Teja. "Periodic Psychosis of Puberty: A Longitudinal Case Study." *The Journal of Nervous and Mental Disease*, 162,1: 52-57, 1976.

Rose E. Frisch. "Critical Weights, a Critical Body Composition, Menarche and the Maintenance of the Menstrual Cycle," in *Biosocial Interrelation in Population Adaptation*. The Hague: Mouton & Company.

Rose E. Frisch and Roger Revell. "Height and Weight at Menarche and a Hypothesis of Menarche." *Archives of Diseases in Childhood*, 46, 249: 695, 1971.

Rose E. Frisch, Roger Revell and Sole Cook. "Components of Weight at Menarche and the Initiation of the Adolescent Growth Spurt in Girls." *Human Biology*, 45,3: 469, 1973.

Chapter 18 The Twenties and Thirties

Gail Sheehy. *Passages*. New York: E.P. Dutton Inc., 1974.

Chapter 19 The Forties

Carl Jung. *Modern Man in Search of a Soul*. New York and London: Harvest Books, 1933.

Chapter 20 Menopause and Post-Menopause

Doris Lessing. *The Summer Before the Dark*. New York: Bantam Books, 1974.

Elizabeth Barrett Browning. *Sonnets From the Portuguese*.

William Faulkner. *A Light in August*. New York: Random House, 1967.

William Shakespeare. *The Tragedy of Hamlet, Prince of Denmark*. New York: Washington Square Press, 1958.

Sonja M. McKinlay and Margot Jefferys. "The Menopausal Syndrome." *British Journal of Preventive and Social Medicine*, 28,2: 108, 1974.

Section VI The PMS Prescription

Chapter 21 Do You Have PMS?

Material developed for our centers.

Chapter 22 The PMS Diet

Jane Brody. Jane Brody's *Nutrition Book*. New York and London: W.W. Norton and Company, 1981.

Adele Davis. *Let's Get Well*. New York: Harcourt Brace and World Inc., 1965.

Mildred S. Seelig. "The Requirement of Magnesium by the Normal Adult." *American Journal of Clinical Nutrition*, 14: 342-390, June 1964.

Chapter 23 Vitamin Therapy

Guy Abraham. "Premenstrual Tension." *Current Problems in Obstetrics and Gynecology*, III, 12: 5-39, April 1981.

Morton S. Biskind. "Nutritional Deficiency in the Etiology of Menorr-hagia, Metrohagia, Cystic Mastilis and Premenstrual Tension, Treatment with Vitamin B Complex." *Journal of Clinical Endocrinology and Metabolism,* 3:227-234, 1943.

Clement G. Martin. *Low Blood Sugar: The Hidden Menace of Hypoglycemia.* New York: Arco Publishing Inc., 1969.

Chapter 24 Getting Physical

Kenneth H. Cooper. *Aerobics.* New York: Bantam Books, 1980.

Chapter 25 Managing Stress

Hans Selye. *The Physiology and Pathology of Exposure to Stress.* Montreal, Canada: Acta Inc., 1950.

Hans Selye. *The Stress of Life.* New York: McGraw-Hill Inc., 1956.

Herbert Benson. *The Relaxation Response.* New York: Avon Books, 1975.

Thomas Holmes and Richard Rahe. "The Social Readjustment Rating Scale." *Journal of Psychosomatic Research,* 11: 213, 1967.

Chapter 26 The Progesterone Story

See bibliography for extensive listing of all related articles. Following are cited in order they appear in text.

S.S.C. Yen et al. "Hormonal Relationships During the Menstrual Cycle." *Journal of the American Medical Association,* 211,9: 1513-1517, March 2, 1970.

Reid, Robert L. and S.S.C. Yen. "Premenstrual Syndrome." *American Journal of Obstetrics and Gynecology,* 139: 85-104, 1981.

Willard M. Allen. "Progesterone: How Did the Name Originate?" *Southern Medical Journal,* 63,10: 1151-1155, October 1970.

Willard M. Allen. "Recollections of My Life With Progesterone." *Gynecological Investigations,* 5:142-182, 1974.

Katharina Dalton. "Comparative Trials of New Oral Progestogenic Compounds in Treatment of Premenstrual Syndrome." *British Medical Journal,* 1307-1309, December 12, 1959.

Doyle W. Frank. "Mammary Tumors and Serum Hormones in the Bitch Treated with Medroxyprogesterone Acetate or Progesterone for Four Years." *Fertility and Sterility,* 31,3: 340-346, March 1979.

Linda Cowan et al. "Breast Cancer Incidence in Women With a History of Progesterone Deficiency." *American Journal of Epidemiology,* 114,2: 209-217, 1981.

Joseph Gilman. "Nature of Subjective Reaction Evoked in Women by Progesterone with Special Reference to the Problem of Premenstrual Tension." *Journal of Clinical Endocrinology and Metabolism,* 2: 156, 1942.

L.A. Gray. "The Use of Progesterone in Nervous Tension States." *Southern Medical Journal,* 1004-1010, September 1941.

David A. Hamburg. "Effects of Progesterone on Behavior," in *Endocrines and the Central Nervous System,* Levine and Rachkiel eds. Baltimore: Williams & Wilkins Company, 1966.

David A. Hamburg and Donald T. Lunde. "Sex Hormones in the Development of Sex Differences in Human Behavior," in *The Development of Sex Differences,* Eleanor E. Maccoby ed. Stanford, Calif.: Stanford University Press, 1966.

Arthur Herbst et al. "The Effects of Local Progesterone on Stilbestrol-Associated Vaginal Adenosis." *American Journal of Obstetrics and Gynecology,* 607-615, March 1, 1974.

IARC Monograph. "Evaluation of the Carcinogenic Risk of Chemicals to Man: Sex Hormones." Lyon, February 4-11, 1974, vol. 6.

Mary-Claire King. "Risk Factors in Breast Cancer," a review of *Hormones and Breast Cancer, in Science,* 214: 1122-1123, December 9, 1981.

Sophia J. Kleegman and Sherwin A. Kaufman. "The Endocrines Concerned with Menstruation and Infertility," in *Infertility in Women.* Philadelphia: F.A. Davis, 1966.

Frederick Naftolin and George Tolis. "Neuroendocrine Regulation of the Menstrual Cycle." *Clinical Obstetrics and Gynecology,* 21,1: 17-29, March 1978.

Gwyneth A. Sampson. "Premenstrual Syndrome: A Double-Blind Controlled Trial of Progesterone and Placebo." *British Journal of Psychiatry,* 135:209-215, 1979.

Gwyneth A. Sampson. "An Appraisal of the Role of Progesterone in the Therapy of Premenstrual Syndrome" in *The Premenstrual Syndrome,* ed. by P.A. van Keep. Lancaster, England: MTP Press Ltd., Falcon House International Medical Publishers, 1981, pp.51-69.

Mona Shangold. "The Relationship Between Long-Distance Running, Plasma Progesterone, and Luteal Phase Length." *Fertility and Sterility,* 31,130: 607-608, 1979.

Pentti K. Siiteri. "Progesterone and Maintenance of Pregnancy: Is Progesterone Nature's Immunosuppressant?" *Annals of the New York Academy of Science,* 286: 434-445, March 1979.

Leon Speroff and Raymond Vande Wiele. "Regulation of the Human Menstrual Cycle." *American Journal of Obstetrics and Gynecology,* 109,2: 232-247, January 15, 1971.

Bruce V. Stadel. "Oral Contraceptives and Cardiovascular Disease." *New England Journal of Medicine,* 612-677, September 10, 1981.

Paul Beck. "Effects of Progestins on Glucose and Lipid Metabolism." *Annals of the New York Academy of Science,* 286: 343-355, March 1979.

Allan C. Barnes and Irving Rothchild. "Experimental Use of Intravenously Administered Progesterone in Advanced Cases of Cervical Carcinoma." *Obstetrics and Gynecology,* 1,2: 147-155, February 1953.

Anne Colston Wentz. "Assessment of Estrogen and Progestin Therapy in Gynecology and Obstetrics." *Clinical Obstetrics and Gynecology,* 20,2:461-480, June 1977.

M.I. Whitehead et al. "Absorption and Metabolism of Oral Progesterone." *Gynecology,* 36,1: 32-33, 1981.

Section VII The Broader View

Chapter 27 Fame Is No Protection

Carolly Erikson. *Bloody Mary.* New York: Doubleday and Company Inc., 1978.

Louis Auchincloss. *Persons of Consequence, Queen Victoria and Her Circle.* New York: Random House, 1979.

Alison Plowden. *Marriage With My Kingdom.* New York: Stein and Day, 1977.

Herbert Tingsten. *Victoria and the Victorians.* New York: Delacorte Press, 1972.

Len Ortzen. *Imperial Venus.* New York: Stein and Day, 1974.

Ruth Painter Randall. *Mary Lincoln — Biography of a Marriage.* Boston: Little Brown and Company, 1953.

W.A. Evans. *Mrs. Abraham Lincoln — A Study of Her Personality and Her Influence on Lincoln.* New York: Alfred A. Knopf Inc., 1932.

Jean Strouse. *Alice James.* New York: Bantam Books, 1982.

Arianna Stassinopoulos. *Maria Callas.* New York: Ballantine Books, 1982.

Christopher Finch. *Rainbow.* New York: Grosset & Dunlap, 1975.

Edward Butscher. *Sylvia Plath: Method and Madness.* New York: Washington Square Press, 1976.

Sylvia Plath. *The Bell Jar.* op. cit.

Sylvia Plath. *The Collected Poems.* op. cit.

Sylvia Plath. *The Journals.* op. cit.

A. Alvarez. *The Savage God.* op. cit.

Chapter 28 The Defense Pleads PMS

Aleta Wallach and Larry Rubin. "The Premenstrual Syndrome and Criminal Responsibility." *UCLA Law Review,* 19: 209-312, 1971.

Katharina Dalton. "Cyclical Criminal Acts in Premenstrual Syndrome." op.cit.

Katharina Dalton. "Legal Implications of PMS." *World Medicine*, 93-94, April 17, 1982.

Diana Brahams. "Premenstrual Syndrome: A Disease of the Mind?" *The Lancet*, 1238-1240, November 28, 1981.

Diana Brahams. "Rejection of Premenstrual Syndrome as a Defence in English Law." *The Lancet*, 1134-1135, May 15, 1982.

P.T. d'Orban. "Premenstrual Syndrome." *The Lancet*, ii, 1413.

Julie Horney. "Menstrual Cycles and Criminal Responsibility." *Law and Human Behavior*, 2,1: 25-36, 1978.

Kenneth K. Fukunaga et al. "Insanity Plea." *Law and Human Behavior*, 5,4: 325-328, 1981.

Peter Arenella. "The Diminished Capacity and Diminished Responsibility Defenses: Two Children of a Doomed Marriage." *Columbia Law Review*, 77, 6: 827-863, October 1977.

R.D. Mackay. "Non-Organic Automatism — Some Recent Developments." *The Criminal Law Review*, 350-361, 1978.

Geraldine Brotherton. "Post-Traumatic Stress Disorder — Opening Pandora's Box?" *New England Law Review*, 17,1: 91-117, 1981.

Chapter 29 Making Progress

References to materials from our center.

Telephone interview with Susan Brownmiller.

Selected Bibliography

Abraham, Guy, E. et al. "Evaluation of Ovulation and Corpus Luteum Function in Using Measurements of Plasma Progesterone." *Obstetrics and Gynecology,* 44: 522, 1974.

Abraham, G.E., and Hargrove, J.T. "Effect of Vitamin B-6 on Premenstrual Symptomatology in Women with Premenstrual Tension Syndrome: A Double Crossover Study." *Infertility,* 3: 155-165, 1980.

Abraham, G.E. "Premenstrual Tension." *Current Problems in Obstetrics and Gynecology,* III, 12: 5-39, April 1981.

Abraham, G.E., and Lubran, M.M. "Serum and Red Cell Magnesium Levels in Patients with Premenstrual Tensions." *American Journal of Applied Nutrition,* 34: 4, 1982.

Ackerknecht, Erwin H. "The History of Psychosomatic Medicine." *Psychological Medicine,* 12: 17-24, 1982.

Allen, Willard M. "Progesterone: How Did the Name Originate?" *Southern Medical Journal,* 63,10: 1151-1155, October 1970.

Allen, Willard M. "Recollections of My Life With Progesterone." *Gynecological Investigations,* 5: 142-182, 1974.

Altschule, Mark D. and Brem, Jacob. "Periodic Psychosis of Puberty." *American Journal of Psychiatry,* 119: 1176-1178, 1963.

Alvarez, A. *The Savage God — A Study of Suicide.* New York: Random House, 1970.

American Psychiatric Assocation. *Diagnostic and Statistical Mannual of Mental Disorders,* third edition. Washington, D.C., APA, 1980.

Andersen, Hans Christian. "The Snow Queen," in *Fairy Tales.* New York: Grosset and Dunlap, 1981.

Appleby, B.P. "A Study of Premenstrual Tension in General Practice." *British Medical Journal,* 1: 391, February 1960.

Arenella, Peter. "The Diminished Capacity and Diminished Responsibility Defenses: Two Children of a Doomed Marriage." *Columbia University Law Review,* 77, 6: 827-863, October 1977.

Auchincloss, Louis. *Persons of Consequence, Queen Victoria and Her Circle.* New York: Random House, 1979.

Backstrom, C.T. et al. "Persistence of Symptoms of Premenstrual Tension in Hysterectomized Women." *British Journal of Obstetrics and Gynaecology,* 88:530-536, 1981.

Baker, H.W.G. et al. "Rhythms in the Secretion of Gonadotropins and Gonadal Steroids." *Journal of Steroidal Biochemistry,* 6: 793, 1975.

Ballantine, R. *Diet and Nutrition: A Holistic Approach.* Honesdale, Pennsylvania: Himalayan International Institute, 1978.

Barker, Montagu G. "Psychiatric Illness after Hysterectomy." *British Medical Journal,* April 13, 1968, 91-95.

Barnes, Allan C. and Rothchild, Irving. "Experimental Use of Intravenously Administered Progesterone in Advanced Cases of Cervical Carcinoma." *Obstetrics and Gynecology.* 1, 2: 147-155, February 1953.

Barnes, A.C., ed. *Progesterone.* Augusta, Michigan: Brook Lodge Press, 1961.

Barton, D.H. "The Conformation of the Steroid Nucleus." *Experientia,* VI (8): 316-320, 1950.

Beck, Paul. "Effects of Progestins on Glucose and Lipid Metabolism." *Annals of the New York Academy of Science,* 286: 434-455, March 1979.

Beecher, Henry K. "Relationship of Significance of Wound to Pain Experienced." *Journal of the American Medical Association,* 161,7: 1609-1613, August 25, 1956.

Belfer, Myron L. et al. "Alcoholism in Women." *Archives of General Psychiatry,* 25: 540-544, December 1971.

Bell, Donald H. *Being a Man — The Paradox of Masculinity.* Brattleboro, Vt.: The Lewis Publishing Company, 1982.

Benedict, Ruth. *Patterns of Culture*. Boston: Houghton Mifflin, 1934.

Benson, Ralph C., ed. *Current Obstetric and Gynecologic Diagnosis and Treatment*. Los Altos, Calif.: Lange Medical Publications, fourth edition, 1976.

Berlin, Fred S. et al. "Periodic Psychosis of Puberty. A Case Report." *American Journal of Psychiatry*, 139, 1: 119-120. January 1982.

Berry, Constance and McGuire, Frederick L. "Menstrual Distress and Acceptance of Sexual Role." *American Journal of Obstetrics and Gynecology*, 114: 84, September 1972.

Bertioli, A. et al. "Differences in Insulin Receptors Between Men and Menstruating Women and Influence of Sex Hormones on Insulin Binding During the Menstrual Cycle." *Journal of Clinical Endocrinology and Metabolics*, 50:246-250, 1980.

Bettelheim, Bruno. *Symbolic Wounds*. New York: Collier Books, 1962.

Billig, Harvey E. Jr. and Spaulding, C. Arthur Jr. "Hyperinsulinism of Menses." *Industrial Medicine*, July 1947, 336-339.

Billig, Harvey E. Jr. "The Role of Premenstrual Tension in Industry." *International Record of Medicine*, 166, 11: 487-491, November 1953.

Biskind, Morton S. "Nutritional Deficiency in the Etiology of Menorrhagia, Metrohagia, Cystic Mastilis and Premenstrual Tension, Treatment with Vitamin B Complex." *Journal of Clinical Endocrinology and Metabolism*, 3: 227-234, 1943.

Boyd, A.E., Reichlin, S. et al. "Galactorrhea-Amenorrhea Syndrome: Diagnosis and Therapy." *Annals of Internal Medicine*, 87: 165, 1977.

Brahams, Diana. "Medicine and the Law: Premenstrual Syndrome — a Disease of the Mind?" *The Lancet*, November 28, 1981, 1238-1240.

Brahams, Diana. "Rejection of Premenstrual Syndrome as a Defence in English Law." *The Lancet*, 1134-1135, May 15, 1982.

Breuer, Josef and Sigmund Freud, *Studies on Hysteria, translated by James Strachey*. New York: Basic Books Inc., 1982.

Briscoe, Monica. "Sex Differences in Psychological Well-Being," monograph supplement in *Psychological Medicine*. Cambridge, London and New York: Cambridge University Press, 1982.

Brotherton, Geraldine L. "Post-Traumatic Stress Disorder – Opening Pandora's Box?" *New England Law Review*, 17, 1: 91-117, 1981.

Bruch, Hilde. *Eating Disorders*. New York: Basic Books Inc., 1973.

Brush, M. "Therapy for the Woman with Premenstrual Syndrome." *Mims*, April 1, 1982, 7-31.

Bullough, Vern and Voght, Martha. "Women, Menstruation, and Nineteenth-Century Medicine." *Bulletin of Historical Medicine*, 47: 66-82, 1973.

Burkhart, Kathryn. *Women in Prison*. New York: Doubleday and Company, 1973.

Butscher, Edward. *Sylvia Plath: Method and Madness*. New York: Washington Square Press, 1977.

Campbell, Joseph, ed. *The Portable Jung*. New York: Penguin Books, 1976.

Carsten, Mary E. "Hormonal Regulation of Myometrial Calcium Transport." *Gynecological Investigations*, 5:269-275, 1974.

Chadwick, Mary. *The Psychology of Menstruation* (Monograph 56). Washington, D.C.: Nervous and Mental Diseases Publishing Company, 1932.

Chesler, Phyllis. *Women and Madness*. New York: Avon Books, 1972.

Chez, R.A. "Proceedings of the Symposium: Progesterone, Progestins, and Fetal Development." *Fertility and Sterility*, 30: 16, 1978.

Clarke, Edward H. *Sex in Education*, 1873.

Colquhoun, W.P. ed. *Biological Rhythms and Human Performance*. London and New York: Academic Press, 1971.

Colt, Edward W.D. et al. "The Effect of Running on Plasma B-Endorphin." *Life Science*, 28, 1637, 1982.

Cooper, Kenneth H. *Aerobics*. New York: Bantam Books, 1980.

Cowan, Linda et al. "Breast Cancer Incidence in Women With a History of Progesterone Deficiency." *American Journal of Epidemiology,* 114, 2: 209-217, 1981.

Crawford, Christine. *Mommie Dearest.* New York: Berkley Books, 1981.

Crawfurd, Raymond. "Superstitions of Menstruation." *The Lancet,* December 18, 1915.

Croucher, M.J. et al. "Anticonvulsant Action of Excitatory Amino Acid Antagonists." *Science,* 216: 899-901, May 21, 1982.

Dalton, Katharina and Greene, Raymond. "The Premenstrual Syndrome." *British Medical Journal,* 1007-1016, May 9, 1953.

Dalton, Katharina. "Similarity of Symptomatology of Premenstrual Syndrome and Toxaemia of Pregnancy and Their Response to Progesterone." *British Medical Journal,* 1071-1076, November 6, 1954.

Dalton, Katharina. "Progesterone in Toxaemia of Pregnancy." *Medical World,* 1-3, December 1955.

Dalton, Katharina. "Comparative Trials of New Oral Progestogenic Compounds in Treatment of Premenstrual Syndrome." *British Medical Journal,* 1307-1309, December 12, 1959.

Dalton, Katharina. "Effects of Menstruation on Schoolgirls' Weekly Work." *British Medical Journal,* 326-328, January 30, 1960.

Dalton, Katharina. "Menstruation and Accidents." *British Medical Journal,* 1425-1426, November 12, 1960.

Dalton, Katharina. "Controlled Trials in the Prophylactic Value of Progesterone in the Treatment of Pre-Eclamptic Toxaemia." *Journal of Obstetrics and Gynaecology,* 69: 463-468, June 1962.

Dalton, Katharina. "Menstruation and Examinations." *The Lancet,* 1386-1388, December 28, 1968.

Dalton, Katharina. "Ante-Natal Progesterone and Intelligence." *British Journal of Psychiatry,* 114: 1377-1382, 1968.

Dalton, Katharina. "Children's Hospital Admissions and Mother's Menstruation." *British Medical Journal,* 27-28, April 4, 1970.

Dalton, Katharina. "Prospective Study into Puerperal Depression." *British Journal of Psychiatry,* 113: 689-692, 1971.

Dalton, Katharina. "Progesterone Suppositories and Pessaries in the Treatment of Menstrual Migraine." *Headache,* 12, 4: 151-159, January 1973.

Dalton, Katharina. "Food Intake Prior to a Migraine Attack — Study of 2,313 Spontaneous Attacks." *Headache,* 15, 3: 188-193, October 1975.

Dalton, Katharina. "Cyclical Criminal Acts in Premenstrual Syndrome." *The Lancet,* 1070-1071, November 15, 1980.

Davis, Adele. *Let's Get Well.* New York: Harcourt Brace and World Inc., 1965.

deBeauvoir, Simone. *The Second Sex.* New York: Alfred A. Knopf, 1952.

Debrovner, C., ed. *Premenstrual Tension.* New York: Human Sciences Press, 1982.

Delaney, Janice, et al. *The Curse, A Cultural History of Menstruation.* New York: E.P. Dutton and Company Inc., 1976.

Dempsey, M.E. "Regulation of Steroid Biosynthesis." *Annual Review of Biochemistry,* 44: 967, 1975.

Deutsch, Helene. *The Psychology of Women, volumes I and II.* New York: Grune and Stratton, 1944.

Diabetes, "ADA Statement on Hypoglycemia." *Diabetes,* 22: 137, 1973.

Didion, Joan. *The White Album.* New York: Pocket Books, 1978.

Doering, C.H. et al. "A Cycle of Plasma Testosterone in the Human Male." *Journal of Clinical Endocrinology and Metabolism,* 40: 492, 1975.

d'Orban, P.T. and Dalton, J. "Violent Crime and the Menstrual Cycle." *Psychological Medicine,* 10: 353-359, 1980.

Dostoevsky, Fyodor. *The Idiot.* New York: Signet Classics, 1969.

Douglas, Mary. *Purity and Danger: An Analysis of Concepts of Pollution and Taboo*. Baltimore, Md.: Penguin Books, 1970.

Duff, David. *Albert and Victoria*. London: Ludgate House, 1972.

Ehrenreich, Barbara and English, Deirdre. *Complaints and Disorders, The Sexual Politics of Sickness*. Old Westbury, New York: The Feminist Press, 1973.

Eichner, E. and Waltner, C. "Premenstrual Tension." *Medical Times,* 83: 771, 1955.

Eisenberg, L. "The Search for Care." *Daedalus,* 106: 235-246, 1977.

Ellis, D.P. and Austin, P. "Menstruation and Aggressive Behavior in a Correctional Center for Women." *Journal of Criminal Law, Criminology and Police Science,* 62: 388-395, 1971.

Endo, M. et al. "Periodic Psychosis Recurring in Association With the Menstrual Cycle." *Journal of Clinical Psychiatry,* 39: 456-466, 1978.

Engel, G.W. "The Need For a New Medical Model: A Challenge for Biomedicine." *Science,* 196: 129-136, 1977.

Epps, P. "Women Shoplifters in Holloway Prison," in *Shoplifting,* ed. by T.C.N. Gibbens and J. Prince. London: Institute for the Study and Treatment of Delinquency, 1962.

Epstein, M.T. et al. "Migraine and Reproductive Hormones Through the Menstrual Cycle." *The Lancet,* March 8, 1975, 543-547.

Erikson, Carolly. *Bloody Mary*. New York: Doubleday and Company Inc., 1978.

Erikson, Erik H. *Identity Youth and Crisis*. New York and London: W.W. Norton and Company, 1968.

Evans, W.A. *Mrs. Abraham Lincoln — A Study of Her Personality and Her Influence on Lincoln*. New York: Alfred A. Knopf, 1932.

Farber, Leslie. *The Ways of the Will*. New York: Basic Books, 1966.

Ferin, M. et al. eds. *Biorhythms and Human Reproduction*. New York: J. Wiley and Sons, 1974.

Finch, Christopher. *Rainbow*. New York: Grosset & Dunlap, 1975.

Fletcher, Eleanor. *Century of Struggle: The Woman's Rights Movement in the United States*. Cambridge: Harvard University Press, 1959.

Frank, Doyle W. "Mammary Tumors and Serum Hormones in the Bitch Treated With Medroxyprogesterone Acetate or Progesterone for Four Years." *Fertility and Sterility*, 31, 3: 340-346, March 1979.

Frank, Robert T. "Clinical Data Obtained with the Female Sex Hormone Blood Test." *Journal of the American Medical Association*, January 14, 1928.

Frank, Robert T. *The Female Sex Hormone*, New York, 1929.

Frank, Robert T. "Hormonal Causes of Premenstrual Tension." *Archives of Neurology and Psychiatry*, 26: 1053, 1931.

Frantz, A.G. "Prolactin." *New England Journal of Medicine*, 298: 201, 1978.

Frazer, Sir James. *The New Golden Bough*. New York: Mentor Books, 1964.

Freed, S. Charles. "History and Causation of Premenstrual Tension." *International Record of Medicine*, 166: 465-468, November 1953.

Freud, Sigmund. *The Case of Dora and Other Papers*. New York: W.W. Norton & Company, 1952.

Freud, Sigmund. *New Introductory Lectures in Psychoanalysis*. New York: W.W. Norton & Company, 1933.

Freud, Sigmund. *Totem and Taboo*. Harmondsworth, Middlesex: Penguin Books, 1938.

Freud, Sigmund. *Civilization and Its Discontents*. New York: W.W. Norton & Co., 1961.

Friedan, Betty. *The Feminine Mystique*. New York: Dell Publishing Company Inc., 1970.

Frisch, Rose E. "Critical Weights, a Critical Body Composition, Menarche and the Maintenance of the Menstrual Cycle," in *Biosocial Interrelation in Population Adaptation*. The Hague: Mouton & Company. 1974.

Frisch, Rose E. and Roger Revell. "Height and Weight at Menarche and a Hypothesis of Menarche." *Archives of Diseases in Childhood,* 46, 249: 695, 1971.

Frisch, Rose E. et al. "Components of Weight at Menarche and the Initiation of the Adolescent Growth Spurt in Girls." *Human Biology,* 45,3: 469, 1973.

Fukunaga, Kenneth K. "Insanity Plea: Interexaminer Agreement and Concordance of Psychiatric Opinion and Court Verdict." *Law and Human Behavior,* 5: 325-328, November 4, 1981.

Gilman, Joseph. "Nature of Subjective Reaction Evoked in Women by Progesterone with Special Reference to the Problem of Premenstrual Tension." *Journal of Clinical Endocrinology and Metabolism,* 2: 156, 1942.

Glass, George S. et al. "Psychiatric Emergency Related to the Menstrual Cycle." *American Journal of Psychiatry,* 128, 6: 705-711, December 1971.

Gold, J.J. and Josimovich, J.B., eds. *Gynecologic Endocrinology.* New York: Harper & Row, 1980.

Gomberg, Edith S. "Problems with Alcohol and Other Drugs." *Gender and Disordered Behavior.* New York: Brunner/Mazel, 1979.

Gordon, Alfred. "Epilepsy in its Relation to Menstrual Periods." *New York Medical Journal,* XC, 16: 733-736, October 16, 1909.

Gordon, Mary. *Final Payments.* New York: Ballantine Books, 1979.

Gottshalk, Louis A. et al. "Variation in Magnitude of Emotion: A Method Applied to Anxiety and Hostility During Phases of the Menstrual Cycle." *Psychosomatic Medicine,* 24: 300, 1962.

Gove, Walter R. "Sex, Marital Status and Suicide." *Journal of Health and Social Behavior,* June 13, 1972, 204-213.

Gove, Walter R. "Sex Differences in Mental Illness Among Adult Men and Women." *Social Science and Medicine,* 1213: 187-198, 1978.

Gower, D.B. *Steroid Hormones.* Chicago: Year Book Medical Publishers, 1979.

Gray, L. A. "The Use of Progesterone in Nervous Tension States." *Southern Medical Journal,* 1004-1010, September 1941.

Greenblatt, Robert B. "Estrogen Therapy for Postmenopausal Females." *New England Journal of Medicine,* 272: 305, 1963.

Grody, W.W., et al. "Activation, Transformation, and Subunit Structure of Steroid Hormone Receptors." *Endocrine Reviews,* 3: 141-163, 1982.

Gump, Frank E. "Common Errors in the Treatment of Benign Breast Lesions." *Drug Therapy,* March, 1982, 67-75.

Hall, Susan M. "Treatment of Menstrual Epilepsy with a Progesterone-Only Oral Contraceptive." *Epilepsia,* 18, 2: 235-236, 1977.

Hamburg, David A. "Effects of Progesterone on Behavior," in *Endocrines and the Central Nervous System,* Levine and Rachkiel eds. Baltimore: Williams & Wilkins Company, 1966.

Hamburg, David A. and Lunde, Donald T. "Sex Hormones in the Development of Sex Differences in Human Behavior," in *The Development of Sex Differences,* Eleanor E. Maccoby ed. Stanford, Calif.: Stanford University Press, 1966.

Hamburg, David A., "Disease Prevention: The Challenge of the Future." *American Journal of Public Health,* 69: 1026-1033, October 1979.

Hamburg, David A. and Trudeau, Michelle B., eds. *Biobehavioral Aspects of Aggression.* New York: Alan R. Liss Inc., 1981.

Hammond, C.B. and Haney, A.F. "Conservative Treatment of Endometriosis." *Fertility and Sterility,* 30: 497, 1978.

Harding, M. Esther. *Woman's Mysteries, Ancient and Modern.* New York: Harper Colophon Books, 1976.

Hart, Ruth Darcy. "Monthly Rhythm of Libido in Married Women." *British Medical Journal,* 1: 1023, 1960.

Haskett, Roger F. et al. "Severe Premenstrual Tension, Delineation of the Syndrome." *Biological Psychiatry,* 15, 1: 121-139, 1980.

Hays, H.R. *The Dangerous Sex.* New York: Putnam, 1965.

Hegarty, A.B. "Post-Puerperal Recurrent Depression." *British Medical Journal*, 637-640, March 12, 1955.

Henriksen, Erle. "The Melancholies of Menstruation, or Premenstrual Tension." *Clinical Obstetrics and Gynecology*, 252-259, 1965.

Herbst, Arthur et al. "The Effects of Local Progesterone on Stilbestrol-Associated Vaginal Adenosis." *American Journal of Obstetrics and Gynecology*, 607-615, March 1, 1974.

Hier, Daniel B. and William F. Crowley. "Spatial Ability in Androgen-Deficient Men." *New England Journal of Medicine*, 1202-1205, May 20, 1982.

Horney, Julie. "Menstrual Cycles and Criminal Responsibility." *Law and Human Behavior*, 2, 1: 25-36, 1978.

Howe, Florence and Ellen Bass, eds. *No More Masks! An Anthology of Poems by Women*. New York: Anchor Press, 1973.

Howe, Julia Ward, ed. *Sex and Education: A Reply to Dr. E.H. Clarke's 'Sex in Education.'* Boston, 1874; New York: Arno Press, 1972.

— IARC Monograph. "Evaluation of the Carcinogenic Risk of Chemicals to Man: Sex Hormones." *Lyon*, vol. 6, February 4-11, 1974.

Icard, S. *La Femme Pendant la Periode Menstruelle*. Paris: Felix Alcan, 1890.

Israel, S. Leon. "Premenstrual Tension." *Journal of the American Medical Association*, 110: 1721-1723, November 21, 1938.

Israel, S. Leon. "The Clinical Pattern and Etiology of Premenstrual Tension." *International Record of Medicine*, 166,11: 469-474, November 1953.

Israel, S. Leon. *Diagnosis and Treatment of Menstrual Disorders and Sterility*. New York: Harper and Row, fifth edition, 1967.

Janiger, Oscar et al. "Cross Cultural Study of Premenstrual Symptoms." *Psychosomatics*, XIII: 226-233, July-August 1972.

Janowsky, David S. et al. "The Curse — Vicissitudes and Variations of the Female Fertility Cycle." *Psychosomatics*, VII: 242, 1966.

Jefferson, J.W. and Marshall, J.R., *Neuropsychiatric Features of Medical Disorders*. New York: Plenum Medical Book Company, 1981.

Johansson, E.D.B. "Depression of the Progesterone Levels in Women Treated with Synthetic Gestagens After Ovulation." *Acta Endocrinologica,* 68: 779, 1971.

Jones, Ann. *Women Who Kill*. New York: Fawcett Columbine, 1981.

Jones, H.W. and Jones, G.S. *Gynecology*. Baltimore: Williams & Wilkins, 1982.

Jordheim, Odd. "The Premenstrual Syndrome." *Acta Obstetrica Gynecologica Scandinavica,* 51: 77, 1972.

Jost, A. "Hormonal Effects on Fetal Development: A Survey." *Clinical Pharmacology and Therapeutics,* 14: 714, 1973.

Jung, Carl C. *Modern Man in Search of a Soul*. New York and London: Harvest Books, 1933.

Jung, Carl C. *Memories, Dreams, Reflections*. New York: Vintage Books, 1965.

Jung, Carl C. *Man and His Symbols*. New York: Dell Publishing Company, 1968.

Jurkowski, J.E. et al. "Ovarian Hormonal Responses to Exercise." *Journal of Applied Physiology,* 44: 109-114, January 1978.

Kane, Alison and Carlson, Eric T. "A Different Drummer: Robert B. Carter and Nineteenth Century Hysteria." *Bulletin of the New York Academy of Medicine,* 58, 6: 519-529, September 1982.

Kapp, M.B. "Prescribing Approved Drugs for Nonapproved Uses: Physicians' Disclosure Obligations to Their Patients." *Law, Medicine and Health Care,* 20-23, October 1981.

Kates, J.E. *Managing Stress*. New York: AMACOM, 1979.

Kempre, C. Henry and Helfer, Ray E. *Helping the Battered Child and His Family*. Philadelphia and Toronto: J.B. Lippincott Company, 1982.

Kerr, G.D. "The Management of the Premenstrual Syndrome." *Current Medical Resident Opinion,* 4 (Supplement 4): 29-34, 1977.

King, Mary-Claire. "Risk Factors in Breast Cancer," a review of *Hormones and Breast Cancer, in Science,* 214: 1122-1123, December 9, 1981.

Kinney, Jean and Leaton, Gwen. *Understanding Alcohol.* St. Louis: The Mosely Press, 1982.

Kleegman, Sophia J. and Kaufman, Sherwin A. "The Endocrines Concerned with Menstruation and Infertility" in *Infertility in Women.* Philadelphia: F.A. Davis, 1966.

Kleinman, A. et al. "Culture, Illness, and Care." *Annals of Internal Medicine,* 88: 251-258, 1978.

Klimt, E.R. et al. "Standardization of the Oral Glucose Tolerance Test." *Diabetes,* 18: 299, 1969.

Kroger, W.S. *Psychosomatic Obstetrics, Gynecology and Endocrinology.* Springfield, Ill.: Charles C Thomas Publisher, 1962.

Lennane, K. Jean and Lennane, R. John. "Alleged Psychogenic Disorders in Women — A Possible Manifestation of Sexual Prejudice." *New England Journal of Medicine,* 288, February 1973.

Lesser, M. *Nutrition and Vitamin Therapy.* New York: Grove Press, 1980.

Lessing, Doris. *A Proper Marriage.* New York: Plume Books, 1970.

Lessing, Doris. *The Summer Before the Dark.* New York: Bantam Books, 1974.

Levi-Strauss, Claude. *Structural Anthropology,* translated by Claire Jacobsen and Brooke Grundfest Schoepf. New York: Basic Books, 1963.

Levine, Lena and Doherty, Beka. *The Menopause.* New York: Random House, 1952.

Lincoln, Victoria. *A Private Disgrace, Lizzie Borden by Daylight.* New York: G.P. Putnam's Sons, 1967.

Lipsitt, D.R. "Who Are the 'Worried Well'?" *General Hospital Psychiatry,* 4: 93-94, 1982.

MacKay, R.D. "Non-Organic Automatism — Some Recent Developments." *The Criminal Law Review,* 350-361, 1981.

MacLeod, Sheila. *The Art of Starvation.* New York: Schocken Books, 1982.

Mann, G.V. "Diet-Heart: End of an Era." *New England Journal of Medicine,* 297: 644, 1977.

Marker, R. "New Sources of Sapogenins." *Journal of American Chemical Society,* 69: 2242, 1947.

Marshall, J.L. *The Sports Doctors' Fitness Book for Women.* New York: Dell Publishing, 1981.

Martin, Clement G. *Low Blood Sugar: The Hidden Menace of Hypoglycemia.* New York: Arco Publishing Inc. 1969.

May, Rollo. *Power and Innocence.* New York: Delta Books, 1981.

McArthur, Janet W. "Common Menstrual Disorders in the Adolescent Girl." *Clinical Pediatrics,* 3, 11: 663, 1964.

McClintock, Martha K. "Menstrual Synchrony and Suppression." *Nature,* 229, 244: 5282, 1971.

McCullers, Carson. *The Member of the Wedding.* New York: Bantam Books, 1950.

McEwen, B.S. "Binding and Metabolism of Sex Steroids by the Hypothalamic-Pituitary Unit: Physiological Implications." *Annual Review of Physiology,* 42: 97, 1980.

McKinlay, Sonja M. and Jefferys, Margot. "The Menopausal Syndrome." *British Journal of Preventive and Social Medicine,* 28, 2: 108, 1974.

Mead, Margaret. *Male and Female.* New York: Dell Publishing Company, 1970.

Mead, Margaret. *Sex and Temperament.* New York: William Morrow & Company, 1935.

Meldrum, D.R. "Weighing Benefits and Risks of Hormone Therapy in the Menopause." *Contemporary OB/GYN,* 17: 157, 1981.

Mindell, E. *Vitamin Bible*. New York: Warner Books, 1979.

Mishell, D.R. "Noncontraceptive Health Benefits of Oral Steroidal Contraceptives." *American Journal of Obstetrics and Gynecology,* 809-816, March 1982.

Mitchell, Juliet. *Psychoanalysis and Feminism*. New York: Pantheon Books, 1974.

Moghissi, Kamran J. et al. "A Composite Picture of the Menstrual Cycle." *American Journal of Obstetrics and Gynecology,* 114, 3: 405-418, October 1, 1972.

Montagu, Ashley. *The Natural Superiority of Women*. New York: Collier Books, 1952.

Moore, Brian. *I Am Mary Dunne*. New York: The Viking Press, 1966.

Moos, Rudolph H. "Typology of Menstrual Cycle Symptoms." *American Journal of Obstetrics and Gynecology,* 103, 3: 390-402, February 1, 1968.

Morton, Joseph H. "Premenstrual Tension." *American Journal of Obstetrics and Gynecology,* 60: 343-352, 1950.

Morton, Joseph H. et al. "A Clinical Study of Premenstrual Tension." *American Journal of Obstetrics and Gynecology,* 65: 1182-1191, 1953.

Morton, Joseph H. ed. "Symposium on Premenstrual Tension." *International Record of Medicine,* 166, 11, November 1953.

Mukherjee. "Premenstrual Tension: A Critical Study of the Syndrome." *Journal of the Indian Medical Association,* 1954.

Naftolin, Frederick and Tolis, George. "Neuroendocrine Regulation of the Menstrual Cycle." *Clinical Obstetrics and Gynecology,* 21, 1: 17-29, March 1978.

Nathanson, Constance. "Illness and the Feminine Role: A Theoretical Review." *Social Science and Medicine,* 9: 57-62, 1975.

Nathanson, Constance. "Sex, Illness and Medical Care: A Review of Data, Theory and Method." *Social Science and Medicine,* 11: 13-25, 1977.

Nillius, S.J. and Johansson, E.D. "Plasma Levels of Progesterone After Vaginal, Rectal or Intramuscular Administration of Progesterone." *American Journal of Obstetrics and Gynecology,* 110: 470-477, June 1971.

O'Connor, J.F. et al. "Behavioral Rhythms Related to the Menstrual Cycle." *International Institue for the Study of Human Reproduction.* New York, 1973.

Okey, Ruth and Robb, Elda I. "Studies of the Metabolism of Women. Variations in the Fasting Blood Sugar Level and in Sugar Tolerance in Relation to the Menstrual Cycle." *Journal of Biological Chemistry,* 65: 165-189, 1925.

Oleck, Howard L. "Legal Aspects of Premenstrual Tension." *International Record of Medicine,* 166: 492-501, November 1953.

Ortzen, Len. *Imperial Venus.* New York: Stein and Day, 1974.

Parker, A. Seymour. "The Premenstrual Tension Syndrome." *Medical Clinics of North America,* 44: 339-347, November 7, 1960.

Parlee, Mary Brown. "The Premenstrual Syndrome." *Psychological Bulletin,* 80, 6: 454-465, 1973.

Pavese, Cesare. *This Business of Living,* translated by A.E. Murch. London and Toronto, 1961.

Pelletier, K.R. *Holistic Medicine: From Stress to Optimum Health.* New York: Dell Publishing, 1979.

Permutt, M.A. "Postprandial Hypoglycemia." *Diabetes,* 22: 719, 1976.

Pitt, Bruce. "Maternity Blues." *British Journal of Psychiatry,* 122: 431-433, 1973.

Plath, Sylvia. *The Bell Jar.* New York: Bantam Books, 1972.

Plath, Sylvia. *The Collected Poems.* New York: Harper and Row Publishers, 1981.

Plath, Sylvia. *The Journals of Sylvia Plath.* New York: Dial Press, 1982.

Pliny, *Natural History,* Book 7, translated by H. Rackham. Cambridge, Mass.: Harvard University Press, 1961.

Ploss, Hermann Heinrich et al. *Woman: An Historical Gynaecological and Anthropological Compendium.* St. Louis: Mosby, 1936.

Plowden, Alison. *Marriage With My Kingdom.* New York: Stein and Day, 1977.

Pratt, J.P. and Thomas, W.L. "The Endocrine Treatment of Menopausal Phenomena." *Journal of the American Medical Association,* 65, 1937.

Price, Trevor R.P. "Temporal Lobe Epilepsy as a Premenstrual Behavioral Syndrome." *Biological Psychiatry,* 15, 6: 957-963, 1980.

Putnam-Jacobi, Mary. *The Question of Rest for Women during Menstruation.* New York, 1877.

Raj, S., et al. "Clincial Aspects of the Polycystic Ovary Syndrome." *Obstetrics and Gynecology,* 49: 552, 1977.

Ramey, Estelle. "Men's Cycles (They Have Them Too, You Know)." *Ms.,* 8-14, Spring 1972.

Randall, Ruth Painter. *Mary Lincoln − Biography of a Marriage.* Boston: Little Brown and Company, 1953.

Rebeta-Burditt, Joyce. *The Cracker Factory.* New York: Bantam Books, 1978.

Rees, Linford. "The Premenstrual Tension Syndrome and Its Treatment." *British Medical Journal,* 1014-1016, May 9, 1953.

Reid, Robert L. and Yen, S.S.C. "Premenstrual Syndrome." *American Journal of Obstetrics and Gynecology,* 139: 85-104, 1981.

Reid, Robert L., "Premenstrual Syndrome: A Therapeutic Enigma." *Drug Therapy,* 33-43, April 1982.

Robbins, Fred P. "Psychosomatic Aspects of Dysmenorrhea." *American Journal of Obstetrics and Gynecology,* 66: 808-815, 1953.

Romney, S.L. et al. eds. *Gynecology and Obstetrics.* New York: McGraw-Hill Inc., 1981.

Rosenwaks, Z. "New Approach to Dysmenorrhea." *Drug Therapy*, 47-53, April 1982.

Rothchild, J. and Rappaport, R.S. "The Thermogenic Effect of Progesterone and Its Relation to Thyroid Function." *Endocrinology*, 50: 580, 1952.

Ryan, A.J. and Allman, F.L. *Sports Medicine*. New York: Academic Press, 1974.

Salhanick, H.A. et al. eds. *Metabolic Effects of Gonadal Hormones and Contraceptive Steroids*. New York: Plenum Press, 1969.

Sammour, Mohamed B. et al. "Progesterone Therapy in Pre-Eclamptic Toxaemia," *Acta Obstetrica Gynecologica Scandinavica*, 54: 195-202, 1975.

Sampson, Gwyneth A. "Premenstrual Syndrome: A Double-Blind Controlled Trial of Progesterone and Placebo." *British Journal of Psychiatry*, 135: 209-215, 1979.

Sampson, Gwyneth A. "An Appraisal of the Role of Progesterone in the Therapy of Premenstrual Syndrome," in van Keep, P.A., ed., *The Premenstrual Syndrome*. Lancaster, England: MTP Press Ltd., Falcon House International Medical Publishers, 51-69, 1981.

Samuels, Alec. "Psychiatric Evidence." *The Criminal Law Review*, 762-770, 1981.

Sanders, Lawrence. *The Third Deadly Sin*. New York: Berkley Books, 1982.

Sandmaier, Marian. *The Invisible Alcoholics*. New York: McGraw-Hill Inc., 1981.

Scarf, Maggie. *Unfinished Business*. New York: Ballantine Books, 1981.

Schwab, John J. "Psychiatric Illness in Medical Patients: Why It Goes Undiagnosed." *Psychosomatics*, 23, 3: 225-229, March 1982.

Scida, Joan and Vannicella, Marsha. "Sex-Role Conflict and Women's Drinking." *Journal of Studies on Alcohol*, 40, 1: 25-44, 1979.

Seelig, Mildred S. "The Requirement of Magnesium by the Normal Adult." *American Journal of Clinical Nutrition,* 14: 342-390, June 1979.

Selye, Hans. *The Physiology and Pathology of Exposure to Stress.* Montreal, Canada: Acta Inc., 1950.

Selye, Hans. *The Stress of Life.* New York: McGraw-Hill Inc., 1956.

Shader, Richard I. and Ohly, Jane I. "Premenstrual Tension, Femininity and Sexual Drive." *Medical Aspects of Human Sexuality,* April 1970.

Shainess, Natalie. "Psychiatric Evaluation of Premenstrual Tension." *New York State Journal of Medicine,* 3573-3579, November 15, 1962.

Shakespeare, William. *The Tragedy of Hamlet,* Prince of Denmark. New York: Washington Square Press, 1958.

Shangold, Mona. "The Relationship Between Long-Distance Running, Plasma Progesterone, and Luteal Phase Length." *Fertility and Sterility,* 31, 130: 607-608, 1979.

Sheehy, Gail. *Passages.* New York: E.P. Dutton Inc., 1974.

Siiteri, Pentti K. "Progesterone and Maintenance of Pregnancy: Is Progesterone Nature's Immunosuppressant?" *Annals of the New York Academy of Science,* 286: 434-445, March 1979.

Silber, Sherman J. *The Male.* New York: Charles Scribner's and Sons, 1981.

Smith, Bushnell and Prockop, Darwin. "Central-Nervous System Effects of Ingestion of L-Tryptophan by Normal Subjects." *New England Journal of Medicine,* 1338-1342, December 27, 1962.

Smith, O.W. and Smith, G. van S. "Menstrual Toxin," in *Menstruation and Its Disorders,* E.T. Engle ed. Springfield, Ill.: Charles C Thomas Publisher, 1950.

Smith, Stuart L. and Sauder, Cynthia. "Food Cravings, Depression, and Premenstrual Problems." *Psychosomatic Medicine,* XXXI, 4: 281-287, 1969.

Sommer, Barbara. "Menstrual Cycle Changes and Intellectual Performance." *Psychosomatic Medicine,* 35, 6: 515-534, Nov-Dec 1973.

Sontag, Susan. *Illness as Metaphor.* New York: Farrar, Straus and Giroux, 1977.

Soranus. *Gynecology,* translated by Owsei Temkin. Baltimore: Johns Hopkins University Press, 1956.

Southam, Anna L. and Gonzaga, Florante P. "Systemic Changes During the Menstrual Cycle." *American Journal of Obstetrics and Gynecology,* 91, 1: 142-165, January 1, 1965.

Speidel, J.J. et al. "Symposium on Oral Contraceptives." *The Johns Hopkins Medical Journal,* 150: 161-180, May 1982.

Speroff, Leon and Vande Wiele, Raymond. "Regulation of the Human Menstrual Cycle." *American Journal of Obstetrics and Gynecology,* 109, 2: 232-247, January 15, 1971.

Speroff, L. et al. *Clinical Gynecologic Endocrinology and Infertility.* Baltimore: Williams and Wilkins Company, 1978.

Spodick, D.H. "The Randomized Controlled Clinical Trials." *The American Journal of Medicine,* 73: 420-425, 1982.

Stadel, Bruce V. "Oral Contraceptives and Cardiovascular Disease." *New England Journal of Medicine,* 612-677. September 10, 1981.

Stassinopoulos, Arianna. *Maria Callas.* New York: Ballantine Books, 1982.

Steiner, Franz. *Taboo.* Baltimore: Penguin Books, 1956.

Steiner, Meir and Carroll, Bernard J. "The Psychology of Premenstrual Dysphoria: Review of Theories and Treatments." *Psychoneuroendocrinology,* 2: 321-335, 1977.

Stengel, Erwin. *Suicide and Attempted Suicide,* revised edition. Harmondsworth, 1969.

Stephens, William N. *A Cross-cultural Study of Menstrual Taboos.* Provincetown, Mass: Genetic Psych. Monographs, 1961.

Stoeckle, John D. "The Quantity and Significance of Psychological Distress in Medical Patients." *Journal of Chronic Diseases,* 17: 959-970, 1964.

Strouse, Jean. *Alice James.* New York: Bantam Books, 1982.

Suarez-Morias, Edward L. "The Psychophysiologic Syndrome of Premenstrual Tension with Emphasis on the Psychiatric Aspect." *International Record of Medicine,* 166,11: 475-486, November 1953.

Szpmtagh, F.E., *Mechanism of Action of Oral Progestogens.* Budapest: Akademai Kiado, 1970.

Tager, Benjamin N. and Kost, Shelton. "Personality Changes in Endocrine Disorders." *Journal of Clinical Endocrinology and Metabolism,* 239-242, 1943.

Tannahill, Reay. *Sex in History.* New York: Scarborough Books, 1982.

Terkel, Studs. *Working.* New York: Avon Books, 1975.

Thorne, G.W. "Cyclical Edema." *American Journal of Medicine,* 23: 507, 1957.

Tingsten, Herbert. *Victoria and the Victorians.* New York: Delacorte Press, 1972.

Timonen, Sakari and Procope, Berndt-Johan. "Premenstrual Syndrome and Physical Exercise." *Acta Obstetrica Gynecologica Scandinavica,* 50: 331-337, 1971.

Tolstoy, Leo. *Anna Karenina.* New York: Signet Classics, 1961.

Udry, J.R. and Morris, N. "Distribution of Coitus in the Menstrual Cycle." *Nature,* 220: 593, November 1968.

Van Keep, P.A. and Utian, W.H. *The Premenstrual Syndrome.* Lancaster, England: MTP Press Limited, 1981.

Vander, Arthur J. et al. *Human Physiology.* New York: McGraw-Hill Inc., 1970.

Verbrugge, Lois M. "Females and Illness: Recent Trends in Sex Differences in the United States." *Journal of Health and Social Behavior,* 17: 387-403, 1976.

Verbrugge, Lois M. "Sex Differences in Morbidity and Mortality in the United States." *Social Biology,* 23: 275-296, 1977.

Verbrugge, Lois M. "Sex and Gender in Health and Medicine." *Social Science and Medicine,* 12: 329-333, 1978.

Verbrugge, Lois M. "Social Roles and Health Status Among Women: The Significance of Employment." *Social Science and Medicine,* 14A: 463-471, 1980.

Wallach, Aleta and Rubin, Larry. "The Premenstrual Syndrome and Criminal Responsibility." *UCLA Law Review,* 19: 210-312, 1971.

Webster, Hutton. *Taboo - A Sociological Study.* Stanford, Calif.: Stanford University Press, 1942.

Weideger, Paula. *Menstruation and Menopause.* New York: Alfred A. Knopf, 1976.

Welner, Amos. "Childbirth-Related Psychiatric Illness." *Comprehensive Psychiatry,* 23, 2: 143-154, March/April 1982.

Wentz, Anne Colston. "Assessment of Estrogen and Progestin Therapy in Gynecology and Obstetrics." *Clinical Obstetrics and Gynecology,* 20, 2: 461-480, June 1977.

Wetzel, Richard D. et al. "Premenstrual Symptoms in Self-Referrals to a Suicide Prevention Service." *British Journal of Psychiatry,* 119: 525-526, 1971.

Wetzel, Richard D. and McClure, J.N., Jr. "Suicide and the Menstrual Cycle." *Comprehensive Psychiatry,* 13, 4: 369, 1972.

Whalen, Richard E. ed. *Hormones and Behavior.* Princeton, N.J.: D. Van Nostrand Company, 1967.

Whitehead, M.I. et al. "Absorption and Metabolism of Oral Progesterone." *British Medical Journal,* 1: 825, 1980.

Whittlesey, Marietta. *Killer Salt.* New York: Avon Books, 1978.

Williams, E.Y. and L.R. Weekes. "Premenstrual Tension Associated with Psychotic Episodes." *Journal of Nervous and Mental Disease,* 116: 321-329, 1952.

Williams, R.H. *Textbook of Endocrinology.* Philadelphia: W.B. Saunders Company, 1981.

Wise, Penny W. *No More Menstrual Cramps and Other Good News.* New York: Penguin Books, 1981.

Witzmann, R.F. *Steroids.* New York: Van Nostrand Reinhold, 1977.

Yager, J. and Young, R.T. "Non-hypoglycemia is an Epidemic Condition." *New England Journal of Medicine,* 291: 907, 1974.

Yen, S.S.C. et al. "Hormonal Relationships During the Menstrual Cycle." *Journal of the American Medical Association,* 211, 9: 1513-1517, March 2, 1970.

Index